flid

Flid

Published by The Conrad Press Ltd. in the United Kingdom 2022

Tel: +44(0)1227 472 874

www.theconradpress.com

info@theconradpress.com

ISBN 978-1-915494-15-3

Typesetting and Cover Design by: Charlotte Mouncey, www.bookstyle.co.uk

The Conrad Press logo was designed by Maria Priestley.

Printed and bound in Great Britain by Clays Ltd, Elcograf S.p.A.

flid

Colin Stewart

We hold these truths to be self-evident…

Prologue

Cathy has a soft spot – asks me how I know him. I tell her I'm writing a book. She pauses, pointing out Pamela Jones as she glides across the hall within, continuing in a whisper: they had a relationship you know…

It isn't true, but I don't correct her.

What about you? I ask.

Me? No… though I've thought about it, she admits, a slow drag sending spirals of smoke sprawling up into the chill night air. I do fancy him, she continues in an undertone, and I think he's an extraordinary person. She holds my eye now, making sure I've heard and understood, before conceding with seeming regret: but I think we're better off as friends.

There were many eulogies that night: some official, delivered from a clearing of chairs at the far end of the room, some only in passing.

When I took a seat next to Pamela Jones, who I didn't yet know by sight, she had almost immediately turned to introduce herself, before asking how I knew Kevin.

I'm writing a book about him, I had replied, smiling despite myself, adding quickly, and you're in it.

There should be a whole chapter on me, she snorted. We went to school together you know…

I did.

Pamela had given her testimonial earlier in the evening, recalling a scene I already knew by heart and had written about, relating – with a laconic drawl – how she had pulled unexpectedly onto the Donnellon drive in her brand new car. Rushing out to investigate, Mrs Donnellon had almost immediately declared that her son would not be driving any time soon.

Kevin would pass his test within a matter of months, Pamela observed, as the room erupted into generous applause – this the sort of reversal they had come to expect of their celebrated friend.

Breathless and red of face, his tongue loosened by the alcohol he had been consuming throughout the day, Mark Holt took to the floor with an unsteady shuffle, before running emotively through the various campaigns they had worked on together over the years. There were tears in his eyes when he detailed his friend's courage, explaining that Kevin had never been one to duck a fight: an inspiration, he averred, despite difficulties he had never made an issue of.

We were here to celebrate Kevin's fiftieth year, the room full of people I had already written about, who I felt I knew despite having never met, refracted as they were by time and perspective.

James Schaer, the nephew, gave a reading next, reciting a poem that Andrew Kavanagh, one of Kevin's oldest friends, had composed for an earlier occasion: forty-eight lines of twenty-four rhyming couplets. I know them both; I have written about them too. The poem was utter doggerel.

As this latest speaker stepped down, I turned my head about the room, only now noticing the photographs affixed at shoulder height to the walls around us. There were others spread across the tables too, like oversized playing cards, each showing Kevin in a different time and place, offering their own florid documentation of his varied life and career thus far: the confidence and exuberance were hard to ignore.

The room is full of thalidomides, all now around fifty years of age, as has to be the case, and – suddenly lost in their incestuous midst – I realise that they will all soon be footnotes, their stories forgotten.

I watch closely as the tributes run on, Kevin's face betraying an increasing, if good-natured, bewilderment at the manner of representation. Those garbled portraits don't seem right, and we both know it, skewering as they do into a reductive parody.

A captive audience, at his own event, volunteering genial bemusement to everything that is said – with smiles and acknowledgements to the guests who plead his attention – Kevin wonders whether he really belongs, what his life amounts to, whether anybody truly knows him. I wonder, too, as recollections of my own return, scenes I had thought forgotten.

But this isn't about me.

What had been clear, from the moment we started to talk, was the precision of Kevin's memory in picking out those sharp pinpricks of detail, the bright particulars that blazed a fevered course through the space of time that lay between, Kevin bringing each lucidly to life.

My own memory, conversely, is grey and tortuous: an ash that whistles through heavy winds over desert flats – dead ends, lacking substance.

But this isn't about me.

She said, simply, 'It's not going to happen,' and whatever trailed after – contrition, apology, reconciliation – he didn't hear. Stood at the kerb, under a quickly-darkening sky, barely aware of the rain that had just started to fall, a heavy burst starching the shirt he had put on specially for the occasion, there was nothing he could offer in response.

'It's not going to happen.'

Did she repeat the words, or is their meaning still ringing from that single pronouncement?

But this isn't about me.

Chapter 1

Kevin Donnellon was delivered at Walton Hospital on 28 November 1961. His mother, Agnes, heavily sedated at the conclusion of the long and difficult birth of her fifth child, was barely conscious.

There was pity rather than wonder when the newborn was revealed, with Agnes still too confused to take proper account of what was uncharted territory and no one knowing if Kevin would last the night. Thalidomide – the 'super drug' – had been withdrawn from the pharmaceutical shelves by the morning, with cause belatedly following effect.

I first came to know Kevin through my brother, Gary, who met him off the back of a six-month youth employment scheme he was forced to attend in the spring of 1984, our relationship initially conducted at something of a remove.

Kevin was twenty-two and, slowly filling out into the man he would become, no longer the child he had once seemed set to remain, though his smooth, heart-shaped face, with its button nose and fleshy pink lips, was ageless, some said cherubic. Initial impressions proved misleading – the squashed-red pug nose, which had been broken on numerous occasions, that of a boxer or a drinker; the chin, *cleft*; the man himself anything but an angel.

Kevin's face was broad and articulate with wide-spread, asymmetric blue-grey eyes, the right of which – its feathery brow lifted in permanent entreaty – like glass compared to its heavy-lidded companion. Rising lavishly over these eyes, on the ridge of a particularly pronounced brow, the untutored supercilia allowed for the full range of expression. Worldly and innocent, candid and calculated, incredulous and naïve – as quick to engage a friend as a stranger – Kevin was a challenge to interpretation.

Behind the bloated, childlike lips that retreat to reveal a gummy, protuberant smile (his most habitual expression), Kevin's teeth are straight, square… and false – '*Crowns*!' he cries, reading over my shoulder, 'they're *crowns*!' – drawing the discriminating eye almost intentionally from the scar cutting a left-right diagonal across the soft convex of his pale philtrum.

His hair, which would suffer any number of revisions over the years was, at the time, a feathery brown mop, his diminutive ears showing like golf balls through the rough, while his upper lip would soon be sporting the bum-fluff moustache which was then the fashion.

By the time I had been properly introduced and first took account of his appearance up close, Kevin was boasting a high-alkaline permanent wave from his recent visit to Smithies (on College Road), having spent the better part of an hour straddling a reclining chair as the noxious glue was applied.

Revelling in the weft of his new pelt, russet gold in full sun, Kevin had felt like a new man when he set off on a celebratory drive. 'A Solid Bond in your Heart' played on the radio and he sang hoarsely along, licking at the footballer's moustache now perched on his upper lip.

The moustache was gone within a month, Kevin shaving smooth after learning of its preponderance within the gay community.

'I had a reputation to uphold,' he chuckles, though the approbation of the herd did little to forestall his next misguided phase – New Romantic.

Kevin, in truth, rarely stuck with anything: his hair, short and sharp one day, might be left to go to seed for the rest of the year. His most dramatic makeover came during the fortnight when he briefly considered himself a punk, his dismayed mother barely recognising her son when he rattled home, a bona fide goth. The jarring effect of the heavily applied eyeliner and the jet-black Liberty spikes was only slightly confused by the chaste check shirt that Kevin wore down below.

'Is that you?' his mother quivered, which seemed an exaggeration.

Kevin's gossamer-thin locks were all too soon receding anyway, and though he made an occasional attempt at the Bobby Charlton comb-over, it was quickly apparent that he was fighting a losing battle. Henceforth, he kept the stylings strategically short, clipping those steadily reducing strands back up with the tide of a naturally high hairline.

The gold glint of stud that idled on the dimpled lobe of his high-set left ear was a later addition and came as a surprise when Kevin called me across, asking after my brother.

'He's in, I think,' I said, just as Gary came striding down the path, kicking up stones.

Kevin turned the engine in reply and, dropping the ball from under my arm, I backed away to watch from a suitable distance as, spinning full circle, the van departed with a sputtering throttle.

Kevin had still been in college when, having seen a girl get it done in Michael John's, he had decided that he would have his ears pierced too, though he was, by his own admission, 'shitting' himself when he finally took the plunge. He was letting out pre-emptive cries before the needle even hit, twisting round for a better view when it was done.

'You're very brave,' the assistants cooed; already considering what to attach, Kevin was too proud to correct the condescension.

That simple gold stud was an unexpectedly elegant first pick, Kevin fitting it into the soft left lobe to make his sexual orientation clear, not that anyone cared. A larger ring, featuring a white-on-black CND insignia, would take its place, with a snarl of political defiance, within a week. The latest constant of a fickle wardrobe, Kevin would soon tire of such ornaments altogether, leaving the punctured holes to seal up in their own good time.

They were nothing but a memory when Paula forced a heated

needle through to prise the rift apart again, after declaring, with undue irritation, 'You looked better with an earring.'

Though way past caring what Paula might have thought by this point, Miss Harrison was a force of nature and hard to refuse.

'As long as you know what you're doing,' Kevin allowed.

'Course I do,' Paula snapped, with a malevolent sneer.

In the event, there was blood everywhere – on the mirror and the walls – with shrieks and squeals of the sort of open laughter they hadn't shared in years. The suture was blistered rather than breached, however, with Kevin indefatigably refusing to insert any sort of ring or stud into that quickly-closing aperture again (or to let Paula anywhere near).

....

Carnegie Library, a rectilinear construction of Accrington brick and sandstone facings, its domed Edwardian clock tower standing proud, without any noticeable face-lift nearly a hundred years on, looks out on College Road, at the junction of Coronation Drive, with a narrow one-way street to the left (that bears its name) providing the hypotenuse.

Stepping out through the rusted iron gates, the established peace is immediately lost to the clatter of traffic approaching the roundabout, where irregular slabs of Yorkshire stone are set onto fine-grade gravel, while paving stones describe a chord for pedestrian passage. Road signs orbit the outer rim.

There are four exits: the first, a left, swings west, up over the burrowing train line, before dropping back down to the coast. The second, a rambling continuation of College Road, splits almost immediately into two, with one branch leading north-west, past a squat Unitarian church, onto Eshe Road, and the other curving due north, after a sharp dog-leg, onto College Road North, and the house where I was raised (number twelve). The third exit, a quarter turn to the right, leads to Coronation Road, where Alexandra Park blooms through the summer, while a fourth traces the circle back around.

We were moving in opposite directions when we passed. After joining Mersey Road at the roundabout, I was proceeding west on foot while Kevin, mounting the lip of the hill above me, was heading east. He was still some way off when I picked out the familiar, Post Office-red van, a Ford Transit V6, the last three digits of the registration confirming the sighting: GRH, or 'Great Rev Head,' as Big Eric had christened his new friend, when he first pulled up on Nunsford Close.

A gentle breeze was rolling in off the coast as I rounded the corner, and I could smell the sea, though – making my way to an unwanted appointment – it barely registered. For, with your blonde hair braided into a tight bun, on a first date of sorts (with nothing yet decided), you were waiting for me back at the house. Encountering Kevin like this, given that I so rarely saw him since Gary had moved to Poland, seemed providential and filled me with an undefined sense of hope. I couldn't wait to get back to you.

Seeking Kevin's face through the glare of the glass, as he bounded down the hill to the corner I had just turned, I was happily preparing a salute, when I noticed a second, muffled figure in the passenger seat. He was barely a shadow and, given that I didn't know any of Kevin's friends, excepting my brother, I didn't even consider him as the van drew level – the horn tooting through the music – and I raised an arm in acknowledgement.

His square teeth fixed in a broad grin, as he roared out a battle cry, the stranger had now thrown his head – a mass of golden hair – from the window, and was pumping his fists to the sky… and, I *knew* him, and in that realisation the whole world shifted.

Bouncing down the hill to the roundabout and away, they were gone again and I was left to wonder why my old friend, Danny Wilkinson, was riding side-saddle with Kevin Donnellon. No mention had been made of their acquaintance before and such an association seemed unlikely.

I have often teased Kevin over his age, noting the statesmanlike seniority, the fact that he had been around in the sixties and the seventies, before I was even born, but there are barely ten years between us. A decade that can be a lifetime – each temperament tempered by the time it inhabits, bearing its own particular frames of reference – but, since becoming friends in our own right, the joke had grown tired.

Raised in the same neighbourhood and breathing the same air, there are many commonalities, yet Kevin was my brother's friend first and I had only ever observed him from a distance, if I dared to cast an uneasy eye to the end of our crumbling path, where he would be sat waiting – an agitated figure – high behind the wheel.

I was eleven years old then, a shy and reserved boy who had too much to fear and, despite understanding, and occasionally coming to the defence of difference (and those who stood alone), I was never truly at ease around Kevin. In his singular presence, I wouldn't know where to look, and – put to question – I would blush unaccountably, passing his message on but relieved to be free of him.

As the frequency of those visits increased, I maintained a studied distance and would sometimes pretend that I hadn't noticed Kevin's van as I kicked the ball back and forth, though we were just metres apart. A child, balking in his tracks at the inexplicable, I couldn't face Kevin during that first summer – he was too large and too strange, and I didn't have the courage to look, or to understand. That situation would only change with the inevitable passing of time.

Standing oblivious in heavy rain, as you stepped lightly into the waiting cab, throwing out a final, sympathetic smile, I was back in that world again, despite the preceding years. I was a child, an irrelevance, with the world running on without me – knowing, then, that nothing had changed.

Thankfully, by the time Kevin had sounded his horn, Gary would already be halfway down the stairs and crashing out, and I would turn back to whatever it was I was doing: Subbuteo perhaps, or football charts. It would be music, later, with every other sound more distant still.

As the weeks and the months became years, I didn't have much to do with Kevin, his presence but a background to everything else now bristling to the fore, in that defining teenage phase. Those initial reservations would recede, with Kevin soon just another of my brother's friends, his distinctive Transit a welcome sight on our quiet, residential street.

Seventeen years would pass before we became friends in our own right and it now seems a matter of fate. There was salt in the air and a seagull cawing overhead when, stepping out of shadow, I saw the van, smiling in anticipation (it had been a while) as I savoured the pleasant pull of nostalgia, a world come full circle.

It was the passenger, once I had him picked out – head hung from the window; bright teeth spread in a devilish leer; thick glasses shielding narrow eyes – who gave me pause, because he was an old friend. Giving an excited whoop as they chased past, the van skidded across the roundabout with no thought for the oncoming traffic.

I had been introduced to Danny Wilkinson several years back, though he had recently broken up with his girlfriend and I hadn't seen him in over a month. He had changed jobs too, I had been told, signing up with the Parks and Gardens Landscape Services Team, while moving into a house his sister was sharing with a friend. I hadn't been over yet, didn't even know the address but, curious to learn how he and Kevin had met, I called him up later that same day.

'I'm doing his garden,' he said, of a project he had started the previous week, 'and it's a proper landscaping job… And,' breathless, 'he smokes weed, too!' laughing now, as he went on to describe a recent trip and the way that Kevin had skipped through a series of red lights just to make it back on time.

Danny was grinning from ear to ear, and I could see the connection.

'He's got porn on his computer,' he continued, finishing the joint (that he turned in the ashtray). 'He showed me some… he's mad,' – a term of endearment – 'takes the piss out of disabled people and everything… doesn't give a shit. You should come round sometime – he's cool!'

He was silent then, wondering if he had gone too far, while I considered the person I had known all those years before: an adult, who had always seemed much more set in life than I was.

Danny had rolled another spliff, and I took what he had told me with the necessary pinch of salt.

In the circumstances, it had felt auspicious – significant – to meet again like that, while the idea of two such distinct characters sharing a room was intriguing. Dan's rambling account had me wondering what else I might have missed, so when I was invited to a party at Kevin's flat the following week, I decided to go, despite the usual reservations.

'He said I can bring whoever I want,' Danny had assured me and it still seemed impossible that they could have anything in common.

The ease of that sudden clearing of the decks was a surprise, and felt like an opening. The last six months had been unbearable. This, whatever it was, was a first step, with Kevin's unexpected reappearance providing the necessary impetus.

'I'll knock round about eight,' Danny told me over the phone, and I found myself agreeing once more.

They had all said, in one way or another, that 'time would heal', satisfied that there was nothing else to do. Six months seemed too long; I had grieved enough, they imagined, knowing nothing of what I had suffered (and still suffer).

I was glad to be left alone, and it was only the unlikely nature of the invitation, following that chance encounter, that had me back on my feet, grateful for that sudden sense of belonging. It was an improbable turning point. I was sleepwalking and all over the place, but at least I was on my feet again.

Respecting the silence of the evening streets, each of us lost in our own thoughts, we barely spoke as we headed over. We *heard* the house before we saw it, then the light over the door, which gave automatically (just as soon as we pressed the bell), Danny smirking at our confusion as he ushered us in.

The hall was dark, with candles burning at strategic points along its length, and we could hear voices and music filtering through from a back room. Danny led us into the lounge and it was obvious that he no more recognised the people there than we did.

The other guests were older and dressed for a formal occasion – the men in jackets, the women in heels – while we had simply come as we were, bearing sagging plastic bags full of beer.

'It's a bit posh,' Danny muttered. 'Maybe we should go home and get changed?'

Backs to the wall, while we considered our next move, we were already regretting having smoked on the way over.

I wanted to leave; couldn't imagine what had possessed me to think I was ready. I wasn't, and I needed to go.

'Where's Kevin?' I asked, seeking to establish some footing. Perhaps Danny had the wrong house (it wouldn't be the first time).

'He'll be here, somewhere,' Dan returned blithely, giving a quick scan over the heads of the other guests, before muttering his apologies and pushing through to the back door.

He had offered no explanation and we could only watch as he stepped onto the patio and struck up a conversation. Still more exposed in his absence, we found ourselves somewhere to sit, with Dan quickly lost from sight.

'Should I skin up?' he asked, on his return.

Deciding against it, he was soon up on his feet again, and addressing himself to the host, who had entered from another room – he didn't think to introduce us – and then, to the food laid out on a table.

We watched Dan giving a suspicious sniff to each of the dishes, to check if they were vegetarian, before dropping various items onto his plate, while continuing to stuff his face with crisps, the mime show drawing genial smiles.

'It's all bullshit,' we heard from across the room, as Dan launched into a conversation with a trio of lecturers (at a guess), their faces ablaze with pique at such a free use of language.

There was laughter, and heads turned, with Dan's new companions seeing nothing but an entertaining floorshow in views and values that were presumably far from their own. I had often taken Dan to task over his outdated ideas. It was ironic to see them accepted with such impunity.

He was grinning like a Cheshire cat when, forcing his way between us, he dropped breathlessly to the sofa.

'I'm in love!' he declared.

We were used to such talk – Danny, even now, was sharing a house with a girl he had previously declared just such a love for (the proposal gently demurred).

'Who are you in love with this time?' I asked, looking across to Ray, who was leaning forward with sudden interest while, giving a coy nod in the direction of the garden, Danny shuffled closer.

'Her,' he whispered, pointing out a slight girl with chestnut-brown hair.

We – all three – turned to watch then, as the girl drew on a cigarette, with a cocked wrist, while continuing to hold court with her friends. *She's alright,* I decided, turning back again, *but nothing special.*

'I'd fuck her all over the place,' Danny spat lasciviously, his flickering eyes following her every move – the gestures she made when she spoke, the thick auburn hair (dark against pale skin), teeth flashing. 'She's lovely,' he mumbled, almost forgetting himself.

'Why don't you go and ask if she wants a fuck?' Ray snorted facetiously, easier now that we were on familiar territory, his crisp black quiff wagging with derision.

Spluttering into his beer, stifling laughter, Danny surfaced with a series of obfuscating coughs.

'That'd be subtle, wouldn't it?' he cried, expressing an offence he didn't feel, part of him wondering if he possibly could.

His gaze trained on that solitary figure, as those around her came and went, Dan was still hoping he might catch her eye.

'Is she looking?' he would whisper periodically, imagining that we could see something that he couldn't.

He was clearly in earnest and, like it or not, we would regularly be forced to look across and make our report.

'She's snogging someone now,' Ray burst out suddenly.

'Who? Where?' Dan barked, in alarm, jumping to his feet before he realised the joke.

We had seen him like this before and were surprised that he never once ventured back. Keeping to his seat instead, he was uncharacteristically subdued. There was no denying the creeping sense of familiarity, however; the idea of having seen her somewhere before.

Dan would never place that earlier sighting – a brief encounter, while he had been over to work on the garden.

'How's it going?' Kevin had asked, stepping up from behind and, squinting into the sun, Danny had reluctantly downed tools.

Once he had Kevin in range and had given a brief rundown of his progress, Dan had found his eye drawn to the girl, who had arrived half an hour before and was now sitting inside with a magazine spread across her lap. She was in profile, the sun picking out the line of her cheeks and chin. Everything suddenly grew still.

'Who's that?' he asked with solemnity, straining for a better view.

'Oh, that's Karen,' Kevin answered, with forced nonchalance, adding drily (despite his dilated pupils), 'she's helping me write my dissertation.'

'She's nice,' Danny drawled, holding his gaze as he hefted up another bag of soil, considering the proposition anew.

'Yeah,' Kevin answered simply.

His thoughts already drifting, Danny was no longer listening. It was barely a conversation and all too soon forgotten, with neither side taking any notice or note.

Chapter 2

'*I'm* intelligent!' Kevin roared, puffing out his cheeks with comic indignation.

I wasn't talking about intelligence. Kevin had wilfully misconstrued, our subject more often now pertaining to matters that were not so easily defined (telling as they might be), while intelligence can take many forms.

Kevin, as ever, was turning our discussion into a circus and I couldn't help but smile, conceding, there and then, that within a certain range Kevin was, indeed, intelligent.

From the moment he could talk, spouting out sentences just as soon as he had mastered words, Kevin's mother was already insisting on this intelligence to anyone who would listen, stressing her son's virtues at every opportunity.

When fetching him home from school, Agnes would stand a pace behind the other parents, examining his supposed peers as they passed out in a series of ungainly staggers, a rueful smile playing over her thin lips.

'He's reading already,' she'd explain, pausing to gauge the effect of her words. 'Can't get him away from his books... and,' clucking, 'the words he comes out with!'

Holding younger siblings up to swollen chests, rocking prams with heavy feet, those other parents – all women – would wearily acquiesce, before taking their leave. *She's stuck right up herself, that one. Got a real chip on her shoulder.*

Later, following the chipper reports that Kevin would give, of afternoons sprawled out on the playroom floor before a series of cartoons, or his equally animated sketches of the entertainers – clowns and musicians; minstrels and magicians – sent in to make those sorrowful children *smile*, a mother's natural concerns would surface. It seemed a narrow approach, with no reference made to the 'three Rs'. What, after all, were they teaching him?

'So, I just leave him here?' she had asked dubiously, when – dropping Kevin off, on his first day – she had been ushered into a large room containing a dozen or more children.

No account had been taken of her son's age or potential and she was already considering that Kevin's talents might be better served in a mainstream environment, that Greenbank – a 'Children's Rest School of Recovery' – was not really much of a school.

There were no desks and no blackboard, while Kevin's breathless accounts of the fun he was having, as he sat, restless, through dinner – barely bothering with the food his mother was trying to feed him – offered little encouragement.

'My little boy,' she would tell *World in Action* some fifteen years later, steel in her voice by then, 'though he was only four and a half, did have a brain, which had to be used.'

She was right, and as it became increasingly clear that Kevin belonged in a school, rather than a hospital, she did all she could to remove him.

They tried English Martyrs, the local primary where all the other children had gone – and where his younger sister, Liz, would follow, in due course – first. However, despite the fact that the buildings were all single storey and thus naturally accessible, and overlooking the fact that Kevin was already a member of their in-house scout troop, the application was refused, with little in the way of explanation.

'It's out of our hands,' the Head declared, seeming sympathetic.

Her eyes drawn along the line of sour faces toward the pale, porcelain Rossellino Madonna at their back, Agnes knew that she wouldn't be asking anything of them again. *Kevin's as good as anyone*, she considered, with gathering indignation, as lost to the Catholic faith as she was to the people who represented it.

A thorn in the side of the local authority and Education Department alike, Agnes refused to yield.

'This is Mrs Donnellon and I'm calling about my son,' she would begin, again, coming to the point before they could stop her.

When she was refused – 'As I'm sure you can appreciate Mrs Donnellon, our primary concern, in such a busy environment, is for the safety of your child' – her response, well-rehearsed by now, was unambiguous.

'I'll say it again, Mr Hewitt, to make it crystal clear – you've no need to worry where Kevin's concerned. He's a tough little boy and, I promise, he can cope with anything you care to throw at him.'

Nothing was thrown but, unable or unwilling to accommodate the perceived needs of Agnes's youngest child, they remained deaf to all such entreaties. Sefton Council, their local authority, which represented one of Merseyside's wealthiest boroughs, wanted nothing more to do with the matter.

Sat in headphones beside a stiff-shirted Rex Bawden, it was Agnes' third guest spot on Radio City that finally drew a response, in the form of an unsolicited call.

Initially thrown by the soft-spoken Southern sibilants, the shilling eventually dropped.

'Am I speaking to Mrs Donnellon?' the caller clarified.

'Oh, yes, yes… Mrs Donnellon,' with palpable relief, '… who is this?'

'It's such a pleasure to speak to you at last,' Miss Skelly resumed, 'the radio station gave me your number… It's Agnes, isn't it?'

'Agnes, yes, Agnes,' she echoed, her heart beating fast at the thought of somebody finally taking her side.

Following in the footsteps of Emily Davies and Barbara Bodichon, Pauline Skelly was part of the first wave of women to be admitted into a university. Reading History at Balliol College, she was awarded a first-class degree with honours, in the summer of 1936.

Passing nervously down the line of professors in her oversized hat and gown, taking each hand as it came, she couldn't see her parents; they were in the hall, though, and she quietly acknowledged their ongoing support.

'I believe that everyone deserves that same chance,' she would explain later.

She was never married – such a state precluded by virtue of the teaching career that followed on her graduation – but made steady progress in her profession. Following ten years in her first posting at Gilmour Council School (on £168 a year), and ten more as a Senior Assistant at Northway (on £422), Pauline Skelly took up the Headship at Dovecot County Primary on 1 May 1961.

By then, with her hair pushed back in a curly bob from a high forehead, and the heavy, round glasses she had started to wear in her thirties now a permanent fixture, Miss Skelly was already showing her age to an almost careless degree. Her eyes were discerning, though, her smile genial – with strong straight teeth set against the pearls strung across the collar of a checked dress.

Arriving under something of a cloud, despite her distinguished career, Miss Skelly would be met in the hall by a welcoming committee of the teachers' wives.

'I really don't understand, Miss Skelly… it is *Miss,* isn't it?' one of them pursued testily, 'but my husband was more or less promised… and now, out of the blue…'

Sipping calmly at the tea that had been passed her on request – cup and saucer both resting in her two nerveless hands – Miss Skelly didn't even begin to unpick, but stood them down and waved them away. She had already signed terms, her position beyond dispute, and had no intention of failing the proud office that had been given her on merit, as she saw it, nor of quibbling over the £1,323, 11 shillings and 6 pence that had been offered as her annual salary.

'Yes, well, *Mrs…*' answering blithely, without pause, 'I'm sure that your husband will be given every chance to advance… but, I really have a lot to do.'

Telling them straight – she simply hadn't the time.

Nine years later, having met, individually, with the parents of the proposed new intake to assess their needs – and the requirements placed on the school – Miss Skelly arranged for a meeting with the parents of the children already on roll.

They must have heard something, she thought, surprised by the weight of numbers crammed into the suddenly undersized hall, long after the final bell – the intransigent arms crossed over bullish chests, the faces set with suspicion.

'Good evening,' she began, knowing – in the circumstances – that she would likely face dissension, 'and I must say how gratifying it is to have so many of you here with us tonight. It reflects well on the strength of our school and the sense of community we seek to foster. Such a communitarian spirit will be vital if we are to take the step that I am to propose; this is a decision that can only be taken together and in unison… '

She paused then, before running carefully through the proposal.

'These children have nowhere else to go,' she noted, after explaining the practical measures the school would have to take in accommodation.

There would be implications in terms of staffing and infrastructure, she said, but the local authority had already promised additional funding to cover such costs, while the children themselves would bring more benefits – 'invaluable lessons' – than they would difficulties.

Silence followed Miss Skelly back to her chair, a low murmur gathering pace as the audience shifted position, cleared throats and fumbled for cigarettes – then, a trickle of applause.

There was undoubted hostility in the questions that ensued, with several of the parents now giving full voice to their opposition, wondering aloud why *they* should be the ones to 'foot the bill' when there were other schools.

'And why take all of them?' someone asked.

Miss Skelly left it to the governors to explain, only rising to her feet again to deliver her closing address. She was a slight figure, just five foot five (in two-inch heels), but the measured tone with which she made her case spoke volumes.

'We each of us need to consider, with an open conscience, what will happen to these children if we turn them away,' she said, 'if we wash our hands of these vulnerable wards – boys and girls just like your own – and leave them to fend for themselves. If we do so decide, we must also accept the consequences.'

The silence that fell then had a different tone, with even the most voluble of that crowd having cause to reflect – Miss Skelly's words and dignified demeanour a passionate force that no one could deny. The applause was scattered once more, but the volume was greater this time.

Then, a show of hands, with Dovecot County Primary School deciding, by a clear majority, that those children were as deserving of an education as any others.

Having suggested, with her customary zeal, that they set up a meeting immediately, Miss Skelly descended on Greenbank the following day and, seeing those children at play, with wooden blocks, or flicking wide-eyed through grubby picture books, she wondered why they had ever been refused.

Poor dears, she thought, completing the formalities in the dim back room that served as an office, while the supervisor proposed the 'compromise' of a four-month trial.

'After which, if the children prove too much, we can always take them back,' she wheedled.

Miss Skelly regarded her sadly, before setting her straight.

'That won't be necessary,' she said, 'we're intent on taking these children for the duration.'

'But, if...' the supervisor trailed off, hardly begun.

'There's no question of them coming back,' Miss Skelly snapped.

It was a reluctant truce, the supervisor following with a heavy step as they weaved back through the building.

'It's this way,' she said, sharply, when Miss Skelly took what she thought was a wrong turn.

There was no mistake; Pauline had taken a detour to say goodbye to the children.

'Why don't you take the others, but leave Kevin?' the supervisor suggested at the door, pointing out the small, ash-haired boy who was the most physically compromised of the group. 'He'd be such a lot of work. Why don't you leave him – that'd be one less to worry about?'

'Kevin comes with all the others,' Miss Skelly said, more sure than ever.

We'll need ramps to the desks, and the desks will need adapting, she noted, touring the premises with a critical eye, *while the staff must be brought on board, the expectations made clear.*

Hearing the cries of the children out on the yard, Miss Skelly was suddenly at peace, considering her recently completed degree (in Educational Psychology) a further sleight of fate.

'There will be challenges,' she told the staff, in a briefing the following day, to which everyone (down to the cooks and the cleaners) had been invited, 'but I genuinely believe that we will all grow from the exchange – as people, as much as professionals.'

It was a pitch to their better natures. Leading from the front, Miss Skelly's dedication would never waver: strangers to her, at first, by the end those children were nothing if not her own.

All twelve would take their first steps at Dovecot County Primary School on 1 April 1969 as arranged; within a week, it felt like they had never been anywhere else.

Compared to the dormer bungalow on Litherland Park, where the family had recently moved – a salubrious property set back from the mature elms lining the kerb – Dovecot was another world.

'Where is it?' Kevin had asked, of his new school.

'Not far,' his mother told him, though it was, in truth, a long way from home.

Enjoying a rare day off, Kevin was taking another run on his mobility scooter, to the sandstone gates that topped the street.

'Are you looking forward to going back?' his mother asked, stepping into his path.

'Oh, yes,' Kevin replied, flashing a gummy smile that drew satisfaction.

'I'll give you a shout when it's lunch,' she called after him, but he was already spinning back towards the house, and didn't acknowledge her, as he set off down the side path that led to the garden (and the paving stones that edged the wide lawn).

She watched him go, fearless and light-hearted as ever, wondering how he would cope in a regular school, with regular children. She didn't say it, not even to her husband, John, but she knew it would be difficult, especially given that Dovecot was an area that predominated in social housing. *At least they took him – warts and all* – she considered, *when no one else would.*

'Why can't I go to English Martyrs, like Joan?' Kevin had asked, when his elder sister came skipping home from school, loosening tidy plaits from under a boater, tugging off her blazer.

Agnes felt a wave of shame, though the answer was obvious – English Martyrs was not the kind of place that would have him. It was an emerging pattern that wasn't lost on Kevin, who was astute beyond his tender years, his politics bearing left long before he was even aware of such an ordinance.

Exiting Queens Drive at Alder Road, taking the third exit off the first roundabout (and the second, off the next), Mrs Donnellon was gratified to find the world taking a turn too, the brick and pebble-dash she had been following for the past half hour giving way to something more bucolic. The sun was shining – *this is more like it,* she thought, as that same light was lost again, to the broad branches of the groaning oaks now providing a verdant bower, the sun cutting through in intermittent bursts. Picking out the colourful flowers and plants that dotted the spacious gardens now passing on either side – some boasting sculptures and fountains – Agnes drew the window down and let in what seemed like fresh air; her car, a Riviera blue Morris Minor, was almost at a crawl now (with no one to rush her) and, her mood lifting, it was all wonderfully propitious.

By the time she had spotted the placard, set before a low stone wall, to indicate the entrance to the school, it seemed like nothing could go wrong. Her mind played over the conversation she had had with Miss Skelly the previous week, trusting to the tone as much as the details.

Her first sight of the school and its tranquil setting – scuttling cautiously in over loose stones – was confirmation. Parking the car, at the second attempt, she smiled, listening with pleasure to the high-pitched calls of the children at play.

She was early, checking her watch, and had time to settle, to cast an enquiring eye over the grounds, the modest main building, and the dress she had picked out (keen to make a good impression). *Dovecot County Primary* read the sign over the door and she even liked the sound of it, watching now as a sparrow skipped across the front step.

A bell rang, the children shrieked in answer and Agnes roused herself, laying a thin coat over her thick sleeve, before turning the lock. Miss Skelly was waiting on the steps up ahead of her.

'It's lovely to finally meet you, Mrs Donnellon,' she said, clasping her elbow. 'If you'd like to follow me in, I'll give you the tour – help you get familiar.'

She was impressive; not a hair out of place.

Originating from 1933, Dovecot County Primary had since been rebuilt, Agnes was duly informed, and now consisted of a single storey building laid out in a figure eight, beneath a pitched roof. Conducted into the central hall which, Miss Skelly explained, had been cleared following the Assembly and was now being set for Lunch, Agnes peered curiously into the thick shadows, picking out the heavy doors at either side. These, she was told, led to the classrooms.

'It's important for us to have an area where we can come together as a school, for Assemblies and worship… and, as you can see, for Lunch, too,' she conceded, with a smile.

'And will Kevin be eating in here, with the others?' Agnes enquired.

'Oh, yes,' Miss Skelly told her, 'none of the new children are to be treated any differently,' and another weight lifted.

They exited onto a light, airy corridor, with windows running along one of the walls and a glass roof overhead.

'These, here,' Miss Skelly said, indicating the doors on their left, 'are the junior Form rooms and *that,*' she added – seeing Agnes's attention drifting instinctively the other way, drawn by the green patch of grass, 'well, that's the Rose Garden. There's another one on the other side, too,' pointing casually over her shoulder. 'We find it brings a certain tranquillity which, as you can imagine, is in short supply in such a busy school.'

Those gardens were strictly out of bounds, she would later learn, that same rule quickly relaxed in the case of the newly arrived children, who were, from the first, regularly taken out for a turn, like prized exhibits. They would be wheeled across, or totter unsteadily, towards the fragrant flowers, sniffing at the impeccable petals – of red, white and yellow roses – gravitating, naturally enough, towards the miniatures, with a wary eye on the thorns, while the other children followed their progress from within.

'Look! Look!' their audience would gasp, noses to the misted glass (knees knocking in short pants and sleeveless pinafores), anything, in that moment, seeming possible.

Long accustomed to such an interest, Kevin took their curiosity in his stride, giving only the occasional glance in return.

'It's like being famous,' he explained, as he was dropped into the bath, taking pleasure from the fact of a whole school jumping to attention (while the orbit, at Greenbank, had been much too shallow).

His mother failed to see the connection.

It was only on an unconscious level that Kevin could appreciate the changes that had been made on his account – the systems and safety nets drawn guilelessly into place. Half a dozen portable steps – four grey rungs, edged with a white rail – were placed at the foot of some of the desks, to give access to the thalidomide children who lacked for legs. Those desks were fitted with writing slopes, to enhance their reach, while typing machines had been brought in to help with extended writing tasks. Emitting high-pitched squeals of delight, Kevin took great pleasure in slipping and sliding up and down the length of a desk made for three (now all his own).

'Look out, Miss is coming!' someone would call at the teacher's jangling approach, with such recreations only initiated once he was properly settled and had overcome the shock of sharing a school with a roll of three hundred.

Miss Kemp, who had followed the new intake from Greenbank, would lead their lessons in much the same way as she had before, her presence lending a familiarity at odds with the natural desire to move on.

'How was school today?' Agnes would ask every evening.

'It was fine. We looked at the seasons with Miss Kemp,' Kevin's reply as blithe as ever.

'Is Miss Kemp still there?' his mother would puzzle.

'Oh, yes,' without pause, 'and then we had our lunch in the Rose Garden… and the other children weren't allowed in.'

The fact that the new group were taught apart from the rest of the school was an early concern, though by the end of the week they were already being merged into one or other of the three standard Forms (of twenty five). There was no more talk of Miss Kemp then, but only of new friends, the names of which his mother was glad to have no knowledge of.

They took lunch with the other children now, too – small hands and missing digits proving no preclusion to the use of cutlery – and the level of integration was so complete that, when a journalist from the *Liverpool Echo* called later in the month, Miss Skelly had almost to invent a story.

'They're a plucky bunch,' she enthused over the whirring tape. 'At least three are university material and one girl even has ambitions to be a pop star!'

She made it sound seamless – easy – though it would be twenty more years before anything similar was modelled in any other mainstream educational establishment. Kevin still wonders at the good fortune that saw him wash up there.

His recollections are inevitably rose-tinted: the signs of summer whistling at an open window, as they fought their way through the morning traffic on that first day – the temperatures rising now – a trick of memory, as much as an established fact.

'Would you take a look at that?' his mother would cry, pointing out some infringement on the road, or a cat that had strayed, but it was all a blur to Kevin, whose thoughts were elsewhere.

'Oh yes,' he offered with a vague nod, accepting with unfamiliar grace the grooming his hair would receive at each new set of lights.

They were getting close and he could feel it: goosebumps flecking his skin at the first sight of the trees running the length of the school, all in perpetual bloom that first summer, as he recalls, with honeysuckle borne on the breeze. The grass was soft enough to fall asleep on and harboured an enviable store of grasshoppers and crickets that Kevin was quick to hunt out, stashing his spoils beneath the seat of his chair as he hurried back to class. Those classrooms – in *memory* – were flooded with sunlight; the teachers each kind and considerate in their own way, his new friends doting and doe-eyed.

Kevin would spend the majority of his day trussed up in cumbersome prosthetics, however, suffering the arduous repetition of the walking sessions he was forced to take, come rain or shine. While his friends played on oblivious, he would be staggering back and forth across the recently cleared hall. He forgets – though the scars remain – the falls he would suffer in making his heightened way about the school, each physiotherapist assuring him, in turn, that he would reap the benefit in time.

'Once you're used to them, you'll be walking like everyone else!' he was told.

Kevin forced a smile, wondering at the difficulty of something that came so easily to others. He would wear those legs home too, his plastic feet jutting over the edge of the leather seat in the cab, and was only free of them when he stepped back into the house.

'My feet were always bruised by the end of the day,' he says, knowing now that it was a price he needn't have paid.

He evokes those times better with practise, his once-settled memories loosening under question, hindsight providing an eyeglass.

'Dovecot's all a bit vague,' he admits, 'though I remember us all going to the theatre, one night, to see *Wind in the Willows*. It was amazing,' he adds gleefully, 'the first time I had been out anywhere without my mum and dad.'

That long-lost evening still resonates.

'Are we there, yet?' Pamela Jones had cried, for the third time, and there wasn't a child among them who wasn't thinking the same.

It seemed an eternity since they had set off, with an excited roar, yet it hadn't been twenty minutes... and they were, in fact, already there.

'Look!' Pamela cried, first again, the great bulk of the coach coming to a halt before the grandiloquent Empire Theatre, its white face bathed in electric light, copper and steel flashing, doors revolving over a plush red carpet.

The high-spirited children, their eyes drawn to left and right, jumped out of the coach into the frosty air, with no thought for the falling temperature. Sat, agog, in his chair, as he was secured – his mouth wide, his breath showing – Kevin was twisting and stretching in his desire to take it all in. The teachers did well to shake him from his rhapsody.

'Don't dawdle!' they instructed, wheeling his wheelchair through the glass doors that were parted by gloved hands.

Descending into the cavernous auditorium, Kevin's gaze turned to the domed ceiling as he was hoisted up out of his chair and then down again, onto a deep velvet seat, his fingers flexing instinctively at the soft material. When the heavy curtains were drawn apart to reveal a line of billowing willows set against a crystal-blue sky, dotted with clouds, with a river receding into the distance – the foreground a wash of wild flowers – his excitement was fever pitch.

Losing all sense of space and time, wonder following wonder, the children were transfixed. When the actors emerged in their suits of fur, with padded paws and bushy tails, the small orchestra below the stage filling the air with their lyrical melodies, they were utterly lost.

Mesmerised, Kevin couldn't deny the truth of it, even if there were clearly people inside the costumes, dripping sweat through the face paint. When the actors returned to the stage to take their bows at the close, Kevin couldn't physically clap, but he roared his approval for all he was worth.

'I want to be an actor!' he told his parents, his eyes still shining at the visions he had seen – the boats, the carts, the trains and the cars, thrust forcefully onto the stage.

Having formed an immediate kinship with the garrulous hero, Toad's delight was Kevin's delight, and it was only with reluctance that he accepted that the day was over and he needed to sleep.

Kevin took his lessons where he could and, at this vital juncture, Miss Skelly's guidance was critical. The first adult of any authority to suggest that he might be worth as much as anyone else and might be whatever he wanted to be – that his life *needn't* be reduced – it was she who set him on the road that could just as easily have been denied. Boasting the sort of education that should be every child's right, Kevin would return from school refreshed and renewed, and with stories to tell.

If Kevin has much to thank Miss Skelly for, his cohort (and peers) were long gone by the time she retired in July 1980, after forty-two years of unbroken service. She would still speak of him, to neighbours and dwindling friends – referring to that notorious intake as 'my children' – and had never forgotten.

'And Kevin didn't flinch,' she would recall, her eyes sparkling at the thought, her whole life consisting, to a great extent, of classrooms and chalkboards.

Miss Skelly had never married, so when she passed and a box of her personal effects came into the hands of a neighbour, it was decided that Kevin (whom she had spoken of with such favour) should take possession.

'Have a look,' Kevin directed, pointing out the box stacked up on his desk.

Cautiously lifting the lid, I found little of interest, at first, in the jumbled pile of papers and cuttings.

'What are they?' I asked, bringing them out, while Kevin talked me through that veritable treasure trove.

Miss Skelly's certificates of qualification were laid across the faded deeds to her first house, with the details of the loan she had taken out for the purchase of her first car tucked below a bill of tattered wage slips, while the cards she had received on her retirement were collected in a tidy stack, along with various drawings made by the children in her care.

The photographs were first to draw my eye, with Kevin – his smiling face dominating the frame – centre stage in the majority, those faded, technicolour prints evoking a long-gone era peopled with thick knitwear and turtlenecked shirts; flared slacks and calico skirts; fat glasses and great mops of hair… And Kevin: squatting before the gymnasium's wooden horse, as speckles of light flooded the floor; or frowning studiously over an exercise book from behind a vertiginous desk (a fat butt of pencil clasped in his stumpy fist); or in profile, strapped to the teacher's back (in a converted rucksack), halfway up a mountain. He was squinting into the sun, a broad smile plastered across his face.

The pièce de résistance was the group portrait, of the whole gang, that Kevin pointed out with obvious pleasure. Arranged in the Rose Garden in two rows of seven, without a teacher in sight,

I could only imagine the stories they had to tell. Moving from left to right, Kevin offered a pen portrait of each: Laura Manning, Kenny Pollock, Marie Pearse, Helen Scott, Pamela Collins, Peter Spiers, David Parry, Pamela Jones, Gillian Draper, Serena Doyle, Michael Casswell, Phil Cooper and Johnny Hinds. They were faces and names – and *souls* – to conjure with.

Although Kevin would pass his eleven-plus with relative ease, his attempt to pick out a suitable secondary coincided, regrettably, with the abolition of the area's last two remaining grammar schools.

Hoping to take up a place along with his brothers and sisters, in the schools they had been admitted to, Kevin found his path blocked, with the usual 'right of appeal' inexplicably waived.

'You didn't have a problem enrolling any of my other children,' Agnes argued, her irritation growing with each new refusal.

Highfield Comprehensive was the only school to offer Kevin a place and sandwiched between Broadgreen and Old Swan it was a full nine miles from home, as the crow flew; once again, Kevin's schooling would require a lengthy commute.

Old Bill's creaking black cab would pull up outside the house, just as before and, squinting through the thin light as they crawled along in the early morning traffic, Kevin felt like he was stuck in a loop. He was too big for a cab, now that he was in secondary school, and too old to be ferried around like a child. His mother's interminable interventions set the tone.

'I've already had a wash,' Kevin spluttered when she drew a flannel over his face once more, this no matter of sanitation, but something closer to bewilderment.

By the time they came to their first pick-up, at the back of the Giro, where Andrew Barber would be waiting beside his Nan, Kevin would be champing at the bit.

'Hurry up!' he would hiss, as the passenger stepped cautiously aboard, continuing to Old Bill, 'he's in now, can we go?' though Andrew had yet to take his seat.

Old Bill was nodding to a rhythm of his own, however, hearing only muffles despite the dull grey sheath of the hearing aid receiver that hung from his elongated lobe.

'Have a little respect,' Mrs Lofthouse, the designated chaperone, seethed from the shadows, 'and show some gratitude…'

Struggling to see what he had to be grateful for, Kevin was even brusquer when it came to their final passenger, who would be unaccountably shaking when she stepped aboard.

'Oh, for God's sake…' he would cry to Old Bill, who was doubled over the wheel, while the girl – whose name still eludes him – dropped to her seat and Andrew tried to force conversation.

Mrs Lofthouse threw a glare and Kevin considered, once more, the necessity of her presence, given the snail's pace that Bill espoused.

As interminable as the outward journey undoubtedly was, the return, with the desire to be done with school almost unbearable, was even worse. Though Kevin had waved on the first few occasions, the sight of the deputy head, Mr West, passing them in the outside lane – his sporty red Capri leaving them for dust – was particularly galling.

Given his poor vision and dulled reflexes, it would ultimately prove fortuitous that Old Bill knew his limits and seldom pushed them.

'You need your eyes testing, you old git. Shouldn't even be on the road!' drivers would bawl, gesturing madness with circling fingers when they pulled alongside.

'Don't tell me how to do my job,' Bill would retort through his gleaming false teeth, but they had already gone and the cars at his back were now beeping too.

It was sad, really, and would prove serious when, taking a short-cut at Hillside – flipping an indicator; adjusting the visor – Bill reconvened with the traffic on the other side and ploughed blindly into the side of a bus he hadn't seen.

The unnamed girl was already screaming, Mrs Lofthouse clutching in fright to the seat that Kevin, face-down on the carpeted floor, had long since vacated, while Old Bill held tight to the wheel (the blood drained, struggling for breath). A letter of resignation was put in the next day and Kevin never saw him again.

He described it all to his mother that night, as a *wheeze*, but he hated that journey and resented the fact that his siblings, who were not even out of bed when he set off, would all still arrive at their schools before he did.

'I want to go to St Wilfred's, like Liz,' he pleaded again, imagining that the brutal loss of his driver would bring a revision.

'Liz is a girl,' Agnes replied tactfully, giving his teeth a final rinse, calling to mind the Education Authority's answer to that very question.

'He'll be with all his friends at Highfield,' they'd said, 'and that's so important at his age.'

Sensitive considerations had little to do with the matter, though Highfield did at least boast a reputation for the provision of 'special needs', while also being the favoured feeder school for children leaving Dovecot Primary.

'It should be our decision, John,' Agnes complained to her husband, not at any point considering those other boys and girls to be Kevin's friends.

'It's just a stone's throw,' the Authority's genial representative added, Agnes chuckling at the thought of throwing a stone nine miles.

They were given little choice and, with the summer dragging on, Kevin was happy to go anywhere, while Highfield Comprehensive, with a roll call of over a thousand, was undoubtedly a step in the right direction (transport, notwithstanding).

Kevin was eleven years and nine months and had long since deposited the last of his milk teeth when, in September 1973, the cab turned in through the gates of his new school. Twisting his head to take in the imposing tower block, that he would learn contained classrooms too – four storeys overlooking the rutted streets of Huyton (where most of the pupils originated) – Kevin was taken with the long, tomb-like building which, miraculously, housed a swimming pool.

His crisp, white shirt was crossed with a green and blue tie, over which flapped a sleeveless blazer bearing the elaborate school crest. There had been no prior visit, and the sheer scale of the place was a revelation, with children of all shapes and sizes emerging from every corner, before heading off in different directions.

'This way, Kev…' It was Kenny Pollock, and having lost his bearings on the way back from Assembly, Kevin welcomed a familiar face. 'In here,' Kenny declared, bouncing the wheelchair up, over the small, ridged step, into the squat, Victorian redbrick where most of their lessons would be taught.

Assuming that he would be placed in a Form with all his old friends, Kevin was relieved to find that there wasn't another thalidomide in sight; furthermore, that in a school of this size, there was no reason to bump into any of his former classmates. If they were to be friends now, it was by choice, not compulsion.

'Which is the best House?' he asked excitedly, on learning that he had been assigned to Thebes (Highfield continuing the grammar school tradition of House groups long after they had lost all relevance), though he never got an answer and soon forgot the question, his prejudices quickly out-stripped.

'This very building,' Mr Johnson informed the class, with a laconic lisp, extending his arms, 'in a previous life, before the construction of this school, was a sanatorium for Broadgreen Hospital, so' – coming to the punch line – 'if you feel like you're losing your head here, in your first few weeks, please do bear that in mind!'

Kevin grinned; they weren't to be treated like babies.

'They're all mad,' he sniggered to his uncomprehending mother later.

It was Geography that first took him up the tower, in a lift that grumbled and groaned (but bore his weight), and it was from a greasy third-floor window that he followed the final laying out of the M62, the dual carriageway that ran along the front of the school now rising up as the new road passed below. The builders, tiny figures in high-visibility jackets – turning the ground with diggers – looked miniscule from such a high vantage point, with Kevin imagining that he could have moved them if he tried, that he could have picked them up and placed them down again (just like the models and figures that littered his train set).

'Donnellon, what do you think of the population problem?'

Caught unawares and fumbling for an answer, Kevin's eyes darted over the open page of his textbook. The teachers, in truth, rarely bothered him; it was enough that he had made it to the lesson.

'It's a drain on the world's resources?' he answered, cautiously.

'A drain on the world's resources, indeed,' the teacher repeated, 'now, Jackson, can you tell me of what, exactly, these resources consist?'

Content to have dodged the tougher question, Kevin's attention shifted back to the scene below, where a crane was now lifting a concrete block into place; the world opening up before him, Kevin had no desire to return to his trains.

Drawn onto a steep learning curve, within a matter of weeks Kevin was no longer telling his parents what he did there, beyond the basics. That subtle shift, in priorities and in attitude, could no more be found in the algebra they were being introduced to (as early as the second term), as it could in the bloody soliloquies, that he learned by heart, or the sprawled innards of a dissected mouse, which brought colour to a lesson that bored him to tears. That Kevin was growing – *changing* – was undeniable, though the terms proved hard to define.

'But the bike sheds are out of bounds,' he had informed his mother, while still finding his feet – and still keen to share – adding, 'unless you're a fifth former,' his mother disapprovingly beguiled.

'But you're happy there?' she asked, '... nobody bothers you?

Because we can always have you moved…'

Kevin didn't elaborate, already recognising that discretion was the better part of valour, his growing ease in the rough and tumble of such a school a fact he was happy to keep to himself.

'It's fine,' he told her.

'And you're able to keep up?'

'Yes.'

Kevin was, in fact, excelling in academic terms, though he was a teenager before anything else and, with the field level as it had never been before, everything was suddenly at hand. This now included *girls*, who – legs flecked with goosebumps and freckles – would send the boys mad when, emerging from the fog of the changing rooms, they would waft guilelessly back into class.

Turning with a smile to the boy at his side in his very first lesson, Kevin was quick to make friends.

'I'm Kevin,' adding quickly, '*Donnellon*' – the surname now obligatory.

'Terry Turner,' the boy mumbled back, extending a hand that Kevin flapped at with a smile; it wasn't long before they were launching paper notes back and forth, or swapping sweets and bubblegum.

'He was tiny – a midget, really,' Kevin clarifies.

Hunkering down to their plots and plans – with an equivalence neither had known before – they were a perfect fit, in a friendship that would last the duration.

'I can't wait to leave all this shit behind,' Terry would start up unexpectedly, as they took cover in the bike sheds, lifting his furtive eyes to take in the surroundings, while the rain puttered at the plastic roof.

Sensing some unexpected weight, Kevin agreed.

'But we're stuck here, I suppose. We can't just walk out… '

'I mean, later,' Terry interjected, with a shake of the head, 'when we leave.'

He turned, to spit.

'Why? Where do you want to go?' Kevin asked.

Terry moved closer then, so they couldn't be overheard, laying out his soul in a conspiratorial whisper, while the boys around them passed damp cigarettes.

'Join the navy – go see the world,' he admitted, shyly.

The confessional blew out just as quick, the weather turning.

A wind rolling through his insides, Kevin sensed that he was losing a friend. In the silence that followed, he could only admire such well-defined plans. He spat, for something to do (the saliva falling short), wondering what they had ever had in common.

He could have asked the same of any one of his friends: Peter Birch, for instance who, with his long, lank hair and crumpled leather jacket – from which he, one day, rather magnificently pulled out a pouch of tobacco and rolled himself a cigarette, like there was nothing to it – was cool.

'Keep Dixie,' he hissed, and Kevin was won. 'Do you want one?' he asked next, to which Kevin, fearing an embarrassing coughing fit, or smoking from the wrong end, was almost ashamed to have to answer 'no', adding, with feigned nonchalance, 'maybe later'.

Kevin would be smoking too, before long, masking the evidence with Polo mints and Juicy Fruit.

'Birchy was the class clown,' Kevin reminisces, his sardonic wit well suited to the secondary modern, as he shrugged off both the threat and the application of the cane.

'It didn't hurt,' he told his astonished classmates, when – the first of their Form to receive the punishment – he returned from Miss Martin, with red welts written over his palms.

Gravitating naturally towards the rebels and the outsiders, Kevin couldn't have been more impressed.

Continuing an alliance that had been struck up in Dovecot, Kevin's best friend was still probably Johnny Hinds, his puffy face running with snot as his infectious laughter rang across the room.

They no longer shared a class – they were in different Form groups and, later, different streams – but would indulge in what could only be described as jousts whenever they met.

Initiated on the dandelion-speckled playing fields of Dovecot County Primary School, such contests had grown ever more elaborate; a sport of sorts, they had never lost their humour.

Commencing with a verbal tourney, to stoke the fires, the trial would quickly turn physical.

'Come on, then!' John would drawl, the oversized arms hanging from his broad shoulders more than a match for the discarded prosthetics.

'Go 'ed, then, ya prick!' Kevin spat back, while John folded away those gargantuan arms, for a fair fight.

'Queensberry rules!' one wag declared as, from a distance of several metres – the floor cleared and the children drawing back – they ran at each other head-on, to cheers and encouragement.

Cracking chests and heads, in a tangle of limbs, the two combatants would fight themselves to a standstill where, smarting from their cuts and scrapes, their eyes would be rolling with tears and their stomachs burning with laughter.

'What wonderful straight backs you boys have!' a teacher might offer, in passing, seeing them righted again (blind to the soiled shirts and twisted ties).

'Anyone gives you any trouble, let me know and I'll sort them,' Kenny Pollock had assured Kevin in their first week.

Following the acrimonious divorce of his parents, Kenny was wild and off the rails; he was loyal, too, though his services were never required.

A head taller than most of their peers, with an unruly scrub of hair and lop-sided ears, Kenny commanded respect and would happily take on boys two or three years his senior. He didn't look for conflict, but – forever taking a swing at the world – he wouldn't run from it either. He saved his greatest contempt for those in authority.

'I was having a ciggie,' he would answer, crashing late into class, without a blazer or a tie; the teachers knew better than to push.

'He seemed to want them to punish him,' Kevin mused, with an incredulous shake of the head, 'and, when they did, he wouldn't even flinch, no matter hard they hit him.'

Lacking a bag, a pen and a PE kit since the first week of their first term, Kenny had no real friends, yet he was fond of Kevin (and had never forgotten).

'It was pissing down, remember?' he began, sliding into the next seat, 'but we were all out in the rain. I don't know where the teachers were... ' Kevin blinked back, struggling to recall. 'And you came out of nowhere,' Kenny mumbled on, coughing the smoker's cough, rubbing at swollen knuckles; it was hard to believe that he was still just fourteen.

Kevin hadn't thought of that day for years – had all but forgotten – but Kenny persisted, drawing the memory out: how Kevin had been hurrying, to beat the bell, when Miss Bailey had, unaccountably, released him; how, carried by his own momentum – his unsteady legs cantering to left and right – he had darted away from her, in an act of liberation.

'We were spinning rope for Helen Scott,' Kenny continued, and it was hardly credible that the scowling figure hunched before him had once played at such games. 'Then you were suddenly on top of us and went flying... I thought you'd never come down.'

Kenny hazarded a smile, relieved to be able to say it, as Kevin thought back to that weightless flight – the way time had stalled; how free he had felt; how light, once the straps that held him in place had ripped loose and released him from those unwieldy limbs.

His face hit the ground first, smashing his front teeth, as his momentum bounced him across the floor, his hands (a meagre defence) scratched raw, the skin on his cheek and chin torn. A thin drizzle of blood led back from the detached plastic legs to the unconscious child, though Kevin didn't feel a thing – no pain, only relief. The skipping rope lay inert and it was all that any of them could do to move again, and breathe.

A sudden rush of voices – some shrieks and cries – broke the silence, then measured steps that, shaking with inconsolable tears, Kevin heard but couldn't place.

'We didn't see you,' Kenny offered again, patting Kevin's shoulder as he rose, leaving his tray and the half-eaten food.

They were the only people left in the hall.

Kevin had found Miss Bailey squatted over him when he came to, and he proffered a hopeful smile.

'I'm sorry… I was going too fast,' he conceded, but it was like a dream now and he could only watch with detachment as she plucked at his collar to straighten his tie, before brushing a hand down his chest.

A scuttle of feet over the wet surface, his ear low to the ground – hisses, whistles – preceded the heavy rumble of a vehicle on the tarmac: flashing lights, blaring horns.

To this day, Kevin can no longer recollect how they got him into the ambulance that he found himself staring back out of, the windows spattered with rain, though he remembers a stretcher of some kind and the children running wildly about, like there was to be no more school. He wondered, momentarily, why he wasn't with them – why they were getting to play out – only really understanding that the ambulance had come for him when they were already passing out through the gates of the school. That was when the pain kicked in.

A safety net for the increasingly vertiginous high wire that those increasingly steep stilts provided, Miss Bailey would supervise most of Kevin's physiotherapy sessions in school. She was on permanent call for the washroom too, and saw more of Kevin during the week than his own mother.

When he was told that he would be staying with Miss Bailey for the weekend, he understood how little he had ever known.

'Well, Kevin, my lad,' the husband, a diminutive figure with a round, hairless head, condescended cheerfully, 'I've heard a lot about you.'

'All good, I hope,' Kevin replied with his usual finesse and, having indicated a passing interest in military history, he was soon talking war with his host.

Kevin was quartered in the spare room where he would spend most of the following day, with the books he had brought along for the trip; on Monday, Miss Bailey would simply drive him back to school again.

'I still don't know why I went,' Kevin says now, with a shake of the head at another stray memory, adding, in some sort of conclusion that opened up a further line of enquiry, 'It was quite a shock when she died… fell down dead in the dinner hall.'

He was smiling now – at the sound of that juicy phrase – and, scrabbling in my bag for a pen, I was pleased to have another tale.

Kevin had turned, at the crash of china, to find Miss Bailey spread like a rag doll across the floor, with her arms and legs twisted beneath her and her tweed skirt hitched up her thigh – one shoe on, one shoe off. He remembers, too, how the contents of the tray, the knives and the forks and the food, were spread wide, while the plate itself was still intact (and could be taken up again).

A silence fell over the room as, struck by an unfamiliar incapacity – knowing he should do something, but with no idea what – Kevin turned numbly back to the table. When he looked again – minutes, or perhaps only seconds, later – the room had already shifted and he wondered how he hadn't heard the tables and chairs being cleared for the arriving paramedics, now crouched over the prone figure.

He was seeing Miss Bailey for the first time: the birthmark on her temple, puffy bags under the eyes (lids shut tight) and the grey streaks in her hair. The touch of a hand on his shoulder surprised him, a soft voice sounding feebly in his ear. It took him several blurred seconds to recognise Miss Skelly.

'Are you okay, Kevin?' she asked. Kevin nodded distractedly. 'Would you like something to eat?'

The talk of food was odd and Kevin shook his head, barely conscious of the fact that Miss Bailey had been carried out on a stretcher. She had suffered a brain haemorrhage and died on the spot.

Kevin had numerous friends by his final year, but it was still a wrench to lose one of those who had been with him from the start. No doubt well advised to opt against the cruel vicissitudes of the public examination system, that wasn't for the likes of him, Kenny Pollock had walked out just as soon as he came of age in April 1976, rapping at the window as he skipped away from his final class.

He was back again the following week, rolling up to the gates in a calypso coral Ford Cortina.

'The instructor said I was a natural,' he grinned, showing them how – by shoving his seat tight to the dash – he could operate a regular car, despite his limitations. 'See?' He had climbed out now and Kevin peered unhindered into the empty interior. 'I've just been to pick it up,' Kenny added, with a tap at the bonnet. 'The Thalidomide Trust sorted it… thought you'd like to see.'

There was nowhere else he could have gone and no one else to show. Kevin was pleased to see Kenny again, but he hasn't seen him from that day to this.

Serving a mixed community, Highfield Comprehensive offered a diverse constituency that was not without its problems, this being the first time that Kevin had met with people who actively wished him ill. If he had previously been an open book, Kevin would now learn to close the cover.

'Oi, spaz!' he would hear, from across the yard, and the first thing to know was not to turn and seem the object.

It was Phil Cooper this time – he recognised the voice – and he kept walking, didn't look back, leaving his potential tormentor to stalk off in search of some other sap.

You could hardly warrant that such an unprepossessing boy – with his left foot bound in a raised shoe and stick-thin arms – could possess such violence, but Kevin had seen Phil at work, slugging for all he was worth, his two balled fists bloodied and bruised. Once he got started, spoiling for fights just to pass the time, Phil didn't seem minded to stop.

'You wan' a go, you spaz?' he would jeer and heads would drop, with no one willing to catch his eye, especially given that his best friend, John Cairns, the putative 'cock' of year, was more often than not standing right beside him.

Dark-haired and stocky, John liked to fight too, though – given his ranking – he was generally more selective. Thus, after the initial reckonings, to settle the hierarchy between the new arrivals, he only ever fought the fights that the school demanded, sending boys home to nurse their wounds and egos (agreed, by fist and feet, that he was their better).

Kevin kept his distance but was no coward, so when, on a trip to Colomendy, the whole gang of them started in on Terry Turner, who they had cornered on his return from the showers, Kevin went on the attack, despite their number.

'Fucking dickheads,' he hissed, not for a minute considering the repercussions, as he shouldered his way through to where Terry lay quivering, his clothes caked in mud, the ground sprinkled with congealed blood. 'Leave him alone!' Spitting down on the cowering figure, John Cairns sneered as he lit up a cigarette. Waiting for a response that didn't come, Kevin coloured. 'Why don't you pick on someone your own size?' he spluttered carelessly – and, now it had been said, it could not be *un*said.

It was, however, a challenge that could not be met.

'You'll be next, knobhead,' John snorted contemptuously, as he flicked his cigarette onto a ground of potential kindling.

Kevin didn't flinch or step away, but parked himself in front of his friend and stayed in place until the crowd had dispersed and the damage could be assessed.

The other children were incredulous, though there were witnesses enough for there to be consequences the next day, on their return to school, with John Cairns hauled off to the Head for a good thrashing – the well-worn rattan cane rattling off his backside, as he grimaced but held back tears.

With the extensive grounds and a new, four-storey stack of classrooms to go with the Olympic-sized swimming pool, Highfield Comprehensive was a school you could get lost in; plotting a necessarily idiosyncratic course through the jumble of lessons and friendships, there was no room for sentiment.

As such, in the headlong rush to survive, it was several weeks before Kevin even realised that Pamela Jones hadn't come along with them, being told second hand that the mousey girl he'd known in Dovecot had secured a place at St Wilfred's, where he had been refused. He would learn the full story several months later, with Pamela confiding in tears.

'They call me names… push me into corners so I can't get out… and no one wants to sit with me. I spend most of my time in the library, just so they'll leave me in peace.'

She was sobbing now and Kevin considered, ruefully, what might have been; the friends he had already made, in comparison.

'Have you told the teachers?' he asked blandly.

Pamela gave a sorrowful shake of the head to suggest that she was, ultimately, powerless, only explaining on a later occasion that her sister, who was two years her senior, had refused to help and wouldn't even acknowledge her when they passed on the corridor.

While sympathetic, Kevin had to admit that he had rarely thought of Pamela since changing school, especially with so many other girls to consider. For, somewhat miraculously, he was now starting to experience the very stirrings he had been given no reason to expect.

'Kevin… is damaged down below… sterile,' his mother had told *World in Action* in 1972 and, though he hadn't understood her at the time, the idea had held.

It had, therefore, come as quite a surprise to find his penis fully erect one summer's afternoon, when Emily – an attractive girl, whose attributes were more pronounced than her peers – had leaned across to whisper into his ear, his cheek brushing her breast (in turning to answer). *Mum was wrong,* he concluded gleefully, his face crimson, as he sought to adjust – another weight lifting at the fact that he was now free to join in without fear, whenever his friends, inevitably, started to beat on about girls.

'I'd shag her,' Kevin had previously conceded, sensing that he had to say *something*, with a rakish grin towards Laura Manning. She was perched on the edge of a table, her skirt hitched up to reveal the long, shapely legs that served as compensation for the flipper-like arms, the hands of which, consisting of three fingers combined, emerged somewhere in the vicinity of her shoulders. 'She's gorgeous,' he added, in a lascivious whisper.

With her long, blonde hair and china-blue eyes, they were all agreed on her qualities, though Kevin had imagined that – being thalidomide – he would have first refusal. This presumption would be sharply disabused one morning when Johnny Gallagher, whose actively Communist father was a close friend of Alexei Sayle, crashed excitedly into class.

'I fucked Laura Manning!' he leered, all eyes falling his way. 'It was amazing!'

Bewilderment washed over the other boys, who were still just talk (the teacher's arrival a relief). Judging the whole affair a personal affront, Kevin would seek Laura out over Lunch.

'Johnny said you did it with him – is that true?' he whined, close to tears.

'What – with Johnny?' Laura replied, expressing incomprehension. 'Who said that?'

The tolling bell gave Kevin the opportunity to slip away before Laura thought to ask just what it had to do with him. He believed her rebuttal but, somehow, couldn't accept her denial, even if his relations with the opposite sex were still just a matter of conjecture.

At Break, Kevin usually stayed inside and, with the corridors free of children, he would race his chair. Barry Laird, Jack Murphy and Daryl Hannigan, the hall monitors, who generally delighted in throwing their weight about, had no such desire in Kevin's case and would take it in turns (one to each arm).

'Faster! Faster!' Kevin would cry, the tears streaming down his face, when they reached the corridor that connected the old building to the new, where a jump was required, Kevin tipping his chair onto the thick rear tyres, as they picked up pace.

Pulling up hard on the other side to negotiate a tight corner, his flailing bulk rattling at the tight belt, Kevin would bring his vehicle to a truncated halt. The distant screech of the tyres – the rubber tearing, in desperation, at the parquet – sounded like someone in pain.

'One small step for mankind!' a quick wit had it.

His eyes shut tight and, praying for safety, Kevin had all but forgotten where he was.

Making strategic play of the privileges afforded in respect of his 'difficulties', Kevin walked a rebellious line.

'Ah, Kevin, take a seat,' was all a teacher would say if he was late for class – dispensing with the troublesome patronymic (in this single esteemed case) – with much of his schoolwork similarly waived.

Given such lassitude, Kevin could do pretty much as he pleased; he was fortunate to find himself interested enough in his lessons to make a success of them, his hand raised as often as anyone.

Just as ready with a barbed quip as a precocious reply, Kevin was in nobody's pocket: he spat like the other boys, wore his tie pencil-thin like they did (the fat blade drawn into the placket of a Fred Perry shirt) and, clearing his throat of the tell-tale smoker's cough, he could curse with the best of them, too. He would never know just how far he acted out of a sense of immunity.

'Did you manage to do your homework?' the teachers would merely broach.

'Nah, I dropped it on those steps in H Block,' Kevin would reply, his voice broad Scouse under question, the seditious tone drawing sniggers from classmates he acknowledged with a sneer.

Accepting that no concession, or deference, would be made to his 'condition', Kevin generally preferred the teachers of the 'old school' who – a heady blend of sarcastic taunts and corporal punishment – still ran like a vein through this establishment, as any other (despite recent legislation).

'You're late, Donnellon!' they would bawl when, heaving at the exertion of manoeuvring a manual, Kevin's unoiled chair rolled into view.

Given the size and spread of the campus, Kevin could hardly be faulted for arriving late and, as an adult, he is nothing if not punctual; we often leave for the theatre hours ahead of time.

In school, such equality was a liberation, with Kevin pleased to take flight along with the rest whenever Miss Martin, the newly installed head, strode out of her office in her cap and gown, with a cane clamped to her thigh.

Having been left more or less to his own devices for the first twelve months, Kevin was surprised to find, on his return the following September, that he was being provided with an assistant.

'This is Mr Bateman – he's here to help you get about the school,' Mr West explained.

Kevin glared across at Mr Bateman, imagining that a support worker would cramp his style and single him out, when he had tried so hard to settle. He was ready to resist but, stepping onto the corridor, he was immediately reassured.

'Slap-head goes on a bit, doesn't he?' Mr Bateman chuckled, by way of introduction.

'Yeah,' Kevin answered casually.

'I'm Mark, by the way... pleased to meet you,' his new companion said, drawing a cigarette from his denim jacket.

Kevin smirked, noting that Mr Bateman wasn't long out of school himself and didn't yet side with the staff. Within minutes, his friends had tagged him 'Batman', on account of his patronymic, and were quickly testing the possibilities.

'Give us a push!' Birchy cried, having climbed up on Kevin's chair.

'Nah, you're too fat,' Batman returned, batting him away to laughter.

'He was cool,' Kevin recalls, 'and totally obsessed with the Beatles... always reckoned they were going to reform.'

Backing them into the next class, while another pupil held the door, Batman gave a playful salute before dropping Kevin to his seat. He was whistling a familiar tune: 'Let It Be'.

Between lessons, with a whole crowd of them gathered around, Batman would run through the details of his most recent date. With no concession made for their relative youth, or the fact that they were pupils rather than friends, he would describe every single kiss and grope.

His muscular presence undoubtedly served as a deterrent too, for anyone who might have thought to challenge or question Kevin's place in the school. This facility would only once be brought into play, when Kevin was nearing the end of his third year and, rattling hurriedly into class (making hasty apologies) Mark started to drop him into place, before suddenly pulling up again.

'Bastard,' he hissed, casting an eye over the room and almost immediately picking out a grinning John Cairns. 'Prick,' he spat, with unconcealed venom, before making a grab at the litter of tacks scattered over Kevin's chair and tossing them towards John, delivering another oath as he stormed from the room.

Kevin, who hadn't seen the tacks, sat on in confusion, surprised to see that easy-going character in such a temper. There was a brief lull before Mr West, the deputy head, crashed in.

'Cairns – here, now!' he roared.

John Cairns shuffled idly over and, taking his collar (once in range), Mr West dragged him out. He was given six of the best, which Kevin would later apologise for, with the two boys forming an unlikely alliance from that day forth.

After a single, abortive attempt, it was decided that Kevin wouldn't be doing PE and would spend those periods in the medical room instead, just as he would his Science lessons, the dreary laboratories all being located up an imponderable set of stairs (and Kevin too heavy to lift).

Tucked away on the far side of the school and overlooking a garden lined with billowing poplars, this medical room would provide a welcome escape from the pressing demands of academia. The school nurse, Ivy McCullough, would keep him company, with genuinely ailing students a rare sight.

'She was mad,' Kevin gleefully explains, 'and she smoked like a chimney.'

It was Ivy, appropriately enough, who passed Kevin his first cigarette, before embarking on another of her lurid tales.

Her age was an open debate, which the gaudy sartorial choices – the low-cut tops and flabby miniskirts – did little to clarify. Her bronzed legs ran with varicose veins; her bare feet were squeezed into sandals (exposing blistered corns), while jewellery swung garrulously from every perch.

'And she had purple hair,' Kevin broke in, excitedly, 'piled up in a beehive!'

Taking down the details of another vivid creation, I could already picture her, just as I could imagine the part Ivy McCullough must have played in that young boy's education.

'Ah, you won't believe it!' she would begin again, recounting a recent trip to the Costa Brava, from which she had returned with a topped-up tan, growing misty-eyed over the waiter she had 'fucked up against the wall' in some dusty side street and the swarthy constable who had taken her aside to show her his 'gun'.

'My own little piece of heaven!' she crowed, in ecstasies, of that gilded coastline.

When, tapping timidly at the door – in a part of the school they had never ventured into before – some sick child would occasionally stumble in, they would more often than not find Kevin and

Ivy in stitches on the floor, in a room full of smoke.

'My stomach hurts,' the child would plead, while Ivy gave a brief touch of the back of her hand to their forehead.

'Take these and see how you go,' she would say, ushering them away with a handful of pills.

Sometimes the child in question would come right out and ask. 'Can I have a ciggie too, please Miss?'

'Don't smoke it in class,' was Ivy's sage advice, as she stamped out the last of her own, waving the worst of the fumes from the window, suddenly self-conscious.

Ivy would retire from Highfield Comprehensive while Kevin was still a pupil, with the job passed on, without interview, to her niece.

Kevin spent many an afternoon stretched out on the wide wooden windowsill in that medical room, his face to the glass. On one such occasion, lurching forward for a better view of the comical figure, shuffling left, then right, in the snow outside – there had been a blizzard that morning – Kevin was momentarily caught off guard.

'It's Jimmy Jameson!' he cried suddenly, at the sight of his stumbling classmate, only gradually perceiving that – despite the visibility of his jet-black Afro against the virgin-white snow – Jimmy was actually trying to maintain his cover, in a vain attempt to avoid the detention that would inevitably follow. 'Daft sod!' Kevin muttered fondly, turning to share his opinion when the pane beside him gave with a crash of glass, under the weight of a tight ball of snow.

Struggling to keep his balance, Kevin turned back just in time to see Jimmy darting off in the direction of the trees, tripping every second step. Wanting no part in the repercussions, Kevin was back in his chair and out on the corridor, in seconds flat, leaving Ivy to pick up the pieces.

'He's pathetic,' Kevin hissed – of Andrew Barber, who shared his morning cab – keen to disassociate. 'The knobhead actually thinks we're friends.'

Carefully noting their reactions, Kevin feared how it must look when the two of them stumbled out of the taxi together, blurring the lines of equivalence. While Kevin made no play of his disability, Andrew seemed to revel in it.

'I've got encephalitis… and spina bifida,' he would announce, with seeming pride – on introduction – and Kevin, who had worked so hard to establish a reputation that had nothing to do with the presence of a wheelchair, wondered at his willingness to be defined in such terms.

'How are you, Kevin?' Andrew would ask, like a sop.

'Marvellous,' the retort, with no attempt to disguise the sarcasm, or his displeasure, lighting up a cigarette just so he could spit the smoke in his companion's face.

Cough, splutter: Andrew, of course, was a non-smoker.

'What lessons have you got this afternoon?' Andrew began again.

'Double fuck off,' Kevin told him, pushing past.

This was on a good day. In a less accommodating mood, the encounter would generally conclude in violence, Kevin liking to sneak up from behind.

'Hey! Help! Watch out!' Andrew would quail when he felt his chair tip, fearing a fall, Kevin breaking into unrestrained laughter at the sight of his flapping arms and cracking a ruler at his knuckles as he tried to hold on.

'For God's sake, Kevin, you'll kill the boy!' Ivy cried when she saw them, and it was no exaggeration, as had been explained: 'water on the brain' was no joke.

'We're just messing about,' Kevin snorted, turning a complicit eye on his temporary friend. 'Andrew doesn't mind.'

Andrew shook his head, grinning along, displaying a loyalty that had no place.

'I was a bastard to Andrew,' Kevin admits – the man he is now, far removed from the boy he once was – before going on to describe the fun they would have at the expense of supply teachers.

Johnny had spotted him first, making his cautious way down the corridor, checking the numbers on the doors.

'Quick – he's coming!' he called, rushing back in, ready to test the newcomer (a ritual point of honour).

There were sniggers and smirks when the Supply arrived, with the pupils all jumping to their feet.

'Morning, sir,' they called, making a show of respect as the Supply, who had long, girlish hair and a chin drawn with spots, took his place at the front.

'My name is Mr Brown,' he announced with a slight stammer – chalking it up on the board – and the snickering began.

'Good morning, Mr Brown,' the facetious reply, Mr Brown turning to find the pupils all standing obediently to attention.

In the circumstances, Kevin's failure to comply looked like a blatant act of disrespect.

'Is there a problem?' the teacher called. Kevin was smirking when he set off down the aisle towards him, the rest of the class stamping their feet and beating at their desks at his approach. 'Are you deaf,' the Supply blurted carelessly, 'or just plain stupid?'

Kevin was still smiling when, considering possible sanctions, Mr Brown rounded on him from the side. It was only as he was about to lay hands on the transgressor that he noticed the wheelchair and gave a furtive peek beneath the desk. Rising to his feet, with his arms hanging dumbly at his side, Mr Brown's face was beetroot as the class erupted.

'I see,' he conceded, without apology, before striding back to the board and scratching the date across it in French. 'Can you all please turn to the next page in your books,' he directed shrilly, seeking the authority of instruction, 'and write the date and the title.'

Recognising that the lesson was as good as done, Kevin was grinning in triumph.

Wholly at his ease and continuing to take as read the privileges that came his way, by his final year Kevin seemed to have already outgrown the place. With the dining room full of 'kids', he would now take his lunch off-site with his friends, the whole crowd of them dumping their sandwiches and lighting up cigarettes just as soon as they were through the gate.

They took it in turns, in different houses, gorging on biscuits and crisps, washed down with Coke, while listening through the Top 40 tape from the weekend chart, winding back and forth through their favourite picks.

Birchy was turning the latest Blondie LP about on his lap.

'I'd give her one,' he said, 'rip her to bloody shreds,' and the boys – coughing and spluttering, as cigarettes were passed down the line – all concurred.

They blew the fumes from the window, a crack of light showing through the thick curtains.

'What about Mel?' Mickey asked gingerly, dropping his eyes to the floor before drawing them level. 'She wears glasses, but she's alright… '

'No chance!' Birchy burst in. 'Didn't you hear Johnny the other day? Said he got her bra off at that party and she had blackheads on her tits!'

Bowing to popular opinion, Mickey snorted along with them.

'What about you and Laura Manning?' Jacko asked Kevin, bringing him up short. 'You getting any yet?'

It was an old line and he knew it well.

'Nah, not yet,' Kevin admitted, though he didn't tell them he had lost interest. 'She's a bit of a flid, anyway,' he added slyly, his punch-line bringing hoots of laughter, as someone else pointed out the time and, flicking the dead stubs of their cigarettes from the window, they snatched up their coats and bags.

They were back late most days – running all the way – though this didn't stop them fooling around with Kevin's chair as they went, tipping it and spinning it (to lusty cheers) while the occupant struggled to stay afloat.

'Kev, you spaz!' Jacko roared, turning him on the spot.

'Fuck off!' Kevin blasted back, drooling with pleasure, while two of their number, their unwashed blazers billowing, took a handle each and resumed their sprint.

Unable to resist a final punt, Jacko listed Kevin forty-five degrees to stern, spinning the wheels vacantly on their pivots, before launching him headlong into the oncoming traffic.

Kevin nearly collided with a car, which swerved; recognising the uniforms, the driver phoned through to the school to complain.

'One of your pupils has just tried to kill me!'

Kevin (it could hardly be mistaken identity) was wheeled away to Miss Martin, where he sat, in petulant silence, through the subsequent telling off.

'I even considered giving you the cane,' he was told.

His eyes down, in seeming contrition, Kevin found it hard to see past the short skirt and shapely calves.

He apologised grudgingly but, having learned by now that there wasn't much they could actually do, he had little to fear. For Kevin couldn't be stood in a corner, as an object of ridicule, if he couldn't even stand, while keeping him back after class would only make him late for his next lesson. Given the need to get him home by some other means if he missed his cab, detentions had proved unwieldy, while corporal punishment had been prematurely withdrawn, with even a verbal rollicking deemed inappropriate in the case of a defenceless cripple.

'They had no way to punish me,' Kevin notes, 'so I got away with absolutely everything!'

Kevin was no delinquent but, just as he was confident in his own opinions, he knew how to play dumb when it suited.

'He's a lovely boy,' his parents would be told on Parents' Evening, the teachers happy to paper over cracks, and Kevin was, undoubtedly, bright – top set for everything – with his grades rarely dropping below a B.

If and when his behaviour left something to be desired, the teachers usually looked the other way.

In the summer of 1978, having passed six of the eight O-levels he had sat, Kevin decided, with misplaced nostalgia, to stay on for his A-levels, despite the fact that most of his friends had already gone. He had rarely looked further than the end of the month before, but here he was signing up for the next two years.

'A proper brain box!' his mother declared, not knowing how Kevin had bluffed as much as he studied; the difficulties he encountered at A-level would confirm those limits.

'Some of you will find A-levels a step up,' the head of sixth form explained, 'but with the right application, there's no reason why every single one of you shouldn't make a success of it.'

Casting his eyes over the room, Kevin turned his head disdainfully but, intent on the lecture, no one noticed, and he realised then that he barely knew those other students (their paths hadn't crossed) and that they weren't likely to be much fun.

The next two years were lost years, with Kevin never able to shift the nagging sense of a world moving on while he stayed still, with his former friends already driving cars or taking out girls.

Agnes's second husband, Jim, would – fortunately – persist, with his insistent rap at the bedroom door each morning the only reason that Kevin didn't simply play truant.

'Have you got everything – pen, pencil?' Jim would still be prompting, as Kevin mounted his chair.

'I'm not a child,' Kevin would hiss in response, too demoralised to argue: *Why doesn't he go himself, if he likes it so bloody much?*

There was some truth in the complaint, with Jim (who had left school at fourteen) repeatedly stating his desire to be given 'the chance that you have'.

'They're woollybacks,' Kevin retorted, of the 'nerds' in his class, when his mother wondered aloud why he didn't invite any of his new friends back, though he was the one who lived in the sticks and they were just local lads made good.

The cream of the crop, the class conversation would inevitably turn to what came next.

'I'll probably just bum around for a bit,' Kevin offered contemptuously, 'perhaps write a book or something…'

There were murmurs of assent – they all liked Kevin and certainly thought him capable – but such games were a drain, with Kevin increasingly subdued as he drifted from class to class. While still studiously taking his notes, he wasn't really listening or paying attention.

'Good luck,' his mother called, when he left for his first exam, respecting the work she imagined he'd put in, with his bedroom door stubbornly shut.

'It's now eight minutes past nine, so could you please turn over your papers and begin.'

Glancing curiously round at his classmates, each an arm's length away, Kevin made a quick start: flicking excitedly through the paper, checking its length, the number of questions. When he slowed down and actually started to read, in more detail, it was all suddenly fruitless. *Fuck,* he thought, working his way through with the sense of a missed opportunity.

A shaft of sunlight came washing over the floor from the far end, Kevin smiling as he turned to the extended questions on the final page, where one of his four choices referred to the poem he knew best.

'Can you please stop writing now,' the invigilating Miss Martin intervened, 'the exam is over.'

But I haven't finished, Kevin thought in a panic, searching out the clock behind the stage. His paper had already been collected, however, and his row vacated.

'Good work, Kevin – well done,' Mr Rawlings whispered benevolently, patting at his back, passing him his pen (a Parker 180).

Clattering through the chairs, exiting the hall in a daze, Kevin couldn't understand it. In the corridor outside, his classmates – huddled together in groups – were already running excitedly through the questions.

Staggering the thirty or so metres back to the waiting car, Kevin left them to it.

'How did you do, son?' Agnes asked.

'Alright,' Kevin answered brusquely, not about to explain that it wasn't a level playing field, that he had needed more time, that it was hard enough for him to use a pen, let alone to write at such length.

There had been no additional time – that wouldn't have been fair.

When the results came, Kevin's teachers found it hard to hide their disappointment, such was the store they had set on his intelligence. There was muted talk of errors and possible re-marks, but Kevin declined, accepting that – 'little wonder' or not – the examining board had it just about right: that he hadn't put in the required work.

'I really am very surprised,' Miss Martin said, handing him the envelope she had already opened, taking an interest only now that it was too late. 'I genuinely believed that you were capable of a lot more than… *this*,' rattling the paper before him.

Kevin acknowledged the assessment in silence; it would be another twenty years before the subtle distinction between 'integration' and 'inclusion' would be fully appreciated. Highfield had been good enough to take him, but it was hardly fair that he had been treated like any other pupil.

With no desire to explain why he was still at school, Kevin decided against re-sits at Highfield, enrolling at Hugh Baird instead, which – with a lift running up to every floor (in the old tower) – was not only fully accessible but also offered a break from the past.

The laid-back, collegial atmosphere that held between the students and the staff – who interacted on first-name terms and couldn't always be told apart – was encouraging, with Kevin further emboldened by the electric typewriter he received on arrival.

'A-levels aren't a test for handwriting, are they?' Mr Smith – Paddy – explained, having discussed Kevin's difficulties last time round. 'We want to know what you think, not how well you can use a pen,' he added, stroking a wave of hair behind his ear.

Looking more closely, now that he was close enough to see, at the badges decorating the revers on Paddy's corduroy jacket – the clenched fist of 'Liberation'; the 'peace sign' of CND; the Red Rose enamel pin sat on his breast pocket – Kevin felt a surge of unaccountable pride.

Though as arbitrary as any of his other choices, Hugh Baird would prove to be one of his better decisions.

'I made friends straight away,' Kevin assures me, forgetting his doubts when he first left Jim at the entrance and made his way in alone, with a sense of having to start over, of retracing steps – fearing the need to explain, once more. He needn't have worried.

'I'm Bernard.'

'And I'm Boris.'

Like Tweedledum and Tweedledee, with the inseparable Streatham House girls – Aileen Howard and Alison Archer – to follow.

'Are you going to wear that?' his mother asked doubtfully, pinning another badge to his already littered lapel.

'Yes mother, stop fussing,' he snapped.

The reprimand was playful now. With his new life and his new friends, Kevin was more or less done with his mother and could thus show magnanimity.

'His name's Boris,' he answered another query.

'Boris?' Agnes floundered.

'Yes, *Boris*.'

'That's a strange name, don't you think?'

'No stranger than Donnellon,' Kevin retorted, glad – for once – of Jim's insistence on wheeling him out to the car.

A sad pout drawn on her face, Agnes watched from the front step, hardly able to credit that her son had already gone so far – wondering if she should possibly call him back.

'What do you all *do*?' she quizzed over breakfast, following one of Kevin's increasingly frequent nights out, never imagining that her son could be part of such a circle – rich kids, *posh* kids (another world) – worrying that they might be playing some kind of trick.

'We're friends,' Kevin replied, 'what do you think we do?'

While appreciating the varied freedoms his new companions brought, Kevin was just as confused as she was.

College itself was – fortunately – a *breeze*, with very little required in terms of work; at their leisure, whole days would pass without their having to so much as open a book.

'Where do you want to go?' one of the girls would ask after Lunch, their lessons complete.

'North Park,' Alison cried, checking her watch (the clear sky having decided her).

'Right, then… last one there's an idiot!' Dick – the sixth of their circle – shrieked, tearing off across the road with the chair, flicking two fingers back at his stranded friends from the other side, as the lights turned green and the traffic resumed.

When it rained, as it did for the best part of January and February that first year, they would take the train to town, darting between shops for shelter, or else stay put, sipping at milky coffee in the college cafeteria. The pitter-patter of rain on the window in the roof marked the slow passage of time.

They should have been studying – these were, ostensibly, 'study' periods – and, hunched over textbooks, most of their compatriots *were*, but such labour wasn't their style and, despite the tight deadlines, they always believed that time was on their side.

'How was school today?' his mother would still ask on his return, eaten up with envy.

Dropping his files and binders to the floor, every inch the scholar, Kevin would turn then, indulging what he considered his mother's dotage with a smile and a shrug.

'It was alright,' he told her, his lip turned in a gesture she struggled to read. 'When's dinner?'

A month in and the routine was already set, with Wednesday afternoons, when all six had free periods, spent in the pub, making merry in either the Jutland (on Stanley Road) or the Merton (opposite). There, in a slur of sentences, their passions getting the best of them, they would set the world to rights. Differences of class, or circumstance, falling away under inebriation, each relished the freedom of release.

At the end of their revels, Kevin would invariably find himself deposited on the front step, fishing in his pockets for his keys, before banging the door down (when he couldn't locate them).

'What a state for a young man to be getting into,' his mother would complain.

'Dumped like a sack of spuds,' Jim noted, searching the road for his companions.

They would offer no help in getting him up the stairs.

Scribbling notes into his pad, as he studied the handouts, his mind alight once more, Kevin would be back in class again the next day. He liked his lessons at Hugh Baird, with the tirades the lecturers, who still had fire in their bellies, delivered there a much better fit than the dry subject matter he had encountered at school.

'In an unmeritocratic society,' the lecturer opined (they were studying Marx), 'those without the means to advancement have no way to improve their situation, whatever their abilities; no way to escape their social position. It is like being locked in ice.'

Kevin enjoyed that flourish, looking on admiringly as he jotted it down, word for word, the lecturer lightly perspiring in an open shirt. He was wearing jeans, and no tie!

Emerging, star-struck, Kevin whispered to Dick, 'Do you think he's a communist?' losing his friend, as he ran into a desk.

'History, inevitably, is written by the victors and fashioned in their image,' he was lectured on another occasion, 'its actual constituents rarely figure in such a telling.'

Kevin made a shorthand note, considering all that he had missed at school: the hours spent getting from one place to the next; the physiotherapist dragging him out of class; the unmitigated waste of time… It had amused him then, as some kind of ruse – and he had bragged to friends – but he wondered, now, why no one had ever questioned such reductive practices, why no one had even noticed.

It was only now, and these lectures were a part of it (though the battle was already done), that Kevin started to understand how he had suffered: how both the state and society had failed him. It was a paradigm shift that was always likely to come and one that never left him once it had.

I recalled Wittgenstein, of course – 'He must, so to speak, throw away the ladder after he has climbed up it' – and considered what it was to understand too late: to look down in wonder when the ladder has already gone.

At Hugh Baird, with everything in place for him to succeed – the typewriter that, tapping away one-fingered, he was soon a dab hand at; the recently installed lift that would take him up to the third floor – Kevin was able to meet his potential and, despite a continuingly haphazard work ethic, he would flourish, both socially and academically.

'University,' he told his mother, without hesitation, when she broached the subject of what he might do next.

'*University*?' she enquired peevishly. He would be the first of his family to go; didn't know anyone else who had even tried. 'University?' she began again.

'Yes… and you'll wear the word out, if you keep using it,' Kevin returned offhandedly, not in the least intimidated.

Rolling enthusiastically along to the first of several open days, Kevin couldn't help but reflect on how little his mother knew: on how old she was. *University,* he mused, passing under the arched entrance of the Victoria Building, his eyes drawn to the tower and the spire, before emerging into the dazzling sunlight on the other side.

'Silence, please,' whispered a sign posted in a corner of the lawn he passed down the length of and it seemed a strange request, *here*

– of all places – where there was such peace, with students splayed out in small groups on the grass, or stooped over thick books, on low walls and wooden benches.

Kevin loved it already, feeling an immediate kinship, despite the fact that everything was still so new.

Spotting a lone undergraduate, with a dark bob and a striped shirt, coming his way, he stopped to ask directions, gazing dreamily at the clear skin and the slender lips, when she answered in a soft voice that sounded all the vowels. There was no hint of impatience, just the clear desire to help.

'Thanks!' he gushed cheerfully, wanting to keep her.

When, turning a corner, Kevin finally rode up to the building he had been looking for, he felt his stomach turn, his joy inexplicably tempered. It was only gradually, as he straightened his tie and kicked out the tail of his jacket – with a brief shake of the mop of hair that was sat on the top of his head – that those instinctive misgivings were resolved. *Stairs* – he hadn't even considered the possibility.

'Hello,' he called across, in something like fright, to a willowy young man with horn-rimmed glasses, who was striding towards him, his long legs coming to an abbreviated halt. 'Excuse me…' Kevin continued hesitantly, doing his best to disguise what was, by then, a broad Liverpool accent. 'I was wondering if you could help me at all?'

'Of course, how can I be of assistance?' the young man answered, drawing his hands from his pockets and stooping down.

Kevin paused, before flipping his hand up in the direction of the building before them.

'I need to get in there,' he said, tilting his head, 'but…'

'Oh, I see, gosh,' the boy replied in confusion. 'And that's definitely the building you want? I mean, you have the right place?'

'Yes,' Kevin said, flapping at the piece of paper in his lap that gave the address.

'That's the only way in, I'm afraid… perhaps you could get a few people to carry you up?'

Feeling stupid, the indignity washing over him, Kevin let the boy go, his face flushed as he considered retracing his steps.

He sat on for several minutes, in something like shock, barely aware of the students streaming by – one bike, ridden at pace; another pushed along by the handles, a satchel over the shoulder, while an excited gaggle of debutants was forced apart just to get past.

He didn't see them, and it wasn't until he heard voices – two towering lecturers, in full regalia – that he looked up again. Sick, disorientated and embarrassed, he wondered now what he was even doing there, how he had ever imagined that he belonged in such a place.

Then, his anger coursing, Kevin turned on his heels, violently spinning the chair before setting its wheels hissing across the gravel. This, after all, was his hometown university.

The same experience would repeat, with wearying regularity, over the following week and Kevin was never able to come to terms with, or accept, that such decisions had been made without his consent.

It was Keele University next, where a dozen jeering steps faced him down from the top of a nineteenth-century mansion house; then the John Dalton Tower, at Manchester Met, where he sat for a full half hour, stewing over the fact that just four shallow steps kept him from the door.

Of a newer red brick, Sheffield's Alfred Denny Building had tight-turning stairs on either flank and refused to yield. It seemed a conspiracy – he could huff and puff all he liked.

Given the circumstances, there was no way for Kevin to attend university in 1981, as he hoped. Having recently made the discovery of the 'social model of disability', as coined by Mike Oliver, he had already decided on Sociology. He had the grades and the desire, but no way to get up the stairs.

Kevin didn't need to be told again. There was galling familiarity in the understanding that such a lack of provision was no malice, simply incomprehension that someone like him would ever want to go.

Dropping the university brochures he had collected over recent weeks to the outside bin – so that his mother wouldn't find them and ask – Kevin consigned to truculent memory the sight of the smiling young scholars who adorned the covers, every race and demographic on display. It was another lesson; the 'personal statement' he had agonised over for the last week, just a crumpled sheath.

'I don't think I would have been ready, anyway,' Kevin tells me now, picking at the thread of what was to come: the varied path that would bring him back, utterly altered, sixteen years later.

So much had changed by the time he took up his studies again, in September of 1997; those earlier days another country.

Edge Hill was just a short drive from the place that Kevin now called home. Specialising in the training of teachers and nurses, it provided a three-to-one ratio of girls to boys. Kevin would, he was told, be provided with an amanuensis: 'a facilitator', the Professor explained, to help him take notes and get about the college.

'Though all the buildings on campus are accessible,' he was cheerfully assured.

Kevin nodded, gratified not so much by the ramps as by the fact that he had made it, at last, and on his own terms.

The idea of needing support was academic, though the moment he set eyes on the girl he was to choose (from a dozen others) Kevin was won, with the two of them almost immediately forging a relationship that far exceeded the professional terms of their association. That she appeared as enthusiastic as he was closed the deal.

'I love it,' he told his mother, an emaciated figure – no longer the influence she had once been – when he went for a visit, not telling the half of it, discerning a veiled pride in her disinterested tone. 'And Karen's great,' he couldn't help but add, already thinking of his new friend, even in her absence.

Yet, as he took his place alongside the other students in lectures, greeting one or two of them as he deposited a notepad, the set books and a Dictaphone onto the desk he had been provided with, it was hard to deny that he stood somewhat apart.

'As we can see from this illustration,' the lecturer opined, clicking onto the next slide, 'in Victorian times, physical disability was viewed as a mental deficiency, with little distinction made between need and capability.' Kevin could have lifted his hand here, to give lived examples, but he didn't. 'It was only when soldiers returned, disfigured, to field hospitals and, after that, to their home countries, that the notion of 'disability' first came under question,' the lecturer providing the inverted commas that such a term now required.

Yes, we know, Kevin thought spitefully, pushing his head against Karen's shoulder. Refusing the distraction, Karen went on writing, though Kevin couldn't have cared less about those notes.

'*Boring*,' he whispered, glancing across the room, noting that his was the only wheelchair in attendance, once again.

He had also noticed the way that the other students would seek him out, for approval or clarification, whenever particular issues came up for discussion. He didn't blame them – could see that the interest was well-intentioned – but had not expected such scrutiny in a place of higher education.

Kevin was civil, but refused to indulge and would race back outside just as soon as the lecture was done, leaving Karen to gather up their belongings.

'Hurry up!' he would call over his shoulder, as they made their way back to the van that could take them wherever they wanted to go.

While scoffing cynically at the comfortable trappings of university life, Kevin couldn't help but be enchanted by the sight of so many young people gathered in one place just to learn. He took comfort from the quickly established routines too, watching with undeniable pride as Karen dated the page in her neat script, before taking down the title: 'Unit 4: Disability, Democracy and The New Genetics'.

Kevin sank into his seat, with a listless yawn, and Karen jabbed an elbow into his ribs to point out that the lecture was about to begin. He grumbled – didn't care – while recognising the privilege of such engaging company.

Sensing the divide between the other students and himself, and with many of his expectations unmet, Kevin often considered that he had come too late. His classmates looked almost bewildered as they took down facts and theories that he had long since ascribed to commonplace – hurdles to be overcome – and he wondered at associating with mere adolescents.

They were from another world, while he was the son of working-class parents, who had negotiated the daily trials of a 'sink' school he had been given no choice but to attend, surrounded by friends who couldn't care less. Since then, he had already lived a whole other life: he had participated in protests; found full time employment; purchased his first house.

He felt old – amongst sucklings – with Karen's presence alone giving permission. Turning to watch as she bent over her pad, a studious furrow crossing her face as she puzzled with a spelling, he knew that his epiphanies would not be found in any book.

She's amazing, he mused, not for the first time.

He hadn't been looking, of course, and it seemed miraculous how Karen had simply appeared, in answer to a question he hadn't yet thought to ask. She had changed him, made him forget, with the studies he had once put such store in now just a distant truth that he hoped, one day, to overcome.

Catching up to his chair, Karen stretched her arms about his chest from behind with an ease and simplicity that thrilled. He had not thought it possible. Hurrying back to the hall, for the final lecture of the day, the thought came to him for the first time in years: *I wish I wasn't disabled.*

Stepping back out into the sun, Kevin made sure to thank Karen for the notes she had taken, though he rarely made any use of them.

I'm in love! He had thought it often enough and, nine months in, his heart increasingly driven to a single point, such love could hardly be denied. Hoping that, one day, she would come to see him as he was: as a man and nothing more – and not for what he wasn't, or what he might be said to lack... the only question now was how to proceed.

Chapter 3

I wasn't talking about intelligence – cruelty would have been nearer the mark. For, while he was ostensibly only following Karen's lead, those stray contributions ran to excess. Forgetting his loyalties, Kevin took too much delight in twisting the knife.

'He's an idiot,' he would spit, gleefully repeating her words, before adding some spiteful benediction of his own.

The anger was a surprise, given Kevin's natural generosity, and – sinking his teeth into the object of derision – the words didn't ring true. Whatever the veracity of those malicious flourishes, Kevin's head had been turned; noting the sheepish grin, I followed the process with growing fascination.

Cretin, divvie, retard: I could almost hear the cruel barbs as they rattled round his head, imagining the comfort they brought (to say the unsayable).

Dan, bastard; bastard, Dan, hissed with joyful chutzpah – the water lapping over his teeth – as Kevin ploughed under (the words lost to their incantatory rhythm).

He liked Danny, of course, but he had Karen's back and was willing to stand his ground.

'I like Danny,' he hastened to explain, 'I really do.'

I hadn't asked; given their friendship, I didn't doubt it. Grinning ear to ear, as they huddled closer, they were like brothers at times.

Hearing out her complaints with a telling sobriety, Kevin's sympathies were clear.

'He doesn't treat you right,' he said, reciting a pre-prepared line.

Glad to have the pool to themselves, Kevin welcomed the

proximity, too – with Karen just inches away – holding her eye as they spoke (ready to do her bidding).

'I'm sorry to keep banging on,' Karen resumed, her mouth resting on the water.

'Don't be – I want to help,' Kevin returned, thinking: *why does she stay with him?*

'I mean, she could have anyone,' he elaborated.

I pulled a face (to suggest that she couldn't have me).

Watching her quick eyes, as she gazed across the pool – the flush of her cheeks fading – Kevin felt closer than ever.

A sharp cry from the far side of the hall – a pair of teenage boys diving in – ended the reverie, Kevin feeling suddenly quite bare. His arms tiring, he kicked his legs to remind Karen of his presence.

'Do you want to go?' Karen asked.

'Not yet,' Kevin replied, as the waves settled.

Dan really is a fool, if he can't appreciate what he's got in Karen, he mused.

'They're finished,' he had assured me, more than once, '—she doesn't love him anymore,' his words falling into silence.

Cretin, divvie, retard, Kevin ran on, thinking of Dan as he kicked at the surface, driven by desire rather than cruelty: for, love is a zero-sum game and they couldn't both get the girl. Either he would go down, or Danny.

Bobbing back and forth in the desalinated water, Kevin looked across to Karen, now perched on the edge of the pool in her glistening black suit: to the smooth shins, the thick knees and the freckle-dotted thighs (which, soft as silk, yielded to the crisp tile); to the swell of her small breasts pushing against tight nylon; the dots of her painted toes tapping at the bristling foam.

'We go swimming twice a week,' Kevin told me, lifting his eyes quickly – from the curve of her hip (where the suit cut in) – when Karen turned.

She was apologetic when she slipped back into the water.

'Sometimes, I just need to get it off my chest,' she said.

'And that's what I'm here for,' Kevin replied.

Karen gave a smile.

'He's an absolute prick, sometimes,' she resumed, dropping the pitch of her voice to take her boyfriend's part. 'I fucking hate kids... I'd end up killing the fuckers.' While he found humour in the thought of Dan delivering such a tirade, Kevin gave no sign of amusement as Karen concluded. 'Sometimes it's like talking to a wall.'

She was calmer now, and – folding back a strand of hair – had come to a decision.

'I just can't live with him anymore,' she said. His small fingers gripping to the edge of the pool, Kevin felt his heart skip. 'I mean, he's not going to change, is he?'

Silence was answer enough.

Sensing that they had gone as far as they could, Kevin dropped onto his back and let the tide take him.

'There's nothing to tell,' he had replied, when Karen asked about his love life, in return, dipping his head under before she had the chance to ask again.

Rueing the fact that she would soon be back in her clothes, Kevin looked on forlornly when she stepped out of the pool ahead of him, his eyes flicking hurriedly up to the crown of her head when she turned.

'Dan doesn't understand her,' he explained, running me through his latest encounter. Not like *he* did.

....

Kevin was eleven years old when he was taught to swim at the Princess Margaret Rose Hospital in Edinburgh – where he had gone to be fitted for new prosthetics – the superior technology deemed worth the journey. Free from the clunky straps and chains his other legs had been burdened down with, these new legs were almost comfortable: the bucket he sat in moulded with greater precision to provide a sense of security, the walker taking to the air like a miracle!

They weren't the only option, with Kevin's classmates, Johnny Hinds and Pamela Jones, both opting for the considerably less secure, but apparently more stylish, legs from Liverpool. Kevin wasn't persuaded and hence those trips up north – eight in total – between the ages of five and eleven.

'We went up together, in a bus,' he begins, placing Johnny and Pamela beside him, though they hadn't, in fact, accompanied him on a single one of those sorties – only stopping himself short, with a shake of the head, the next time we spoke – 'No, but Johnny and Pamela weren't there then, were they?'

He hadn't been paying attention. For, while he welcomed the escape, this was no holiday, even if his indefatigable mother insisted on pointing out the places of interest along the way (Kevin feigning sleep).

He was too old, he considered, to be travelling under his mother's supervision; if the other children seemed happy enough in their parents' care, Kevin considered that – save for their destination – they had little in common. Watching as they were dressed, calling 'mummy' across the dorm room without an ounce of shame, Kevin considered them spoiled and cosseted.

Carefully folding the shirt he had taken off, for himself, Kevin drew out his neatly-pressed pyjamas, before starting up on one of the voluminous tombs he had brought along for the trip (*The Wolves of Willoughby Chase*, on this occasion).

Then he remembers, again, that it was a train they had taken, not a bus, meeting the Manchester sleeper at Preston, before dividing back out at Carstairs, South Lanarkshire (which gave routes through to Glasgow and Edinburgh).

'It was just me and my mum... sometimes Aunt Lucy,' he

clarified, the pleasure of that journey returning; the world passing at pace from the windows; towns and villages vanishing in the blink of an eye.

Such a lengthy excursion had necessitated an overnight stay at the hospital's 'special' unit, a single-storey structure dating from the mid-sixties that offered little in the way of critical adaptations. The bathrooms lacked hoists, the doors were too narrow, while the decorative spots and stripes suggested the dubious comforts of a holiday home. Kevin, who liked to be on the move, welcomed the change of scene.

'I remember having haggis there,' he recounts excitedly. That would have been in the communal dining area, with their meals brought across from the main building on squeaking trolleys (under metal cloches). 'It was revolting!'

There was a small kitchen to the rear, where breakfast – cereals and toast, tea and juice – was prepared, with the dining room doubling as a play area once the plates and cutlery had been cleared (with Lego and Tonka dragged hastily from fraying boxes). The communal lounge, with wide windows offering grandstand views over Arthur's Seat, boasted a 12-inch Peto Scott television, on which Kevin, dating it clearly enough, remembers watching *Andy Pandy*.

Of the four bedrooms, Kevin usually got one to himself, for some reason, and he can still bring to mind the colourful parade of elephants that circled the shade on the bedside lamp, his mother and Aunt Lucy (if she came) taking the room next door.

The bathroom was huge – though everything seemed huge to him then – with a steep, oversized bath pitched up against the far wall. After filling the tub to the brim, with an almost ritualistic fervour, Kevin would set about the icebergs of lathered foam with a whistled breath or ploughing nose.

'I'll unpack, while you run the bath,' he would tell his mother on arrival, welcoming the familiarity.

Taking a turn about that same unit, on later visits, Kevin would note, more scrupulously, that the leaded windows, though decorated with brightly coloured curtains, opened no more than a crack; that the heavy doors had automatic locks; that, despite the abstract art lining the walls, the place had an institutional feel.

'They treat us like babies,' he grumbled, on learning that the eight o'clock curfew would mean them missing the end of *The High Chaparral*. 'It's still light out,' he hissed. 'At home, I can stay up as late as I want…'

Tentative murmurs followed from the other children, whose parents were not so broad-minded, with Kevin proving good to his word when he had his mother persuade the nurse to let them stay up until the end (though he was the only one left to see John Cannon making fragile peace with the Apache). For Kevin, it was a typical flexing of muscles.

'Johnny – hurry up!' he whistled to his best friend first, on another visit, sliding stealthily between the beds, 'let's go!' shaking Pamela awake next – as he *recollects* – before moving on to the others, one by one, in the dark.

Together, they not only managed to force the heavy doors, giving egress from their narrow quarters, but also to set off, under cover of stars – a cast of nocturnal crabs – towards the main hospital.

They stopped, to catch their breaths, before heaving themselves up the grass slope to the rear, in order to communicate with the patients in the windows above them, joyfully waving their fingers and flippers.

'No one can hold us!' Kevin cried into the still night, his voice hoarse, his breath short.

It was a rare taste of something they couldn't yet quantify, the children warmed to their souls even as they shook with the cold (none of them had thought to bring a coat). Kevin was eleven years old now, and he wouldn't be back.

The next morning, after breakfast, they were measured up for their prosthetics before being taken along to the hospital's on-site swimming centre. Fifty metres long, this was the biggest pool Kevin had ever seen, and he stood in the doorway for several seconds, along with the rest – the room a glorious silence – none of them daring to break the pellucid tranquillity. It was a stunning sight and, for once in their young lives, they had the floor to themselves, with no need of legs to walk it.

Fitted into ill-fitting trunks and swimsuits, with bright, inflatable rings attached to their hands and feet (or to waists, where they had neither) the novitiates were almost immediately started out on the water.

Letting out high-pitched squeals of delight whenever they bumped up against the side, or another child – the lukewarm water lapping in and out of their panting maws – the children moved with surprising confidence.

By noon, having progressed into single armbands, they were encouraged onto their backs, floating more calmly, and with greater control, as they found their balance and rhythm, their eyes trained on the high ceiling, where the flickering light played on the plated glass (the world turned upside down).

With practise, and belief, came buoyancy, and they were all soon criss-crossing the pool at will, and unaided, even if the direction of travel was wholly arbitrary. It was a beautiful moment, strangely staggered – something akin to a dream – when they realised just what they were doing (and doing for themselves).

'Mum! Mum! I can swim!' Kevin whooped, spotting his mother, who was sat at the side of the pool.

With a cautious smile, Agnes pulled her son up, onto dry land, from where he was able to watch as the others went solo, too (sharing in their pleasure).

'I'm going for two lengths, next!' Johnny – plumped down beside him – promised, and suddenly anything seemed possible.

I can swim, I can actually swim, Kevin thought, that same thought holding him in thrall (and disbelief).

Proud and content, with a little more of the world opened up to them, those temporary colleagues slept like lions that night and would return to the family home eager to press their new-found skills.

'I've only learned the backstroke so far,' Kevin twittered, with guarded authority, his father's big arms wrapped about him, 'but I'm going to learn the crawl next time.'

'We'll have to find you somewhere with proper supervision, first,' his mother broke in anxiously, turning a shirt on the ironing board. 'We don't want you sinking without trace now, do we?'

She wasn't the only parent to see the dangers inherent in the newly acquired skill-set, nor to experience the difficulty of finding a suitable pool.

'Well, I'm very proud of you,' his father repeated, with affection (and a warmth he would miss).

Kevin never did manage the front crawl, or the breaststroke: it had been enough, on the day, that they could all swim (with the backstroke much less reliant on serviceable arms). Given the damage that would have likely accrued to his spine, a spine already bearing the bruises of those new prosthetics, it is probably a good thing that Kevin was never turned and taught to swim on his front. With his heavy head a lead load on the ship's bow, and his puny hands and feet nowhere near sufficient, it was all a matter of balance. Kevin *can* float on his chest, temporarily, if turned, but will quickly succumb if unsupported for any length of time – a dead weight, dropping to the chequer tiles.

Founded in the first flush of Lady Hoare's compassionate patronage, the Princess Margaret Rose Hospital was demolished in 1983, taking every last physical trace of that liberating day (an emancipation of sorts) along with it. Kevin rarely saw any of those children again, after their final visit in 1973, excepting when one of them would appear on a documentary and the memories come flooding.

'I know him,' Kevin would whisper, giving an involuntary cry in the struggle to recall the figure on the screen.

So much had happened in the interim, their lives too complicated to hold such simple times.

'I'd forgotten all about that,' Kevin said, glad to be prompted, shaking his head at the whitewash of his unconscious.

In the summer of 1976, despite his limited capabilities, Kevin – who was now fourteen – was called upon to compete in a sponsored swim at his school, in aid of the NSPCC. The event provoked a media scrum, with an outside broadcast crew from the BBC joining journalists and photographers from the local press in jostling for position as the litter of thalidomides took to the pool.

With the voices of the children' cutting shrilly through the responding calls of the supervising adults and the chamber lined with hard surfaces, the sound would carry and echo back to a chaotic degree (that had heads shaking in confusion). Kevin, who was accustomed to being the centre of attention, was unconcerned, though the overriding tone was up for debate.

'It's marvellous what these poor children are doing to help other unfortunates,' he heard an elderly woman telling his mother, when he stopped for a breather, smiling blankly back.

'You and your little pals are making quite a splash,' his mother quipped when they were alone again, 'you should be very proud.'

Pretending he hadn't heard, Kevin dropped back down.

When it came to the celebrities, who were out in force, Kevin was far from reticent, and – on dry land, once more – he was soon making himself known, wheeling up to Billy Butler (a local radio presenter) first.

His head rocking back and forth, in what he considered infectious bonhomie, the some-time comic bowed down to shake Kevin's shrouded feet, while giving a wink to the proud parent. Les Dennis, who had won *New Faces* with a record score the previous summer, came next, offering Kevin words of encouragement with tears in his eyes. Giving a winsome smile, Kevin wasn't sure who Les Dennis actually was.

Having lived his whole life in the public eye, Kevin wasn't fazed by the chance of mixing with the stars, though seeing the full *Blue Peter* team idling at the side of the pool, in their tasteful slacks – cheering as he passed by – was admittedly surreal. When Miss Judd gave an enthusiastic wave, he blushed, having always quite fancied her.

Arriving in their full club colours, to cheers from the gallery, the Everton football team caused the greatest stir, with Kevin keen to meet his own particular favourites, Bob Latchford and Mickey Lyons, who both posed for pictures before providing autographs.

'What happened to us this season?' Kevin teased – a mid-table finish following a near-win the previous year – and they grumbled along with him, surprised to find Kevin as able to joke as they were.

A lifelong Blue, Kevin was pleased to learn that the Liverpool team were away, in Bruges (for the return leg of the UEFA Cup Final) and couldn't attend, though he was, admittedly, star-struck when Bill Shankly – who he didn't immediately recognise – ambled across to start up a conversation with his mother.

'Agnes,' she told him, when asked, her face colouring, 'but I don't much like the name.'

'Well, that's a real shame,' Bill returned gently, 'when it's such a pretty name… and my wife's too… though we call her Nessie,' he clarified, with a genial bow, before hitching back up to his feet.

He stayed for the rest of the morning, to show his support, even if he seemed more interested in the mother than the child.

'That voice,' Agnes would sigh later, offering her husband a confession, 'and a genuinely lovely man.'

'I wish some of our players were as brave as this wee boy,' Bill would joke, when Kevin was hauled out of the pool after his second swim.

'A Boot Room norm,' he told Agnes, as he helped with the rubdown.

Taking turns, each of the swimmers would complete ten full lengths of the twenty-five-metre pool, before coming up for air.

Kevin had already swum close to a mile when, having finished the fourth leg of his swim, his day was prematurely curtailed.

He had been treading water, waiting to be pulled out when, flipped briefly onto his front – without the energy to object – the hands that were holding him let go (and he fell).

'Kevin!' the lifeguard cried in panic, when she turned to find him gone, scanning the still plate of water – where he had been just moments before – shock and confusion washing over her, while the room went blank.

Then, in a rush of adrenalin, she threw herself in and dove down after him, finding her charge on the floor of the pool, his dark bulk breaking the tile line, the ghost of a smile floating up to his lips, as the chlorine bit.

She had Kevin's small, rigid body back up to the surface within seconds, pulling him off to the side to check his pulse before placing him in the recovery position.

'Can you hear me, Kevin?' she asked, tapping at his bloated cheeks. 'Are you there?'

Coughing up a full chest of water, Kevin gave a sheepish smile.

When he could, he told her, 'I'm fine, really… that last swim must have taken it out of me, and I had nothing left.'

'Well, you're not going in again,' his mother declared, lifting him onto her lap, where he was wrapped in the thick towel she had brought from home.

Seeing Shirley rushing across, with a look of concern, Kevin was glad that the swimming was done.

'You were brilliant,' she whispered, crouching down to him.

'I could have swum another mile, at least,' Kevin boasted.

'I'm sure you could,' Shirley agreed, resting her chin on top of his head and wrapping her arms about his waist, 'you're a much better swimmer than me.'

Kevin basked in that embrace – in a scent he knew by heart. Being pulled from the water, in such circumstances, had been a stroke of good fortune if it meant he got Shirley to himself – no one else in that vast auditorium mattered.

The older sister of a friend of Kevin's younger sister (Liz), Shirley Duggan had introduced herself by means of a note brought back from one of his sister's visits. She was, to all intents and purposes, Kevin's first proper girlfriend.

'Open up,' Liz hissed, rattling softly at his door – their ailing father 'not to be disturbed' in the next room – 'I've got something for you,' listening for the thump on the floor that meant her brother had heard. 'It's a letter,' she told him, when he peeped out.

'A letter?'

'From Shirley,' Liz teased, handing him a Manila envelope with his name scrawled across the top, the perfume coming off on his fingers. 'Rebecca's big sister,' she added.

Kevin pulled the door shut, without a further word, and it was only when he was safely up on his bed again that he tore into his prize, noting immediately that it was a girl's script, with fat curlicues and thick dots over the i's – and, that fragrance (stronger now). It was the first letter he had ever received.

Hello Kevin!

We haven't met yet, but your sister has told me all about you – she said you like Queen? I do too! Why don't you bring your albums round to my house some time and we can listen to them together?

Shirley xx

It was all so unlikely and, his heart beating fast as he read the words over, Kevin felt himself colour.

It was Sunday, early afternoon. Determined to go and see her at once, Kevin examined his profile, briefly, in the mirror, working the point of a pencil beneath the scab that still sat to the right of his nose (from an earlier fall). When it came loose in one clean piece, he was oddly emboldened – wanting, for some reason, to make a good impression.

He changed into a fresh shirt and even allowed his mother to run a cloth over his face, before rattling off on his mobility scooter, taking the straightest route to the address his sister had given – less than a mile away – bumping his wheels up against the door to announce his arrival.

'Good afternoon,' he greeted the stooped man who answered, his wife a step behind, 'I'm Kevin Donnellon and I've come to see Shirley.'

A smile passed between the parents, before Mrs Duggan called up the stairs to their daughter, and there she was, skipping two steps apiece, before skidding to a halt in the hall, seeming – only then – to size Kevin up, with a cautious wave and a generous smile.

'I can't believe you came so soon!' she exclaimed, gliding across the tiled floor for a closer look.

'No time like the present,' Kevin declared smoothly, his mind already turning to the records stacked at his side, and to which he'd play first.

She seemed nice and seemed to like him.

'You'd better come in,' she said, breaking the spell; only then did they consider how they would get him into the house.

There was chemistry from the start, their time together passing in a blur (just as it would on subsequent occasions).

'Hello…' Mrs Duggan ventured, eventually, making a check on them, 'Kevin's mum will be wondering where he is…'

Their faces shining with pleasure, they were surprised to learn that it was so late.

'Oh yes, sorry Mrs Duggan,' Kevin stuttered, as he shuffled to the end of the bed and dropped to the floor, hardly believing that a dull Sunday afternoon had turned into this – that rushing over, headlong, to meet the summons, he now had a new friend. They weren't even in the same school.

'She's great,' he told his mother, while she dressed him for bed, 'and she's got great taste in music.'

Combing through his hair to free the knots, Agnes nodded distractedly. She didn't understand and nor did Kevin, who would spend the rest of the evening running back through their conversation for clues.

He would come to know Shirley better over the forthcoming weeks, finding that they had a whole lot more in common than he had first thought, that there was more to their friendship than Queen (or music, even).

'And I told her she can come over here, next Sunday,' Kevin continued breathlessly.

Agnes paused, the steaming iron still held in her hand.

'That'd be lovely,' she said, 'your little friends are always welcome.'

They were soon meeting up on a regular basis, most often at the Donnellon house, given the vexed issue of accessibility.

'It's like a palace,' Shirley whispered, when he gave the tour.

'Wait 'til you see my room,' Kevin replied, blushing at the thought, but desperate to escape his mother now that she had started in on the photographs on the mantelpiece.

'And that's my eldest, John, who we haven't seen in years.'

Shirley wasn't to get an explanation.

'We need to go,' Kevin urged, pushing away and indicating that Shirley should follow.

'She's lovely… your mum,' Shirley declared, when they were alone, wondering at the warnings he had given.

'You don't know her, yet,' Kevin muttered, letting the rest pass, glad that she already felt welcome and at home.

Trying gently at his conscience, Shirley would regularly come to his mother's defence, with a single look usually enough to break his resolve.

'She's your mum… and she does so much for you,' she would point out.

Turning to find that she was already propped up on the bed (with her small shoes lined up at the wall), Kevin wouldn't argue, but start up another record, instead.

Once a galley-kitchen, with cupboards spanning the wall opposite his squat single bed – and a sliding door opening, handily, onto the hall – Kevin's room ran the full width of the house. The sockets, switches and handles were all within easy reach (about a foot from the floor), with a sturdy writing desk cut away to give access to his chair and a typewriter sat proudly on top.

A second door led out to the garden, where a paved path circled the lawn, the previously mildewed pantry now an en suite, with a walk-in shower, a knee-high sink and a spanking new Clos-o-mat.

'This is amazing!' Shirley gasped, taking a turn.

Kevin followed a pace behind, drawing her attention to the state-of-the-art Panasonic he had recently installed (with its fifteen-watt speakers), while his mother pushed in with a plate of sandwiches and glasses of fizzy pop.

Giddily singing along with their idols, Kevin would hop down to turn the disc when it ran out, the crackle of needle a prelude to an escape they increasingly thrilled to. There was Bowie and Sparks… the material pointing forward, their tastes showing sophistication beyond their years.

'I don't know what you two kids get up to in here,' Agnes mused, when she came to tell Shirley it was time to leave. In believing that they were still children – and that she still had some hold – Agnes was missing the point. 'It's a school night,' she noted, trying another tack, 'and I've still got to get Kevin ready for bed.'

The humiliation was one that Shirley took no account of, or was too careful to notice.

'I'll do you a copy of those albums,' Kevin continued, disregarding his mother.

'Thanks again for having me, Mrs Donnellon,' Shirley said, ignoring Kevin, in turn.

This was no dissimulation; Shirley, who couldn't help but see past and beyond *Kevin's* disability, could only ever see the good in others, too.

'Can I give you a hand?' she asked, bouncing off the bed to join the search.

'It's here, somewhere – I had it the other day,' Kevin muttered, acting the curmudgeon.

'Then, we'll find it,' Shirley admonished, playfully, 'and don't be such a grump!'

Spotting the recalcitrant sheath, Shirley pulled it out from beneath Kevin's rump – where it had been the whole time – and the air was filled with laughter.

'We're best friends,' Shirley giggled to her sister, under interrogation, continuing breathlessly, 'he's cool… and he's funny,' thinking suddenly of something they had been in fits over earlier in the day.

'She's called Shirley,' Kevin was just as quick to inform his friends, with a swell of pride, appreciating the fact that, because they didn't attend the same school, he wouldn't have to share her.

They were soon inseparable and if one of them had to cancel they would exchange letters instead, with Liz the dutiful emissary.

'What did she say?' he would ask, on her return.

'She's got relatives over,' impatient now, 'but they'll be gone by the weekend… oh, yeah, and she'll phone you later.'

Kevin climbed up onto his bed to read the letter, which was usually just a prosaic run-through of her day at school (or something she had seen on TV), but it was contact, at least, and boasted of an intimacy that none of his other friends could attest to.

Turning to the foot of the letter first, Kevin would look to the kisses scratched beneath her name, which seemed as significant as the scent by which they were sealed. He could read whatever he wanted into those ink-blotched kisses, often considering the letter he would receive as worth the loss of an evening. *She loves me; she loves me not,* he would muse, touching his face to the page, drawing in the familiar bouquet, though he hadn't yet a thought to do anything more about feelings that remained shapeless and inchoate.

Looking down from the bed, as she reached up to him, it came as a surprise to learn that she had breasts inside her thin blouse, and was a woman – dropping his eyes away (his heart in his mouth) – and no longer a child. He could only hope that he, too, was becoming a man.

He was soon looking again, more closely now, as she groped about on the floor for an album she had a sudden desire to hear, understanding, at last, that everything had changed (while he had stood still).

'What do you think?' she asked, and he wasn't sure what the question was, or what she wanted his opinion on, gazing back with a shake of the head as he sought his footing.

He mumbled, 'yes,' while committing to nothing, seeing with a new manner of objectivity.

Still soft with puppy fat, grafted close to the bones of pronounced cheeks, the face was longer now, the unruly, curly hair cut crisp to the shoulder; set fair against pale skin, her lips were fuller, with a delicate trace of down brushing the vermilion border. Tucked under, in ankle socks – or knock-kneed in a short, flared dress – Shirley's legs had, sometime in between, gotten taller.

'She looked like a doll,' Kevin registers fondly, 'so pretty… but down to earth, too,' feeling regret at what he hadn't yet thought to explore.

There had been some adjustments already, of course – in acknowledgement of changing circumstances – but these had somehow eluded him. While they still shared the bed and bumped up together quite freely, they were more circumspect in the way they touched; they would kiss cheeks in greeting, but elsewhere respected the need for a clear definition of personal space.

If it was a sign of previously unconsidered possibilities – showing Kevin that he need be no different to other men – it was unwelcome, too, with Kevin seeking the very proximity that was now refused him. As his desires were refined, sometimes just the soft touch of her fingers or the smell of her freshly laundered hair was enough to send him into ecstasies.

'Are you two alright up there?' Mrs Donnellon would call and, in all honesty, Kevin would have to admit that he wasn't, with Shirley's visits now far from simple.

Huddled close on his childhood bed, with a duvet over their

knees and the screen flickering in the dark from across the room – their attention drawn with hallowed intensity – they watched films now, as often as they listened to music.

Feeling Shirley's body beside his own, Kevin could think of little else, surreptitiously turning his eyes to take in the side of her face – illuminated in the half-light – and the slightly cracked upper lip, imagining what it would be like to kiss or to hold her. He knew he wouldn't – and *couldn't* – but, in those moments, time would stop and the world would change (and one day, he would – he *could*)...

They continued night after night, in the same fashion, as the seasons and the years turned – talking with intimacy and freedom, so close that they almost touched. Lacking the weight of undue expectation, afforded a purity they couldn't yet appreciate, it was perfect. After a quick glance at her watch, Shirley would suddenly straighten up her skirt, before jumping down from the bed, as Kevin caught at his breath once more.

That it had to end was an inevitability they couldn't appreciate, with 3 June 1977 – when they went to see Queen at the Liverpool Empire Theatre – proving an apotheosis of sorts.

'It's a date,' Kevin told his friends at school, though it was never that, and while they weren't all necessarily the biggest Queen fans, with 'Bohemian Rhapsody' still casting its shadow – and tickets so hard to come by – they had to admit to jealousy.

'We'll need to go straight from school,' his mother explained, 'and go in by the stage door before they open up to the public.'

'Will we be allowed backstage?' Kevin asked, his eyes wide.

'Probably,' Agnes replied, thinking of her contact at *The Echo*, who had organised the tickets, and the 'stories' she had given in turn.

There were already queues outside when they arrived, with numerous small groups gathered in the vicinity: children standing with their parents (bunking school); teenagers sharing cans of cider; drainpipes and mascara.

Agnes hadn't expected such a crowd and suddenly doubted the wisdom of handing her young charges across to the bouncer who was waiting for them at the stage door, almost pulling them back as they stepped into the dark.

The children were nervous, too – with each soft turn of the wheels echoing along the empty corridor (and drawing attention) – but they tried not to show it as, climbing through the bowels of the venue, they came up into the light of the auditorium. Then there was music, and their fears lifted.

'Look,' Kevin whispered, nodding excitedly up to the stage, where Brian May was standing in silhouette, with a guitar strapped to his hip.

'Okay?' he shouted across to the desk, after playing a run of chords, silence taking the room.

Kevin noticed then that Shirley was shaking and, in that moment, rooted to the spot – their guide already several steps ahead of them – Brian May turned and, seeing them, gave a wave with one hand while shielding his face with the other. The bouncer moved them on, with a smile.

'It's Brian May!' Shirley whispered, her arms lashed about Kevin's chest.

The ensuing night was everything they could have wished for, with the two friends perched in the pit between the band and the crowd, and – as promised – taken backstage at the end, where they were surprised to find Freddie Mercury, so flamboyant just a half hour before, now oddly subdued.

Giving a cursory nod when they were presented, Kevin went ahead and asked, securing them the autograph he knew Shirley wanted over all the others.

Tripping away in a star-struck daze, they quickly set about filling out their programmes with the autographs of the rest of the band.

'Freddie Mercury…' Shirley purred, and it was something like a dream (that they dared not wake from).

'It was cool,' Kevin now admits – expecting an argument – 'but the best thing was spending time with Shirley.'

Welcoming the chance to give something back, Kevin had savoured the sight of her shining eyes and unbroken smile, as they circled the room. They were holding hands the whole way round, their hearts as one (never wanting it to end).

If it was the most beautiful evening they would ever share – with Kevin still just fifteen years old – it was the end of something, too. For, when Chris Stocks, Kevin's cousin, came for a visit three weeks later, everything changed.

With a mottled cigarette cusped casually behind his studded left ear, his firm jaw churning energetically at gum, the tall and muscular Chris was barely eighteen, but he was wily and streetwise.

'He had thick blonde hair,' Kevin sneers helplessly, 'like Rod Stewart… thought he was God's gift,' and – as free with his fists as his heart – such an assessment had yet to meet much resistance.

'Hey mate, how's it going?' he asked now, his eyes scanning the room. He turned, when there was no response, to clarify: 'Any birds on the go?'

'Not at the moment,' Kevin replied coolly, giving nothing away, and breathing more freely only when Chris had gone prowling out to the garden (seeming led by the nose).

Kevin could already hear him, in full flow.

'Yeah, I'd like to play for Everton, one day – go down for a trial, like…' and could readily imagine Chris taking, with a swagger, to the field, alongside Howard Kendall and Duncan McKenzie. 'Or, I might become an actor,' he continued, giving a theatrical spin while winking playfully at a passing cousin (a teenage girl). 'I won't be round here for long, I know that much,' he continued, with a disparaging nod, 'so, catch me while you can!'

'He was in a band, too,' Kevin recounts, with a smirk, 'he was the lead singer!'

Chris was soon off again – to 'mix and mingle' as he called it – announcing himself with a wide beam to the next group, his tanned face and bright teeth indicating rude health (and no shame).

'How you doing?' he'd ask, when they parted to give room, pulling out a cigarette and flicking a lighter – a smooth operator – before he even deigned to begin.

Chris was witty, Kevin allows with a snort, 'like a young Mike Yarwood,' remembering his humorous turns of phrase and the accents he would adopt to deliver them. While able to admit that Chris was *cool*, with the whole world at his feet, Kevin wasn't particularly impressed. He had charms of his own; he had Shirley, too, and needed nothing more.

He would soon learn that he wasn't the only one to appreciate her qualities; by the time he saw the danger, it was already too late. For, despite Kevin's close and attentive proximity, Chris was making a move within a minute of spotting his prey.

'Where you been hiding?' he asked, stepping across to offer a cigarette, which Shirley took unflinchingly, clasping her hand to help her light it, flashing his teeth. 'Do you come here often?' he quipped, and he was nearly on top of her now, pushing a strand of hair back behind her ear; blushing, Shirley didn't correct him.

'Do you want a drink?' Kevin asked hurriedly.

'I'm okay, thanks,' Shirley replied, with a quick glance, before turning back to her new acquaintance, who was now whispering something into her ear.

The effect was immediate and awful, with Shirley's acquiescence resulting in her being dumped to the grass, Chris pinning her wrists as he straddled her waist, while forcing up her floral skirt. She would wonder, later, at the stains.

'Shall we go in and listen to some music?' Kevin tried again, when they were back on their feet, flinching at an unfamiliar distance, even as Shirley returned a smile, Chris's triumphant leer matched by the ease of her submission.

Chris pulled Shirley tight again and she swayed, light-headed, into his arms; Kevin knew he couldn't stay. When, half an hour later, he stepped out again, he found Shirley standing up against the wall that ran along the side of the house, while Chris worked his mouth over hers, his kisses slow and tender at first, and then deeper, and with greater force.

Front row centre, Kevin stood and watched, with growing nausea, while considering his next move. *It's my house*, he thought, figuring that he couldn't leave, though he could hardly demand their departure.

The beer in his hand had no taste, as he took a sip, light on his feet. *She's just like all the others*, he considered bitterly, with no idea who he was comparing her to. *I love her*, he mouthed, in despair, *and I thought she loved me.*

The breath had already left his chest, as he turned away, seeking distraction – someone else to talk to – but the thought of how close they had become and the changes brought about in a single afternoon, was too much to take. All that time they'd had together and he had never laid a finger on her, or made any kind of approach – he had been the complete 'gentleman', and now… *Chris. How could she fall for Chris?*

Kevin turned back, instinctively, to find them still going at it, and he felt his legs buckle and his stomach churn (though he had already eaten).

He had thought Shirley was different and, waving her bravely off at the gate – numb now – he couldn't hide his disappointment or his sorrow, at the sight of her squeezing nonchalantly into Chris's low-flung two-seater. However careful her smile, all he could see was her betrayal, with loss and irrelevancy stalking. If Shirley was Kevin's first love, her loss also represented his first heartbreak. Hurrying inside, he vowed to never see her again.

Wrapped beneath the covers, complaining of a headache and refusing all calls, there was no rousing Kevin the next day, though each time he revived, he would moan and mumble: *I'm pathetic – how could I think she'd be interested in me?*

These were thoughts he had never voiced before, though there seemed no escaping them now; shedding tears that he could hardly account for, the scale of defeat was clear.

'She was my first love,' he tells me, and it is hard to imagine that forty years has passed.

For all his suffering, Kevin's tone is fundamentally upbeat when he recalls those bygone days; they had shared so much together that there can be few regrets. Chris Stocks' late arrival was a mere footnote.

'We were just kids,' Kevin can concede, 'but, at the time, it felt like the end of the world.'

Yet, through Kevin's recollections of what was essentially just 'puppy' love, a crush, at a point in his life when there was very little sense of time – everything seeming set to run on, forever – I had not seen Chris coming; when Kevin was through with the telling, his was still just a minor role.

'When we were a bit older,' Kevin resumed, his eyes shining – far from finished – 'we'd go into town every weekend, on the train,' telling of Shirley's struggles with the chair, how she would heave it aboard as the doors drew shut, collapsing breathless onto the tartan seat when she had him in, before spinning to face him.

'Bloody hell, Kev, you're getting fat!'

There was no trace of Chris here; he had known nothing of their life, or what they shared – those lost weekends – Kevin's face coming alive with the rich memories of emotion.

'We'd wander round the shops,' he continued, 'trying things on, for a laugh; get a portion of chips… just the two of us, in our own little world… I was totally infatuated.'

They were both, ultimately, confused; they were happy, too.

'She used to bring cigarettes,' he snorted, suddenly, 'I don't know where she got them… probably off one of her sisters… and we'd find a quiet spot where we could shelter from the wind, while we got them lit… smoking them quickly, so we wouldn't get caught.'

He looked at me over his glasses, to see how I took to this latest revelation (though I had heard it all, by now), before erupting into laughter at another recollection – of a grand larceny.

'Yeah, and one time we stole a pack of crisps from the Marks & Spencer on Church Street,' the vivid particular opening up the floodgates, his delight palpable. 'They were prawn cocktail!' he fairly yelped, beaming with pride.

The pack had rustled as they left the store, even though Shirley had stuffed it beneath the blanket Kevin's mother always insisted he carry (against the cold), the two of them chasing away in utter fright, adrenalin kicking in as they made a run for it.

Chris, of course, knew nothing of that, and never felt the pangs of romance and love that they did, as they moved, together, through adolescence – as scared as they were exhilarated – knowing only that they wouldn't be anywhere else, their lives irrevocably tied, in ways they couldn't yet know.

'Shirley helped me decorate my room in Litherland Park,' Kevin began again, 'because I was always moaning about the wallpaper... She said we could fix it up; it'd be fun – that we could make a day of it,' arriving there, the following weekend, with her hair tied back and a decided bounce in her step.

Kevin had sent his mother out for paint and the pots were laid out on the floor, beside an assortment of brushes, though neither of them had considered the stripping and scraping they'd have to do first.

Kevin doesn't remember that now, only the destructive glee they took in ripping the old wallpaper down – the floor around them soon filling up – before pinning up its replacement, a plain, textured paper, just as much of the paste on the two friends as the wall. Still, it ultimately came out well and any unevenness in the finish was soon enough concealed beneath the posters Shirley had brought over – spares from her own collection – as a finishing touch.

'We make a good team,' Kevin declared, when they were done, imagining that one day they would have their own house and be decorating the whole place.

Kevin was in love and the pictures Shirley took that day, on her plastic Instamatic (a Christmas gift), capture everything, their faces shot through with pleasure, as the drizzle slapped at the window and the afternoon progressed into evening.

'She had this thin woollen top,' Kevin recalled, in a tremor, 'that she often wore around that time and it was a really tight fit… and she had just started to get breasts – she looked amazing.'

Her frayed denim skirt was cut to the knee, opaque tights tracing the curve of her calves, as she stretched up to a corner Kevin couldn't reach.

'Is it straight?' she'd call down from the step ladder, gazing back at him, her button nose already smudged with paint.

Transfixed by the revelation of those thighs (and scared to look further), Kevin did well to react, directing her with sudden sobriety.

'Yeah, yeah, that's great… perfect.'

She was slight and light, and lithe, and moved with a delicate grace, freckles dotting the backs of her upper arms – hope in her heart.

'She was stunning,' Kevin concedes, 'and I fancied her like mad,' delivering those words so tenderly that it seemed he had only just learnt it.

Shirley still has the photos she took that day: a full roll of twenty-four that she sent off to Max Spielmann for processing. A conjurer's trick, they show what – blinded by sobering familiarity – Kevin couldn't see at the time.

Chris had only a single dog-eared strip of 1.5 inch passport shots, which they had taken 'for a laugh', fairly tripping into the booth and then pulling faces over one another's shoulders. He probably wouldn't remember; he certainly hasn't kept them. Yet, whatever their relative merits, within a single hour of their introduction, Chris had taken from Shirley what Kevin had not yet even thought of.

Giggling uncontrollably, Shirley was barely recognisable the next time they met.

'He's very mature,' she explained, and it was strange to think of her viewing Chris in such a way, that such a steady head could have fallen for such a poser. Picturing his cousin's playful sneer and careless swagger, he struggled to see what the two could have in common – she was worth so much more. 'But it's okay,' Shirley continued, giddily – and he had forgotten she was speaking – 'he said he's happy to take it slow.'

Kevin's face had dropped and his breath was tight, yet smarting (and bitter too) he somehow met her eye and hazarded a smile, as she babbled on.

'He told me about the other girls he's been with… said he didn't want there to be any misunderstanding, but… that I'm different and he wants us to go steady.'

Kevin looked across at Shirley, flushed in the telling and, though he hoped above everything that they wouldn't last, he hated the thought of Shirley being just another conquest.

'What about you – any birds on the go?' Chris asked, the next time he was over – he had brought Shirley, too – leaning in to take advantage of her brief absence (she was making use of the facilities), with a conspiratorial tap at his chest.

Wondering at how Chris could think he could want anyone other than Shirley, Kevin could have hit him. Trying a smile, he refused to answer and was relieved when Shirley skipped back through and broke the conversation, Chris scooping her up onto the bed – *their* bed – to delighted squeals.

Excusing himself, Kevin didn't venture back until they were on their way out again.

The 'happy couple' were – fortunately – all done within a couple of months, Shirley announcing, quite unexpectedly, that, 'we've decided to call it a day.' That got Kevin's attention and, looking closer, he saw that there had been tears.

Yet, there was to be no return to their former life, as he hoped, Chris's arrival (and departure) seeming only to have suggested the possibilities. The world had shifted and, while Kevin edged quietly towards the periphery, Shirley almost immediately moved on to other boys and other bases, and he could hardly stand around and watch as one anonymous figure after the next vied for her affections. He didn't know how he hadn't seen it before, but Shirley was beautiful, an absolute 'catch', and there were always going to be boys.

Kevin hung in as long as he could – as best friend and confessor – but, finding himself bundled up in the back of the latest boyfriend's car (an orange Austin Allegro), with the wind whipping wearily at its paper-thin roof, while his companions petted away on the front seats, he finally gave in to the inevitable.

'Is it okay if you drop me home?' he asked, 'it's just, I'm going out later...'

It was a lie, the first of many, but he couldn't play gooseberry like that, not with Shirley.

He stopped calling, stopped taking her calls – that continued long after what might have been expected – Shirley faithful to the end, in every way but the one that came to obsess him. He sees it all differently, now.

'She probably didn't even know how I felt,' he says, and perhaps he's right, 'But I wish I'd been more pushy, like Chris,' he adds, with a smirk, 'I mean, I didn't even put my tongue in her mouth when we kissed!'

These were the regrets. Just as Kevin would adapt to other processes that were beyond his control, he would adapt here too, recognising, as he moved forward, that there had never been a cross or false word, just the kindness and generosity of a simpler age. As the years passed, he would come to appreciate that.

Chris is all but forgotten now, but the time Kevin spent with Shirley moors him like no other. He regrets not having put up a fight and his refusal to accept the changing nature of their relationship, or to see Shirley for what she was – a loyal friend, who had his back. He regrets little else, though Shirley did eventually stop calling.

'I just couldn't do it,' he concludes sadly, and I can understand.

Later still, with Shirley now a mother – though he didn't know it – Kevin, embarrassed at the fact that he had ever been a Queen fan, would deny her once more, when quite freely giving up his signed programme of the concert they had attended together all those years before. Kevin liked the Smiths and Aztec Camera, now… and *everything* had changed.

Shirley, with three children of her own (by two different fathers), was more measured in her nature and would keep her souvenir safe through every change, just as she still has the photos that record their youthful friendship – from 1971 through 1977 – thinking of Kevin always, with a fondness no way diminished by time.

It wasn't cruelty, either – there was no malice; it was love that drove him, that blinded him… and the almost visceral need he now felt for Karen. I could see it and I understood, but I could also see where Kevin was, once more, wheeling himself, just as he had with Mary, just a month ago (and what a tangle that had been).

It was hard to believe he couldn't see the parallels, wouldn't learn the lessons – that, leaping feet-first, he could be so self-destructive. It was hard to watch such flagrant vulnerability.

I, of course, advised caution at every step, but Kevin was too far gone and there was no speaking to him anymore – those dialogues were a pattern of our own, redundant to purpose. I still advised, but Kevin would only hear what he wanted to hear.

'Yes, yes, but this is different,' he maintained, dismissing me again, with misguided bluster.

………………………………

Boxing Day 2011, and Everton see out a much-needed 1-1 draw against a rejuvenated Sunderland (Goodison Park a mix of groans and cheers). Stepping up from his front row perch (on the Gwladys Street Stand) at its conclusion, Kevin hears someone call his name and turns to find his cousin Chris, edging down the gangway.

'I'm divorced, now,' he is informed, the forgotten voice rising over the bustle of the departing crowd to explain, as though it was ever a question, that he never did become a professional footballer (as hoped).

Kevin notes, wryly, that the blonde tresses are gone (replaced by a rough receding hairline), that the once chiselled jaw is slack and lax, the chest narrow, an extruding belly pulling at his belt.

'You thought you were Rod Stewart!' he sniggers.

'Well,' Chris retorts, with little trace of his former eloquence, 'I guess we've all got skeletons in the cupboard,' taking a final drag on his roll-up, before flicking it into the stands. 'And, you can't talk – you liked Status Quo, for fuck's sake!'

He was laughing now, warm-heartedly, offering a salute as he turned, his frosted breath showing in the air around him.

'I didn't like Status Quo', Kevin assures me, when he recounts the story later (as though any of that matters).

Chapter 4

Kevin was ecstatic when he recounted the morning's events at Park Pool. I said I needed the toilet, his voice following me through to the hall. I was sympathetic, knowing what it was to be smitten.

The first of two doors at the end of a short passage opened out on a box room, containing a toilet, pushed up against the far wall, and a blue sink, sat in shadow. The last prosthetic legs that Kevin had ever tried to fit into – in a long-ago attempt to woo a girl, in college – were propped up on the toilet's porcelain tank, their repulsive chains and straps a torrid souvenir of an archaic age (and a stark reminder of the person Kevin had once been).

The posters fixed to the walls presented a showcase of the campaign years, those humble plastic pins serving – in the context – as a pointedly political object. It was hard to imagine Kevin ever having forced himself into those clattering contrivances, and – considering the implications – I would shudder whenever I saw them (those legs saying nothing of the friend I now knew).

Pushing into a room bright from a recent refit, having decided on the 'disabled' toilet, I remembered the light cord, fixed to drop to within a careful foot of the floor, and pulled on it, before making a studied turn of the first of the two handrails flanking the bowl. After shuffling carefully into place and lifting the frame of the oversized plastic seat, I reached down to set the flush in motion.

It had still not lost its novelty, though thirteen years later, following further renovations, I would step in and find two showers fitted into this same space – one up and one down. This was a careful inversion (of Kevin's own) to the 'legal responsibility to provide accessible toilets', a statute that had been imposed on all publicly trading businesses in 1997 (in an extension to the Disability Discrimination Act). By then, I would be spoilt for choice.

There was no good reason to look up, as I finished off, though some subtle compunction compelled me and I lifted my eyes… discovering, with crude immediacy, the dark, misshapen shadows that covered much of the ceiling: *bats*!

There were a dozen or more of them, some stretched out on their fat backs – black eyes aslant – while others hung head-first, from gnarled claws (defying gravity): life-sized, lifelike replicas, their thin, raggedy wings spread about them like kites.

Smiling, despite myself, I considered those new additions to Kevin's growing menagerie, planning my line of attack – with a snort – as I made my way back to the living room. We had often debated Kevin's questionable aesthetics, his avowed taste for the gothic (that he would protest) – this was yet more ammunition: *bats, for fuck's sake*!

Toilets: Kevin had known from the start that, if he was to be any sort of a man, he would need to go alone; he had shown no desire to prolong the process of potty training, or to have his mother's hands on him for longer than necessary.

'I'll have you done in a jiffy,' Agnes would croon, in seeming high spirits, announcing herself to anyone who happened into the vicinity, as she set about the task with disturbing gusto – rubbing gently at the distended anus rim and then at the soft, stately buttocks (using her own tissues).

Kevin, who would experience shame long before any of his contemporaries, wanted only to be free of her. He hadn't the means, however, and even when, as a teenager, he *was* able to go alone, his mother would intervene at every opportunity, his helplessness something she had no desire to relinquish.

'Are you ok?' she would call at the door, with a rap, when he vainly attempted to make independent use of the public facilities.

Ignoring her, Kevin would pray that there was no one around to take note, while his soul slipped imperceptibly away. The frustration only increased as he matured, but the truth was that he often *did* need help – whether to get him into a cubicle, or onto a seat, or back out again (when done).

Such questions – of agency, and privacy – were only exacerbated at school, where differences he had hardly even known, grew suddenly pronounced.

'Miss Bailey, here,' he was told on his first day – a nod given to the robust lady beside him – 'will help you to get about the school… and, to use the toilet.'

It was a galling introduction, but there was no other way, even if Kevin would only ever raise his hand (for the bathroom) in desperation, cursing at the eyes that followed him out.

At Highfield Comprehensive, where he would yield less frequently to the 'call of nature', the school nurse would be called (some kid sent sprinting off to her room) and later still there was Batman, who – with his willingness to 'take the mick' – Kevin preferred over all the rest.

'In you go,' the helper would say, as he was manoeuvred into a stall and lifted up onto the seat – with the lid raised – Kevin's feet flapping gracelessly as he sought for purchase.

'Are you on?' they would ask then, as – perched precipitously over the bowl (that lacked armrests and lumbar support) – they made a grab for his pants, forcing them over his feet while Kevin shuffled into position.

'Give a shout if you need anything,' he would be told, when all he wanted was to decant, in peace – to force out what he could, so that he wouldn't have to go again.

With his shirt and tie both still incongruously in place, he could only hope that he wouldn't be disturbed, or forgotten, though they *did* forget on one occasion, with Kevin left dangling from his seat for the best part of an hour – the cold wood chafing his skin, while the pipes gurgled.

'It was awful,' he admits, still incredulous after all these years

– 'and the whole time I was panicking in case someone found me,' his thoughts naturally turning to John Cairns and his cronies.

'It was only when another pupil stumbled in, that they came and got me out,' he explained, remembering how the nurse – who had been in charge that day – had returned at a run, her face a wash of perspiration.

'Oh, God, Kevin – I'm sorry,' she cried, placing a hand over her mouth at the shock of finding him still just where she had left him, his pale skin flecked with goosebumps. 'My mind went blank…' she stuttered in apology, helping him down, before bundling him back into his pants and giving the toilet a final flush. 'Poor love… you're froze to the bone!'

'It's fine, honestly Miss,' Kevin said, hazarding a smile, 'at least I got out of class for the afternoon,' he added with ready wit, noting her distress.

The event was not forgotten, however, and determined not to make such a mistake again, the consequences proved far-reaching.

'I'm still claustrophobic,' Kevin explained, 'hate to feel shut in.' We were stuck in a lift, between floors, at the Manchester Cornerhouse. 'I'd get really stressed if I had to stay in here for any length of time,' he added.

'Really?' I pursued, given the opportunity – there was so much I hadn't known – considering the way Kevin had always seemed to recoil in the shadow of a locking lift, how quick he was to open up the windows in his van, bounding down the path before the ramp was even shut.

It was the same with his flat, now I considered it, the front door usually standing ajar whenever I called, Kevin operating an open house, in both physical and emotional terms; it was only now, as I delved deeper, that I could appreciate the difficulties of a barred door or a stacked step (how easy he was to derail).

'Just don't forget I'm here,' he would stress each time, as one helper or another took their leave, making light even as he forced eye contact, impressing on them the need to remember.

He would take other steps too, as he matured, and by his early teens he had developed an almost Zen-like control of his bladder and bowels. Boasting of taut pelvic muscles and tight sphincter sinews, with the caverns of his vesical increasingly implacable, Kevin was a medical wonder.

'I could probably last the whole day without having to go,' he bragged, when I was caught laughingly short again (and forced to relieve myself in an alley).

Such a studied force of loins had not been required at home since the arrival of a Clos-o-mat, when Kevin was in his tenth year, his ablutions having previously been the sole reserve of his doting parents. An undoubted luxury, this single addition would release him, at a stroke, from what had once seemed intractable.

'Give it a try,' his father suggested, leading him through to the 'special surprise' that had been put in over the weekend (with Kevin away).

Ushered inside, Kevin struggled to see what he was expected to do.

'It looks good – thanks,' he conceded grudgingly.

'Get in, have a go,' his mother clipped.

Sniffing at the still-fresh sealant, Kevin pulled the sliding door by the handle at its base, before taking an investigatory turn of the room – hopping experimentally up and down the wooden steps, to the cistern seat (and back).

Satisfied to find that the controls were all within easy reach, Kevin bumped his head to the surprisingly sensitive flush, listening with gratification to the swell of the water. It only gradually dawned on him that there had been no oversight – that toilet paper was, quite simply, redundant in such a configuration. (His dad had made the steps, which would follow him all the way to Briar Moss.)

'Does it work?' he was asked, when he emerged.

'Yes,' he mumbled, red-faced, though he had yet to put the contraption to practical use – to feel the hiss of the jet (to which he would grow accustomed).

Kevin knew enough to know that, freeing him from the constraints of the average bathroom, as it did from the hands and manhandling of various adults in embarrassingly close quarters, this was a form of revolution.

Kevin could now go when he wanted and he could go alone.

That night, safe in the knowledge of the toilet that resided behind the sliding door at the end of his room, Kevin dreamt that he was floating in a vast pool of water, paddling in peacefully slow circles, without a soul in sight.

If somewhat weightier and more functional than a traditional toilet, the Clos-o-mat – with its fully incorporated 'wash and dry' system – was a godsend, Kevin having only to apply pressure to one of the two levers that flanked it to set the flush in motion and wash the excretion away. A jet of cool, then cold, water – a 'douche' – follows, to rinse the sitter, then warm air, in a series of waves that could last for anything up to three minutes.

Kevin took to the device like a duck to water and it is no exaggeration to say that this single installation changed his life more than any other, though the same toileting problems would repeat every time he stepped out of his front door (with this solution fixed firmly in place).

When, at the (illegal) age of seventeen, Kevin started to go out drinking, his difficulties were front and centre once more, with the toilets in public houses among the least accommodating.

'I didn't care – just as long as I could get out of the house,' he admits.

Thus, keen to join his sister and her colleagues from the Giro, on Friday nights at the Stand Farm, he had to accept the fact that the toilets were inaccessible and deal with the consequences.

'I wouldn't have a single drink during the day,' he explains, 'just so that I wouldn't have to go again later.'

He met my eye – candid; forthright – not, at that point,

elaborating on the fact that he would wring out every last drop, on his final visit to the bathroom, with the taxi due (hoping beyond hope).

Such precautions proved ineffective as the beer started to flow, with Kevin garrulous in company and keen to keep pace with his new friends (who each had several years on him).

'I need to go,' he would confess, through gritted teeth, after his second or third pint of frothing best bitter, knowing how Neil resented the role of chaperone.

'You've only had a couple,' Neil would spit, 'you shouldn't even need to go,' adding informatively, 'the human bladder has a capacity of six pints – can't you wait?'

'I can probably hold on for a bit,' Kevin allowed, though he had already been holding on for half an hour and was in excruciating pain.

He forced a grimace, no longer taking any pleasure in the evening's fraternisation, before appealing once more to his sister.

'I'm desperate – can you ask Neil?'

Joan caught the look he gave and, knowing her brother's difficulties as well as anyone, could see he was in trouble. Her husband was selfish – she would freely admit it – and the way he treated her brother a contributory factor in the eventual dissolution of their marriage.

'Kevin needs the toilet,' she said, pushing at Neil's chest, 'and don't dare try to get out of it!'

'Alright, fucking hell,' Neil muttered, swilling down the rest of his pint, before grabbing at Kevin's chair. 'Come on then, hop-along...'

Kevin gave an apologetic smile, having no desire to pull at the threads of a fraying relationship and ready to acknowledge that they got on well enough when sober.

'I really appreciate this,' he mumbled, as he was bashed recklessly through the bar.

'Stupid fucking chair,' Neil cursed, when the wheels caught at the carpeted step, bumping into a man with a tray of drinks on the other side.

It was left to Kevin to throw out shrugging apologies, while Neil stumbled on, banging the frame of the chair at the door of the 'men's room' to force it through. Once inside, Neil guided them into a cubicle, by means of a series of uneven jolts (his elbow grazing a wall).

'You're too fucking heavy,' he grumbled, bracing himself, before hauling Kevin up out of his chair and down onto the plastic seat.

Neil, who was already several pints into the session, and physically out of shape, was wheezing when he got him down – sweat staining his armpits. After tugging Kevin's jeans over his heels, he stepped out with a snort of contempt.

'Thanks,' Kevin coughed, only now registering that the rim was wet and he was straddling another man's urine (Neil hadn't bothered to check).

The relief coursed through his hunched frame when he started to piss, however, and everything else was forgotten.

There was no getting around the facts, but Kevin had no intention of putting an end to the jaunts that offered such liberation. His mother, who could sense that she was losing him, was actively obstructive (in word, if not deed).

'I expect you're off out again, later?' she would ask (knowing he was).

'Yep,' Kevin replied, her disapproval a further spur.

'And you'll be back late, again, I suppose?'

'Yep.'

'Drunk and stinking of ale?'

'No doubt,' Kevin deadpanned.

The stale routine did neither any credit, with both sides knowing that Kevin would be going out, regardless: that nothing either side could say would sway the other.

For, in giving Kevin the chance to mix with adults who didn't see him as anything other than what they were, Stand Farm's humble setting proved a lifeline, and as the weeks passed – in such mixed company – Kevin had the sense of finally finding his feet.

Staggering back in a joyfully inebriated state, Kevin could see little to recommend the family home – in comparison – save for the comfort and ease of an accessible latrine. If he could have pissed in his pants, he might have stayed out all night.

His mother would be up, waiting.

'I need the loo, I'm bursting!' Kevin would cry, pushing past, taking her disapproval as the price he had to pay for stepping out on his own.

Over the years, Kevin would seek out many different solutions to the vexing question of the public restroom, the most outlandish being the brief trial he gave to the urine collection bag. *I wouldn't have to bother Neil*, he considered, wondering why he hadn't thought of it before.

He sought out the chemist after college and rushed straight up to his room, with the box stashed under his jacket, to read over the instructions. Consisting of a 200 ml capacity plastic pouch, secured to the penis by an external catheter, the device looked simple enough on the box but, out of the pack, it was a different matter, all tubes and ties (that were hard to fit); such difficulties seemed only to foreshadow the disaster to come.

'I should have known,' Kevin declared, as I waited for him to continue, explaining that it hadn't felt right, even when he had tried it at home – his natural lack of leg, making also for a lack of trouser leg, in which to secrete the unsightly bulge.

Following any number of adjustments, cursing as he went, Kevin had eventually laid the contraption across his gut, deciding that the soft crest of flesh that over-hung his jeans was the best place.

'It was like wearing a dildo,' he joked, 'or a medieval codpiece!'

On a frosty night at the Stand Farm, testing the device for the first time, Kevin welcomed the chance to keep pace with his doughty companions and was very soon drinking to excess.

'Pint?' Neil offered, giving a respectful nod when Kevin

immediately downed what remained.

'Yeah – and keep them coming!' Kevin cried with a smirk, while his sister glared across.

She was the only one he had let in on the trick; bubbling with pride at his own ingenuity, he wondered whether anyone else would guess.

'Calm down,' Joan advised, as Neil staggered off to the bar.

Kevin was starting in on his third pint when, dizzy – and already slurring his words – he heard a dull pop from the region of his chest, his head spinning in confusion. Then, fortunate to have forewarning, he felt it, a thin drizzle of liquid seeping through his cotton shirt.

Beating a hasty retreat through the obstacle course of tables and chairs, Kevin crashed out to the street. Two or three vigilant steps astern, Joan came tumbling after, freeing her flailing brother from the paraphernalia that was still strapped to his waist – the tubes, the caps, the faulty pouch – before launching them across the street in an arc of urine.

Writhing about on his dripping seat, Kevin was muttering that he 'should have known' and cursing the fact that he would never learn – recalling, suddenly, how once, in the hope of making a good impression on an ill-fated date (in a one-handed play against the facts), he had taken to his prosthetics again. Nobody had been fooled on that occasion; he should have known that he was fooling no one now.

'I'll ring you a cab,' Joan said, with a nod towards the dilapidated booth.

'Fuck off,' Kevin bawled, turning a circle, as he set his chair for home, his shoulders burning when he finally pushed up the ramp.

Kevin was already in his mid-twenties, and independent in every other way, when he purchased his first electric chair and was finally able to manoeuvre with a degree of freedom. He was out most weekends then and sometimes during the week, with both the Firehouse and the Paradox boasting fully accessible toilets and becoming – in consequence – Kevin's nightclubs of choice, the all too familiar door staff only too happy to help him up the steps. With such a clearly defined accent, they took him for one of their own.

'To what do we owe the pleasure?' they would ask, dipping into a courteous bow.

There was a freedom he hadn't expected in such clubs and, with the silver Radar key safe in his possession (giving access to the accessible toilets), Kevin no longer had to worry about his trips to the powder room.

'Coming through,' he would announce, and anyone inadvertently in his path would immediately clear a space (in awed silence).

Several minutes later, Kevin would come wheeling nonchalantly out again.

More was to follow, with disability rights gradually forcing its way to the fore and starting to enshrine such changes of attitude and perception into law. For Kevin – so often at the mercy of backwaters and outliers – the issue would remain a live one, however. Only last summer, for instance, he would steadfastly refuse to come to a mutual friend's birthday meal because of the steps barring entrance to the restaurant.

'I looked on the website,' he returned brusquely. 'It has steps at the entrance,' refusing any offer of strong hands to lift him in; hardly the most sociable by this point, I suspected that he was simply looking for an excuse.

Girls, when they came, brought further complications, with the weekends Kevin took away with Paula – which were, in effect, a series of one-night stands – a cause for tension on both sides.

'I like it here,' Paula would bleat, '—can't we stay another night?' cursing at Kevin when, wary of extending their break, for fear of increased exposure, he refused. 'You're a mean bastard, you really are,' she would complain, thinking she had him pegged, but Kevin wasn't mean and would – in fact – have liked nothing more than to stay.

'I've got work on Monday,' he dissembled, glancing at Paula to see if she took the line (accepting the inevitable sulks).

Given her disgust at the bare mention of a bodily function (able or not), Kevin could see no alternative. He sometimes wondered whether Paula even realised that he had to defecate, just like everyone else, or whether she imagined that he secreted by some other method.

'Why do we have to talk about it?' she would snap, if the subject ever arose – as dumb as she was cruel – though circumstances would regularly press them into honesty.

'You're going to have to help,' Kevin quailing – and forcing her hand – when there was no other option. 'I'm desperate.'

Thus, Paula would reluctantly work his chair into the bathroom and lift him onto the toilet – Kevin, disrobing on the way – before he called her back in again (to help him clean up).

'I don't see why you can't do it yourself,' she hissed, Kevin glad – for once – of the pause his disability gave even such an unfettered creature as Paula.

He was oddly comforted when, with a malicious leer, she declared him a 'spaz' – her malevolence one of equal opportunities.

Splashing water from the tap to my face and combing back the hair that had fallen, I took a slow breath, unable to deny what the reflection returned: the raw, puffy eyes (dull and listless); the thin, dry mouth (flat and inexpressive); the chin, glistening with a rough-cut, six-month beard.

I stared back, hoping to force a reaction, to wrench myself from a mood that followed me, that never gave a moment's rest. I couldn't go on like this…

I stood, rooted to the spot, for a further minute – those same dull eyes staring right back – until the thought of something Kevin had said suddenly set me smiling. He was like a child sometimes, rattling on with such enthusiasm, and it was hard not to be affected by his optimistic bent. Kevin didn't miss a beat, or suffer a single regret, and I admired that, alien as I was to such an open approach.

He was sitting just where I had left him, in the living room (hunched over the computer) – seemed hardly to have noticed I had been away.

'Do you want to make a cup of tea?' he asked, his eyes never leaving the screen, and I stepped out again, knowing the order well enough: a tea for Kevin, in his oversized mug (with just a splash of milk), while I would take a coffee, with a generous heap of demerara sugar.

Struggling, as usual, to find the light – the switches all fixed to within a foot of the floor (and difficult to locate) – I stumbled through the cupboards for cups and then tea bags, before uncovering the kettle (stored at that same incongruous height) and bringing the drinks through.

Having sent the email that he'd been in such a hurry to send, Kevin resumed the narrative: he had been telling me about his latest trip to the public baths, the thought of which was still bringing him pleasure.

'I was absolutely knackered,' he smirked, '... clinging to the bars just to keep afloat. But I didn't want to get out, either.'

'Shall I hold you up for a bit?' Karen had asked, with typical consideration.

Tightening his grip on the rail, Kevin gave no sign of having heard, as Karen moved around him, brushing at his flank as she passed. When he felt her arms tighten about his chest, to take his weight, he relinquished the rail, sending his small fingers flapping to the surface.

His head on her chest – drawing slow breaths even as his heart kicked a feverish beat – he was sat up on her thighs, while her fingers played over his skin. The cavernous room reverberated and, finding his voice – in a panic – Kevin gave a whoop up to the roof as his feet thrashed at the water, disturbing the surface to conceal the rock-solid erection that was pushing at his trunks.

With Karen pressed up close, there was nothing more he could do, so turning, abruptly, onto his front, he took himself under. He was coughing and spluttering when Karen, who had heard all the stories of near-drownings, dragged him back up again.

The shock of the water, taken in through nose and mouth, following on his breathless re-emergence, had served the purpose… dissipating the blood and sending the pulse away from that single, fixed point.

'You had me scared!' Karen cried, brushing through his wringing hair.

When she started out of the pool ahead of him, Kevin's eyes were fixed on her sinuous curves.

'Slowcoach!' she called over her shoulder, her voice steeped in the usual affections.

Scrambling out of the water in pursuit, Kevin could reflect on an invigorating session that had seen Dan's stock fall still further.

'Is she one of the lecturers at Edge Hill?' she asked.

Kevin would neither confirm nor deny.

They were dressed again, and he had been expressing his frustration over a 'date' of the previous summer – an abject failure, as he saw it – sensing that, *quid pro quo*, it was his turn to share.

Struggling briefly with his food – bits and pieces of tuna salad falling carelessly from his mouth – Kevin spluttered on, covering for what was an unusual bout of reticence with a melodramatic sigh and a self-deprecating shrug.

'I'm probably impotent, anyway.'

Karen brought her fork slowly down to her plate, her eyes narrow.

'Oh, I think we both know *that's* not true,' she said, in a tone that invited silence, giving him to understand (he believed) that she had not only been aware of his earlier erection – had seen it, possibly felt it – but that she wasn't in the least concerned: thought it in the normal way of things.

Kevin's head span at the possibilities – hope and hopelessness, in equal measure – as he gave his flushed report. I shuddered at the growing familiarity, at how far I was unwittingly drawn.

'You said you loved Mary,' I reminded him.

The reply was quick, punched out with persuasive clarity.

'That was just an infatuation – this is love! – and Karen's brilliant!'

I was already smiling, knowing that I hadn't a chance, as Kevin – who welcomed the attention – played to the gallery. Through the bluster of indignation, however, there was no denying the truth: that Karen would never see him as anything more than a friend.

'She's still with Danny,' I said, sensing a sadness we hadn't yet approached, a lull to the usual cat and mouse.

'But she doesn't love him,' he retorted, 'and she's always telling me how much she loves me.'

'It's not the same,' I insisted – having recently shared a similar misapprehension – continuing, in abstractions. 'You're friends…'

'We're more than friends,' Kevin snapped, 'we see each other every day… and we're always talking on the phone – I know her much better than Dan does!'

I wouldn't deny their obvious rapport – given the way they acted around one another – nor the fact that Karen and Dan looked awkward in comparison.

'She works for you, she's your employee,' I said, trying another approach.

'No, no, it's not like that,' Kevin returned, with clear exasperation.

'And, what about when she gets another job?' I asked.

'That won't change a thing,' he replied defiantly, '—we'll probably end up seeing even more of each other.'

I was standing now, ready to concede the point, but the truth nagged and I couldn't resist.

'What about Danny?' I said.

'Danny's an imbecile,' Kevin fumed, 'he doesn't deserve her!'

'But they're still together, so she must still have some feelings…?'

'And, what would you know?' Kevin hissed, his top teeth showing.

I let the comment pass – didn't counter what was a misconception.

'Well, I hope you'll be very happy together,' I said instead, offering a truce.

'We will, thanks,' Kevin answered facetiously, before giving a conciliatory smile: he hadn't meant what he had said.

Then, he really should take more care.

If I continued to judge and to question the limits of their relationship, I was also the only person he could really tell and was, therefore, chief witness to every phone call and email he ever sent. I alone understood the looks that passed between them.

'She's lovely,' he sighed, after playing through a recording of her voice, surprised to find that I was not similarly enraptured.

But my thoughts were all elsewhere.

◊

I could hear the train booming away as I chased down the concrete steps to the platform, the memory of an evening spent in such engaging company receding, too. The rain was heavier now and – playing helplessly through the day's events – I wondered why I had even tried to make that last train.

I was soon running, again, hoping to take up where I had left off (with my new friends).

Earlier in the day, taking what proved a convoluted tour, over several dual carriageways and through a couple of parks (now in vibrant bloom), we had met for the first time. I had not wanted to, had no desire to make a new acquaintance at this point, but Martin had insisted. You were going away, he told me, and – besides – he had something he needed to give you.

Four or five sharp stabs at the bell brought the sound of rapid steps on the stairs and – stepping back from the door – Martin turned to smile, with something like an apology.

Grove Park, a detached double-fronted Victorian property, had seen better times, though there were traces of its earlier incarnation in the deep windows, wide ledges and the spacious stairways that wove through the building.

The carpets were worn thin throughout and the furnishings – an occasional cabinet or table (pushed up against a wall) – sparse. Exposed bulbs swung from high ceilings (that were patched and stained), while the cracked walls were unevenly skimmed. Most of the residents were students, though there were artists and musicians, too (in welcome receipt of housing benefit).

With your unassuming head drawn low and your bleached-blonde hair held in a tight ball on a pale nape (dashed with freckles), you bowed slightly in greeting, giving a shy smile. Your face was open and engaged, even as you stepped nervously back in those heavy shoes. I liked you.

'Hi,' rasped in an undertone, your protuberant eyes flitting between us. Then, smiling again (*that* smile) – if you had ever stopped – and I caught just a glimpse of your straight teeth, behind the thin, cracked lips. 'Come in,' you continued quickly, tripping over your feet as you backed away.

Your warmth was natural and effortless... and, in that moment, I felt a tug I hadn't expected.

Flinging his baggy sleeves around you in a bear hug, Martin had quickly stepped inside, leaving me to shuffle in from behind, tendering an awkward hand (which you shook), while noting those attentive eyes and how little you seemed to miss.

'Come up,' you said, in a deep voice, leading us up the first flight of stairs.

Martin grinned across, as if to say he had told me so, though I still wasn't sure what I was supposed to see, or why we had even called. I had to admit to liking Caroline, however – that was the name Martin had given (making the introductions).

There were branches crowding the windows of her first-floor flat, and we were invited to sit, while our host stepped across to the open-plan kitchen. Splashing water to the counter, in filling the kettle, Caroline sniffed suspiciously at the milk while waiting for the kettle to boil. She was humming absently, as she slopped it in regardless, squeezing out the teabags with the water still pale.

Moving with a slovenly grace that I found sympathetic, your pretty, unassuming figure sounded a chord I couldn't yet place; Martin, who had dropped his tobacco to the table and was already skinning up (his narrow legs crossed at the heel), was right – you were cool. I turned my head about, to take in what was a sizeable bedsit, with a living room at the front, a small kitchen to the rear and a door leading to what I presumed was the bathroom. Beyond the narrow glass-topped table, where we were sat, was a single, unmade bed.

It was charming – *bohemian* – but watching, as you finished up in the kitchen, I realised, suddenly, that I didn't know a thing about you: whether you were single, or had a job.

Tapping the filter at the table to settle the tobacco, Martin turned a knot in the opposite end, smiling when Caroline skipped across with a scrunched-up bag of granulated sugar. An acoustic guitar was propped against the bed and I remembered that that had been one of the reasons Martin had given for our coming over.

'You'd like her,' he had said, trying at persuasion, 'she's in a band,' adding – when I showed no particular interest – 'and, it's on the way...'

He did this a lot and I hadn't expected anything to come of another random encounter, Martin having introduced me to a dozen different people over the years, who I would meet once and never again.

This already felt different, though I couldn't have said why, Martin piling three spoons of sugar into his tea, with a solicitous smile, while I noted the Velvet Underground poster pinned to the far wall (wondering how Martin always managed to meet such interesting people).

'Colin's in a band, too,' he said, turning the wheel on his lighter.

While I didn't welcome such a clumsy intervention, Caroline seemed enthusiastic, so I told her what we were called and what we did (keeping it brief). Passing her the joint with a gracious bow, Martin broke in then, to ask her when she was planning to leave.

It was the first I had heard and the thought caught me short – the sense of the world passing me by – as I recalled how often I had imagined something developing, a friendship in its own right, only for nothing to follow.

I listened – she was working in a factory for a couple of weeks and then possibly going on to France with a friend – but I wasn't really listening, knowing now that it didn't matter: that I would, most likely, never see her again.

Still, I watched with pleasure as she turned the joint, to make sure she had it the right way – and that it was lit – before taking two short puffs and passing it on again. I rose to meet her, a little too late, and we bumped heads, our eyes catching in apology.

Observing us, with a wry smile, as he took a chunk of hash into his mouth, and bit into it, Martin seemed to see something.

'Here,' he said, turning the broken pieces about on his hand, before passing Caroline the largest portion. 'Thought you might like to take some away with you,' he added, his face smoothing out.

I envied the smile she gave him – 'Ah, thanks Martin!' – though now that she had the hash, she didn't seem to know what to do with it, rolling the dark smudge about for the best part of a minute, before laying it down beside her tobacco. 'That's so nice of you,' she continued, her voice moving, within a single line, from a chesty bass to a lilting mezzo-soprano.

She was funny – ***kooky***, as Bowie would have said – and I could see why Martin liked her.

The conversation had moved on again, to the demo that Caroline had recently cut, which Martin insisted she play. She did that – with little reluctance – clambering up to her feet and inserting an unmarked cassette into the tape deck on her bedside table, already apologising for the levels as it stuttered into life.

It was a home recording – 'we did it on Lars' four-track,' she explained – of uneven quality, but it was original and authentic, with a physicality I could appreciate. Martin nodded, tapping out a rhythm on the table, while I struggled to pick out the words, with the distorted, ethereal voice proving more of a soundscape.

Her eyes shining as she hummed along, delightfully out of time, Caroline's generosity was infectious and I felt a connection I couldn't explain. There were no words, no sign had been given, yet it seemed, suddenly, that it was Martin who was no longer required.

Moved by some ineffable texture, knowing only how comfortable I already felt in your company, it seemed like I had known you forever.

Then, just as quick as we had come, we were leaving again, Martin jumping up decisively and herding us out ahead of him. Caroline saw us off from the top of the stairs, shuffling away before we were even halfway down. I wanted to stay. I felt like shouting it.

'I said we'd pop over to see Nat and James,' Martin explained, with a glance at his watch as we stepped outside and I nodded back, fearing that the day was already done.

We met up in the Masonic later: four of us, now – Caroline had brought a friend – bunched tight into a corner of the bar on an upholstered leather bench. Going for a round of drinks, we left the girls chatting, Martin squeezing in next to the newcomer when we returned, while I nudged in on the end.

Martin was almost immediately drawing laughter and admiring looks as he ran them through various anecdotes, swaying in close with an ease I would never know, his gestures already suggesting further intimacies.

This wasn't the plan, but when Nat and James had declined the invitation, Martin had decided to invite Caroline out instead.

'She's going away soon,' he had reasoned, sheepishly, thinking I wouldn't approve; in this case, it had been a reprieve.

I was nervous when I saw that Caroline had brought a friend, and glad that Martin – naturally – took the lead so that I could acclimatise at my own pace. It was only after the first round of drinks that I felt able to undercut the steady flow of Martin's flirtatious braggadocio, with a series of sly, teasing digs. This was our general practise and Martin didn't mind, though I was surprised to find Caroline so taken by those dry asides, her eyes flashing appreciative smiles even as she nodded along. There was an understanding in the look we shared.

Martin had soon caught on and – playing for sympathy, with a penitent shrug – he was quickly working the situation to his advantage. The impetus was lost, however, and – as the conversation flagged – I was almost relieved to find him hunched over his tobacco when I returned from the bar.

Dropping the drinks to the table, to provide extra cover while Martin finished up – crumbling the last few grains of hash into his palm, before flipping the contents onto the single, king-sized paper he had laid across the top – I took my seat. Placing a cigarette filter into one end, before smoothing a moistened finger down the overlapping join, Martin pulled the tube tight, making a twist of the surplus. It had taken him less than a minute.

Flashing nervous glances towards the bar, the girls seemed impressed, while, taking a nonchalant swig as he tidied away, Martin was hangdog.

The joint was now laid on his lap, and it wasn't clear what he planned to do. For, though we had built up (and smoked) weed in the dark recesses of nightclubs and on the top decks of rumbling double-deckers, and at Anfield too – huddled into the folds of our heavily-wrapped coats – we weren't in the habit of smoking in open view like this, especially in such a small pub.

I caught his eye, but made no comment, so when – clearly showing off – he actually lit the thing and started to smoke it, I found myself playing along, taking the joint from under his cupped hand, before drawing in a deep, practised breath. I held the smoke, briefly, before releasing a gentle stream to the floor and passing it on.

By the time I had made it back to the pub, my friends had left and the bar was closing up, with only the occasional figure still huddled over a drink, finishing off. Slightly disorientated, I wandered up the street, while the rain beat on, in the hope of seeing them.

Knowing that Martin had planned to go to Nat's, but with no desire to spend the night in an unfamiliar house (with people I hardly knew), I considered the possibility of calling a cab, before counting up my inadequate change. The night seemed to have only just begun, anyway.

It still surprises me, looking back, that I had ever thought to take such a step, but without once considering the practicalities (and implications), I decided then that I would call in on Caroline instead, to see if she was awake. I could sleep on the sofa, I thought vaguely, wanting – simply – to see you again and knowing, somehow, that I couldn't let the opportunity pass.

I set off at a run, round the park – through the driving rain – feeling something like elation, with no more questions or doubts.

Dropping to a walk as I slipped through your gate, almost surprised to have found my way again, I stood, for several seconds, at the foot of the steps that led to your door, as I caught my breath. It was then that I realised, looking over the steep column of bells, that I didn't know the number of your flat (and there were no names).

I gave a gentle tap to buzzer five, pressing down with greater force when there was no response, while listening through the patter of rain for some sign of life (for those feet on the stairs). It seemed like a lifetime since we'd first called and it was all, suddenly, impossible.

Knowing that, having come so far, I couldn't just leave again, I turned towards your window – a brick bay on the first floor – where a light was showing through the curtains, and pitched up three moderately-sized stones in succession. There was silence, but for the rain dripping off the gutters and hissing through the trees, as I waited.

Stepping away, to find more stones, I turned back to discover a silhouette in the window. I waved, but the shadow moved away again, and – with the wind momentarily still – I questioned what I was even doing there, calling uninvited on a girl I barely knew (and throwing stones at her window).

The wind had picked up once more and – stepping onto the street again – I started to run.

I didn't tell Martin what had happened when he welcomed me in and showed me where I could sleep – in the living room, under a blanket going spare, with my coat as a pillow.

I was too excited to sleep at first and woke, with a cough, just as soon as the sun was up (and blazing through the uncovered windows). I left before anyone else had emerged.

I never told you. In all the years that we would eventually share, you never knew that I was there that night, tapping at your window. Perhaps it would have all been different if I had?

Chapter 5

Appreciating the intimacies that such a role afforded, Kevin was attending with uncharacteristic patience as Karen vented and her pale breasts bobbed.

'He says my friends are all too posh,' she resumed – they were discussing Dan (had been for months) – 'and that that's why he won't come out with us… Oh, but he likes you,' she added, drumming at his chest – 'but, then, *everyone* likes you!'

'I'm sure it's just a bad patch,' Kevin suggested, hardly able to account for the pleasure of her words.

'Oh no, it's more than that…' Karen returned, as her friend dipped under.

'I wish I could talk to Dan like I can talk to you,' she said, resurfacing, while Kevin – catching at every inflection – struggled to hide his emotions.

Danny Wilkinson (Kevin's occasional gardener) and Karen Baker (his ongoing facilitator) had been unwittingly introduced just eight months before. It was August 1998 and they had rather spuriously decided to commemorate the end of their second academic year with a party.

'Why the hell not?' Karen declared, with her customary zeal.

Without stopping to consider just how easy it had all become, or how much they were taking for granted, Kevin assented.

'Let me know what we need and I'll send out Auntie Pat,' he added with a chuckle, that brief conversation starting a week of preparations, with Kevin proud to include many of the lecturers (he now classed as friends) on his guest list.

Parking the van in the disabled bay near the store's entrance,

Kevin hurried ahead, leaving Karen to collect the trolley. Watching her employer forcing his way through the idling shoppers, in single-minded pursuit, Karen felt a swell of pride. By the time she had caught up, Kevin was already passing bottles back over his shoulder.

'We'll get a dozen red… and some dry white,' he muttered, 'oh, yes and champagne, too… we might want to celebrate.'

Even allowing for his natural largesse, Kevin's mood was infectious, with the customarily frugal Karen – who still had to pay off her student loans – soon adding items of her own (from the delicatessen this time).

'What about these?' she would ask, pointing out the samosas, or a quarter slice of quiche.

'Yes, yes, chuck them in!' Kevin would cry, helpless, Karen having only to sample a square of cheese (on a stick) for Kevin to have the assistant wrap the whole wheel, or to linger over a cupcake, for her patron to order ten. 'I suppose we'll need to feed the carnivores, too?' Kevin eventually allowed, leaving the acquisition of the meats to Karen.

The invitations, some delivered by hand, Kevin grinning out at the recipient from the van, and some mailed (just for the fun of attaching a stamp) had been sent out at the start of the week, leaving them plenty of time to prepare.

Music brought the first dispute, after Karen had laughingly claimed to have no knowledge of either Steve Harley *or* Elvis Costello (Kevin's excited suggestions).

'You're a dinosaur,' she goaded, 'and, it's a party, remember – we can put all that gloomy stuff on when everyone's gone to bed!'

'It's not gloomy,' Kevin maintained, 'it's beautiful!'

'Like you,' Karen shot back, with a peck at his cheek.

Playing the curmudgeon with relish – their apparent differences only drawing them closer – there was no offence, though he knew more about Karen's musical preferences than he liked to admit.

'Is it straight?' Karen called down from the ladder.

'Yes, but be careful.'

'Yes, dad,' the teasing reply, as Karen dropped to the sofa and nearly bounced him off.

There were streamers and balloons hanging from every wall, a table set for the food they would distribute later, and strategically placed scented candles (Karen particularly proud of this conceit).

Tasting the wine on her breath and the subtle deodorant he knew by heart, Kevin nestled closer. In recent weeks – under the influence – he had been feeling more like a teenager than a man in his middle-thirties: he loved her, no less, and this was the afternoon to confirm it.

'Aren't you too old?' his mother had fretted, when he first announced his intentions.

Taking a turn of the campus, Kevin had wondered, too.

'Not really sure what I'm doing,' he confided, to Andrew Kavanagh, over the phone.

'Nor me,' his former colleague quipped, 'but, I guess it's better than joining the massed ranks of the unemployed.'

'Yes, yes, very droll,' Kevin returned, rolling his eyes towards Nicky (who was picking at her nails on the couch).

'I've never known anyone who's gone to university before,' Nicky would confess, with rueful pride, when Kevin saw her out.

'The students are so young,' he complained to his sister next, 'and, what am I trying to prove?' he added, lapsing into silence, the very idea of an academic footing suddenly seeming absurd.

Seeing the students he so admired carousing on the lawn outside the Union bar, without a book in sight, had been a further discouragement, with Kevin almost walking across to remind them of their privilege.

'Give it a couple of weeks,' Joan suggested – knowing her brother of old – 'and see how it goes.'

Kevin grudgingly took the advice, never imagining the galvanising effect of his hired help.

'She's great,' he was gushing, by the following week. 'Did a Media degree at Edge Hill… her dissertation was on Mills & Boon.' Here, he glanced up, over his glasses. 'She's from Worcester, but she's not stuck up at all.'

'She sounds nice,' Joan allowed, with faint praise.

'She is, she's brilliant,' Kevin returned, glad to be able to say it.

Given the fickle nature of his passions, Joan was surprised to find him still waxing lyrical six months later, with Karen not only helping him to settle at Edge Hill – Kevin now quite at home among his youthful peers (more her age than his) – but bringing other changes, too.

Up early, to shower – singing, with glee, into the steamed-up glass (his heart singing, too) – Kevin would be gone by the time Auntie Pat arrived, climbing into his van in his recently purchased clothes. With his baby-smooth chin and close-cropped hair, Kevin was well preserved, and – taking his place, beside Karen, in the lecture hall (with brief acknowledgements to his fellow students) – he no longer had any doubt that he belonged.

The preparations complete, Kevin and Karen would spend the afternoon of the party on the couch in the back room, without so much as glancing out onto the sun-drenched patio. Yet, the recently completed garden, which now had an accessible ramp leading up to the house, had been one of the reasons they had given for their celebration.

The freshwater pond was the undoubted centrepiece, with Kevin still chuckling about the way they had raced back from the nursery with the greater part of its bulk hanging from the boot. At each bump and turn, Dan – who had taken what weight he could (with ropes tied to his waist) – would let out an excited whoop, while Kevin pushed on, full throttle, in an increasingly frantic attempt to get them home before the haul was ejected.

After laying the plants down on the lawn, Dan was soon explaining how he planned to arrange them. Giving a distracted smile, Kevin suggested they have a cup of tea.

'Just as long as I can get my chair out,' he called back, from the door.

Though the landscaping was now complete, the two friends didn't venture out. Close enough to taste her scent, a subtle vanilla that would outlast all the later fumes, of all the later guests – arriving with such bluster – Kevin could have stayed like this forever. With the house to themselves, they resembled a couple completely at ease (and in the first flush of love).

Laughter filtered down the hall that flickered with candlelight, while spirals of smoke issued from incense. Struggling to keep his feet, through the cacophony of voices clamouring for attention – and the music pouring, at random, from the unmanned stereo – Kevin was already half-cut.

'Good evening… welcome!' he would engage newcomers, with a slur, 'how are you?' flicking a smile (in the struggle for recognition), as he floated through a seeming dream – and everywhere he looked there was yet another face, and yet another smile (when all he wanted was Karen).

She's here, somewhere, he mused, turning tipsily, full circle – the rest of the room mere stage props to that more revered presence – to find himself surrounded once more. Then, in a gap between two hoary professors, he saw her, and positively reeled, knowing that, despite having already spent the better part of the day in her company, she was still the one person he wanted to see.

'Hi, hi, good evening,' he continued, distractedly, with the bosom friends hardly able to suppress their delight as – finishing off one another's sentences – they greeted the new arrivals.

'Hang your coat here,' Kevin said, with a nod to the heavily-weighted rack. 'There's beer in the fridge, and wine… and help yourself to the food,' Karen – the hostess – continued, with her hand on his shoulder.

(And I almost forget – we were there that evening, too, in a staging post of our own.)

Karen was grinning when she staggered back from the stereo, having changed the CD.

'Dance!' she cried, brushing her lips into Kevin's face, before taking up his hands and turning his chair in an allemande. 'Dance!' she commanded.

Confused and disorientated, Kevin was also transfixed.

'No,' he said, shaking his head, his colour rising (and they were suddenly the only two people in the room).

'I love you,' she told him, planting a sloppy kiss on his cheek.

It was as simple as that – as clear as those three words can ever be.

'Don't be daft,' Kevin spluttered, forgetting where he was.

'I do, I love you – you know I do!' Karen repeated earnestly, her voice cutting through the music.

At the end of the song, Karen wheeled away but, for Kevin, who was rigid in his chair, there was no going back.

That party was the glorious climax of two years of gradual approximation, during which they had shared everything, with meditations on love and loss peppering their daily discourse and Karen even suggesting that, one day, they should get a place of their own.

Having had his head turned before – and his heart broken – Kevin knew better than to give too much weight… knew to be grateful for what he had. He had Karen's ear and her confidence, after all.

There had been tears when Karen explained how she lost her virginity, wild hoots of mirth when she described her second proper boyfriend and his malfunctioning penis.

'I said, "it happens to everyone," and it shrank even more,' she cackled. 'I could hardly see the thing in the end!'

Running the rule over the cruelties inflicted, by Paula (among others) – 'I can't believe she actually locked you in the bathroom!' – Kevin, speaking up for the first time in his life, was released.

'I don't know if she ever really loved me,' he said of Klara – and he had never quite put it like that – telling Karen what he had never previously been able to tell.

'You loved her, didn't you?' Karen said simply, when Kevin detailed his cousin's coming and Shirley's subsequent loss.

'Oh, yes, she was my first love,' he admitted, and Karen hugged him tight, before running through some heartbreak of her own, each shared confession bringing them closer.

Much as I would caution Kevin for his guileless candour, there was no reason to doubt his sincerity.

'She's my best friend and I love her,' he would tell me, and – given an awareness of her faults – the appraisal was clear-eyed.

He had seen her anger, too. When, with her nostrils flaring, she had turned on Dan for the first time – the attack seeming out of all proportion – Kevin had hardly known where to look. Dan's equally taut response had settled any doubts over his loyalty.

Quick to yield, in a play of influence that rarely ran the other way, Kevin was happy to acquiesce and almost immediately took to Karen's tastes as his own: they watched *Cold Feet* and *Jonathan Creek* on the small screen; *The Full Monty* and *Boogie Nights* at the multiplex.

By the following autumn, when I had first started to call and first made an inspection of Kevin's CDs, I was surprised by what I found, given his friendship with my brother. It was only when I reckoned with his latest muse and learned where that music was coming from, that I understood.

Actively encouraging such indoctrination, Kevin never once thought to trouble Karen with the subjects closest to his heart, just as he was glad to forgo *Newsnight* and *Question Time* if it meant that Karen was still keeping him company at such an ungodly hour.

Driven by curiosity, Kevin had wanted to know everything at first. He would *tell*, too, when asked, but was more interested in listening and learning. Extremely forthcoming, they were barely an hour into their association when Karen started to explain that when she wanted a man, she simply went out and got one.

Increasingly out of step, Kevin had initially found reassurance in her confessions (and the understanding they brought), but – as the friendship deepened – he had come to believe that Karen was wasting her time on such suitors (when she could do better). Almost inevitably, he had grown protective.

Seeing the perfunctory way she would throw those boys off, when she was done, drew more doubts and, sensing some slight in those indignities, Kevin had sought out a subtle separation, his cool sobriety suggesting a brother rather than a peer.

When Karen snickered about the size of some rejected lover's penis, or the sexual prowess of another, who – disappointingly – had 'nothing between the ears', Kevin's adopted diffidence gave him the space to think (as he turned a blind eye).

She's worth so much more than that, he would brood, wondering why Karen would ever resort to compromise – *when she could have anyone* – or how the generous, open-hearted girl he knew could be so shallow.

'Don't look now,' Karen hissed, dropping to the floor, 'but that guy, there – on the left,' gesturing towards a cluster of students.

'What about him?' Kevin asked, after a disinterested glance.

'We fucked… last night,' Karen returned, in a whisper.

Kevin turned to look again, but all he could suddenly see were young people, *everywhere* (and he so utterly old).

He remembered, now, that they had met the boy in question after a lecture the previous week. Stumbling at the misdirection, his pinched eyes picked out the tall, athletic figure (a head higher than the pack).

'What do you think?' Karen resumed.

Noting the broad chest and the olive skin, Kevin brought to mind Karen's stated ideal – 'a great big lump of a guy!' she had slurred, on one of their first nights out. Resenting the jet-black hair draped casually over his shoulders, as much as the shrill, overconfident laugh that erupted at regular intervals, he could grant that this latest model fitted the criteria.

'I can't tell from here,' he replied, grudgingly.

Looks like a member of a boy band, he snorted, while Karen set about describing the night they had just spent and the fact that she had gone right up to him at the bar and asked.

'He was just what the doctor ordered!' she cooed, laying her head on Kevin's shoulder as the group dispersed.

Wrong-footed, Kevin – who was glad he was already sitting down – could think of nothing to say. *You can fuck me if you want,* he considered suddenly, shuddering – though the sun was warming his back – at the thought of how Karen would react if he ever gave voice to such words.

There was, thankfully, no repeat performance and no further mention, and they were soon back playing at all their old routines, with Kevin teasing Karen over possible (theoretical) suitors, once more.

'Beggars can't be choosers!' he would chuckle, as Karen thumped at his arm.

When, against Karen's stated disavowal of all men (of any description), Kevin had first proposed Dan, declaring him a 'hunk', he had only been joking and had thought nothing of it. He would regret having ever opened his mouth when, with galling inevitability, his stray comment bore rotting fruit.

Karen and Dan had met at that same party, with Karen immediately stating an interest. Offering up the gardener's details with a grin, Kevin had imagined that they were still playing. When a relationship ensued, he took comfort in the fact that, despite the fanfare, it couldn't last: *they're ill-matched,* he considered, *and Karen won't put up with any rubbish.*

They were, predictably, fighting before the month was out, with Kevin merely waiting for the moment when Dan would be cast aside. Yet, the fling persisted and Kevin could only look on in bewilderment as Karen made allowances and excuses.

Though the once-settled boundaries of their relationship had shifted, Karen would still throw her arms about his chair whenever they met, while continuing to share the salacious details of her amorous pursuits. While bragging of their late nights, and the way they would cuddle up on the sofa, Kevin had no choice but to accept the sincerity of Karen's ambiguous proclamations of love (when they came).

Despite the changed circumstances, the adjustments were surprisingly slight; with the continuing overfamiliarity of close quarters bringing disorientation, Kevin was no longer sure where he stood.

'Men are a total waste of space,' Karen mumbled mournfully, sniffing through a hangover.

Accepting that he had no place in such an appraisal, while welcoming the entitlements of singularity, Kevin never sought to ask the reason.

'At least we don't have to worry about all that romantic guff,' Karen would conclude another after-hours session, while Kevin suffered a sadness he couldn't explain.

Back at the beginning of the previous academic year, when he was first starting out – it was now August, nearly two years hence – Kevin had been invited to a meeting of the twenty or so 'inclusive learning facilitators' taken on to provide support for students with additional needs.

'They're there to help you take notes,' the dean explained, 'and to make sure you can access the curriculum.'

While appreciating the gesture, Kevin – who didn't see that he needed any help – was an unwilling participant in the interviews that followed, though he welcomed the opportunity to snoop around the rather grand senior staff room, with its oak-panelled walls and leather-bound books.

Uncharacteristically late to the arranged meeting, it was Karen who would describe the tension that had held between the candidates in the lobby.

'I was nervous as hell,' she admitted over lunch – the ice broken by then – tugging at her unfamiliarly tight skirt.

She had bought the suit for a funeral, she told him, pulling her hands free of the oversized sleeves to check her watch, nibbling at her nails (until she remembered to stop).

'Watch out, everybody!' David Johnson, the department's senior lecturer, had suddenly called out, settling nerves, 'because any minute now, Kevin Donnellon will come bashing through those doors!'

Turning their heads with tentative smiles, struggling to make sense of that odd declaration, Kevin had duly clattered in, as predicted, with the anxious new recruits breaking into hesitant applause.

Noting, with weary irritation, that he was the centre of attention once more, Kevin barked back, 'what are you lot laughing at?' his eyes quick to alight on the grey-suited Dave Johnson, who was shaking with laughter (and now gave a wave).

'May I present, Mr Kevin Donnellon!' he declared.

'Yes, very good,' Kevin muttered darkly, his eyes nevertheless shining as he took a look about the room, offering his audience a lopsided grin.

He was now thirty-five years old, his hair thin and greying, though – youthful in spirit (his head held high, his chin up) – his maturity seemed a matter of distinction rather than age. He was venerable, had seen it all before, and his discerning, blue-grey eyes – reflecting an undeniable intelligence that (taking on all-comers) he didn't seek to hide – suggested as much.

It was the wide, garrulous mouth, from which his words would fall with such regularity, that drew the eye (and the ear) first, the sharp chatter being what got him, initially, through the door (along with an accessible ramp). Kevin could talk to anyone, was as engaging as he was engaged, his natural warmth breaking down barriers; he seemed a friend, even if you had just met.

The face was a face he had grown into, a face that had been *earned*: a face that – with its rearranged teeth, its oft-blackened eyes and the diagonal welt running from the nose to the mouth – was filled out by experience. It was boyish, too – the skin pink and waxy, the flesh porcelain-smooth. At times, when that exterior veneer would drop away, Kevin could seem, momentarily, punch-drunk – lost, in his own world – while, in the next instant, leaning forward to offer some pithy rejoinder, glasses perched professorially on the end of his nose, he was every bit the intellectual he one day hoped to become.

Kevin Donnellon sent a mixed message without even trying.

'What the bugger's going on!?' he cried, his voice carrying full pitch, as he clowned – hangdog – the atmosphere perceptibly shifting once the guests realised that the exchange (between professor and favoured son) was collegiate.

'Late, as usual, Mr Donnellon,' Dave Johnson boomed in response.

'Traffic!' Kevin roared, in exculpation, as the professor called the meeting to order and the prospective employees were introduced.

Noting how nearly all of those assembled were either former, or current, members of the college, Kevin wasn't paying much attention. When, making his own rapid round of the room, he rolled up to Karen, he found her oddly unyielding. Looking closer at her freckled cheeks, which were working up and down, he realised that she had her mouth full.

'Biscuits,' she offered informatively, after swallowing. 'I couldn't resist,' she admitted, with a delicious smile.

Then, remembering why they were there, she gave a playful curtsey before presenting her slim hand – and its brightly coloured nails – in salutation, after only the briefest establishing glance.

'Good afternoon,' Kevin said.

'I'm Karen!' his interlocutor returned.

Still carrying the telltale signs of those flat, pottery vowels, her accent lay somewhere between Brummie and Cov, though the tone had grown more refined, with the time spent away from home making her harder to place.

Kevin, for whom voices hold a particular charm, was immediately drawn, even as he struggled to delineate.

'Karen Baker,' she added, sensing that something more was required.

Five foot five; eight stone six; her small feet flayed from the heel – he had forgotten they were talking.

'You studied *Media* didn't you?' he asked quickly, catching his breath, pleased that at least some of her introduction had registered, pinning her wavering green eyes with his own as he played for time.

'I'm impressed!' she shot back, looking more closely now, at where – and how – Kevin's hands eventually emerged from his sleeves, continuing cheerfully, 'very observant indeed, young man!'

She was a whirlwind, though Kevin retained the presence of mind to take advantage of the confusion and get a good look at her, noting the rich, reddish-brown hair, the gleaming teeth and the grey-green eyes (that caught the light)... *she's beautiful*, he thought, quickly asking another question.

'And what did you do in Media, exactly?'

'Well, my thesis...' Karen began, with a wink, 'was on Mills & Boon,' smiling at all she had omitted.

'*Mills & Boon*?' Kevin balked, with a comically raised brow.

'That's right, Mills & Boon... because, well – basically – because I like Mills & Boon!'

Then, with her head thrown back, she was laughing – a full-blooded laugh – and seemed released. Thrilling to her company, Kevin, who had already decided on both her beauty and her character, was struggling to find his words.

'I pretty much fell in love with the place, on the open day,' she was saying, 'so, when I finished my course, I decided to stay on.'

Her expansive gestures and emphatic turns of phrase were charming. Kevin could only nod and smile, to show that he liked her, his enervated senses taking her in all the while.

Short and slim, with full hips and thick shoulder-length hair, she had bright, clear eyes, and a subtle spray of freckles dotting the bridge of an aquiline nose. *She's lovely,* he thought again, registering the lack of make-up, or pretension: she was a natural, in every sense. Catching once more at her infectious smile, his mind was a blank.

'He's in the army,' she continued, talking about her brother now, and Kevin nodded eagerly, 'I haven't seen him in ages… but we always get together at Christmas.'

'It's a bit soon to be thinking about Christmas!' Kevin interjected, fearing to lose her to the room.

'And, what about you?' he heard her ask, as he unaccountably blushed.

'Oh, there's nothing much to tell,' he returned cautiously… and on they went, already seeming a natural fit.

When they were led through to the adjoining room, where a table had been laid for lunch, Kevin wheeled in beside her, Karen pulling a chair out of the way, before ushering him into place with an ostentatious bow. *Karen Baker*: even the name sounded familiar – like he had known her for several months rather than half an hour.

'You can go and talk to some of the others, if you like,' Karen assured him – in a lull – 'don't feel obliged to stay with me.'

'Oh, no,' Kevin said quickly, 'I'm fine with you, if you don't mind?'

'Suits me,' Karen told him, 'I was getting bored going over the same old questions, anyway.'

Relaxing, now that he had her safe, Kevin ran Karen (at her request) through a few biographical details of his own, elaborating on his 'crazy old mum' and 'dotty Auntie Pat'.

'She said to watch out for rowdy students,' he sniggered, of the latter.

'Well, you're okay with me,' Karen returned with a smile, before adding that – in view of some of the boys she knew at Edge Hill – she was inclined to agree with Auntie Pat. 'But, then, most men are useless, aren't they?' she declared, 'present company excepted…'

Their uninhibited laughter spilling across the otherwise muted table, it was all so easy.

They kept each other company after lunch too, with Kevin setting his chair in pursuit when Karen skipped off to examine an oil painting of some long ago dean – drawing him in with a hiss, tipping her nose in judgement.

'That'll be you one day,' she exclaimed, 'a baldy old professor!'

'Less of the old,' Kevin chided, hoping she hadn't noticed his hair.

Taking his wheelchair by the arms and propelling him forward, she wondered at its top speed; he told her, as they skidded through to the main room to find that the meet-and-greet had already been brought to a close. Pumping his hand in enthusiastic farewell, Karen insisted that she would be seeing him again very soon.

He hadn't moved an inch and was casting about the book-lined walls in something like despair when Jeremy Sharp, who suffers from spina bifida, made himself known with a bold declaration (his dark eyes boring through his thick glasses).

'I'm having the blonde one!'

'What?' Kevin mumbled in reply.

'Emma,' Jeremy continued, without drawing breath, 'I saw her first!'

'Oh,' Kevin conceded with a smile, recalling that he had seen her, too.

She was young and blonde, but he hadn't been paying much attention. *He can have her,* he thought, scrawling 'Karen Baker' out in block capitals on the form provided.

Stepping out of an SWP meeting on 'Capitalism in Crisis' in the low-lying Art block the following week, Kevin's eyes were still adjusting to the bright light outside, when he nearly ran, headlong, into a unkempt-looking student in a leather jacket, who was handing out fliers. Curious to see what she was selling, Kevin steered round to the front, where he was met with a bright beam of recognition.

'Kevin!'

It was Karen, from that day forth his new employee, the partnership confirmed by email. He hadn't recognised her in less formal attire – and approved – though before he could even start to reassess, Karen had seized his collar and flung her arms about his neck in a flood of perfume, before sweeping down to peck at his cheeks.

Stepping back, Kevin noted – wryly – that he was old enough to be her dad (*or her uncle, at least*). He was only just starting to think about the arrangements they would have to make, when his companion suddenly turned and set off across the quadrant – at full, ungainly tilt – in the direction of a fellow student.

It was Neil, her boyfriend, she would explain, with a subtle blush, when they were alone again, Karen wrapping her beloved beau in a smothering embrace, before pulling away so she could get her mouth at him.

Looking on with interest, Kevin was quietly relieved to find that Karen was happy and settled – there had been confusions enough in the past. If he also experienced a stab of envy, he hid it well, as he considered how slight she looked at that distance.

'Well, what do you think?' she asked, when they were alone again.

'He seems nice,' Kevin replied.

They *had* looked good together, he thought, and – after recent tribulations – it was a relief to be a disinterested spectator.

'Oh, stuff it!' Karen declared, drawing him from his reverie, as she stepped across to the bin to dump the rest of the fliers before taking up the handle of his chair. 'I'd much rather spend the day with you.'

Neil Bradley, to give him his full name, would finish with Karen within a matter of weeks and, despite Kevin's sincere assurances that they would be 'back together again soon, don't worry' – Karen dropping brisk tears, her graceful fingers circling his small hands – there would be no such reversal.

Karen Baker was single again, with Kevin soon installed as her best friend and closest confidante.

Chapter 6

It was August 1981 and Kevin was still twiddling his stub opposable digits – after the conclusion of his studies at Hugh Baird – when Sefton Social Services unexpectedly came to call.

'I'm his mother,' Agnes stated, wondering what they could want after all this time.

Still resentful over what she saw as the council's dereliction of duty in former years – at how little they had ever done for her son – she passed the phone to Kevin like a hot coal, with no desire to re-establish a connection that had long since soured (those earlier exchanges another lifetime).

'I'm fine, thanks,' Kevin answered, when asked, his response meeting with a silence broken by the rustle of papers – *resuming*, eventually…

'We're calling to see whether you're aware that this year has been officially designated as the International Year of Disabled Persons?'

'No,' Kevin replied, implacably.

'Essentially, European funding has been set aside, in the form of grants, to provide support for the disabled community,' the woman continued, her confidence growing, 'and, well, we were hoping to persuade you to take advantage of the scheme.'

Kevin glanced back to his mother – eavesdropping, as usual – but he couldn't have told her what this was, even if he had tried.

'I don't understand,' he returned grudgingly.

'In simple terms, Mr Donnellon… *Kevin*,' – again, the shuffled papers (the tone suddenly enthusiastic) – 'we'd like you to come and work for us, if you're interested?'

'Work?' Kevin quizzed; having been all set for university until a month ago he had given no thought to the idea of gainful employment. 'I've just left college,' he returned, high-pitched.

'And that's why we had you, specifically, in mind,' the caller broke in – the trap sprung – 'the fact that you've recently completed A-levels makes you an ideal candidate… more than able, we believe, of taking on the extra responsibility.'

Wondering, idly, if he would still be able to hang out with his friends – and get drunk – if he accepted, Kevin looked to his mother again, still not actually sure what they wanted.

'What would I have to do?' he asked, seeing no other way to end the conversation.

'You'd be based in the Deaf Centre, opposite the Five Lamps, on Liverpool Road…' – and, again, the optimism – 'and you'd be helping to set up a 'welfare advisory service' for the disabled… it'll be one of the first of its kind in Europe.'

'When would I start?' Kevin batted, uncomprehendingly, back.

'In the next week or so… as soon as possible, really – if you're available?' *Available,* Kevin mused – *what the fuck else am I doing?* 'You'll have to come for an interview, but it's just a formality… the job's yours, if you want it…'

His mind running briefly over the likely responsibilities, Kevin considered that he was nowhere near ready, though the thought of his friends, who had all left school at sixteen, standing in line outside the Job Centre, was enough to give him pause.

Sensing hesitancy, the caller resumed.

'The contract runs for twelve months initially, and – to be honest – it shouldn't be very taxing… more like a paid holiday,' she explained, with a smile in her voice. 'You'll be getting some practical experience in the workplace, which is invaluable however you see your career progressing… oh, and,' – she was selling it now – 'all travel expenses will be reimbursed.'

Kevin hadn't once considered a career – had no thought of even getting a job – yet, despite wondering why they would want to offer him such a position in the first place, he had to admit to being flattered by the interest. He could picture Jim's face, when he told him – just as he could imagine the grief, if he turned the offer down – while recognising that anything that got him out of the house and from under the thumb was a good thing.

Prophecy lies beyond the wit of man and Kevin was not to know, then, that such an inauspicious temporary posting – his first – would see him right through to his mid-twenties (and exert a greater influence on his life than he could have imagined).

He would meet my brother at Ellesmere House – forging a friendship that would hold for more than a decade – and Andrew Kavanagh, whose civil partnership ceremony he would attend (as best man) all of twenty years later. There was 'mad' Nicky Mathers, too – lest we forget – a screeching, shrieking banshee, who would still be popping over to visit well into their late fifties, each character bearing their own distinctive brand of influence: bringing colour to this new stage of life.

As Kevin moved unsteadily into adulthood – and the memory of school receded – these were the friends he would come to rely on.

'What do I have to do?' he conceded, at last, sensing that he had no choice.

'Well, first I'll take down some details and then we'll send out a contract.'

The woman sounded delighted. Swallowing hard, Kevin told her what she needed to know.

Arriving at Ellesmere House the following week, with the best of intentions, Kevin was confident of being able to step up to professional standards he thought were expected. He had bought a suit at the weekend – along with several shirts and a chequered necktie – and rolled up to the entrance with a notepad and a dozen or so pens stuffed down the arm of his chair.

He was almost immediately disillusioned.

'It was a sham,' he tells me now, grinning. 'The council needed to prove that they employed disabled people, in order to qualify for the grants... I just happened to fit the bill!'

While waving Jim and his mother off each morning with a seeming sense of purpose – choosing not to disabuse them – Kevin would lose his tie and loosen his collar before he even reached the end of the street (mussing up his already bedraggled hair, to keep with the lawless tone that predominated in his new workplace). The 'welfare advisory service' they provided would prove a complete waste of everybody's time and money, but it was fun, too (while it lasted).

Ellesmere House: I hadn't even noticed the place before, despite having driven past a hundred times and having – undoubtedly – gone along with my mother, on occasion, to drop my brother off.

You see what you want to see, so when I drive along Liverpool Road now, I cannot fail but be drawn to that sombre, oversized building and imagine what it must have been like for Kevin to set foot there for the first time (knowing the extent to which it would subsequently shape him).

'It's where I became a man,' Kevin snorts, the euphemistic phrase covering a multitude of sins, and I think of that comment whenever I pass.

For, Ellesmere House, a detached, double-fronted Victorian property, of four stacked storeys, still stands opposite the Five Lamps, as a testament of sorts, with ivy reaching to the upper walls and the windows boarded fast.

Originally commissioned for a shipping magnate with connections to the slave trade, the building bears a troubled heritage, which the welfare advisory service – and its sister schemes – would go some way to overwrite. It was heartening to see BT Openreach vans parked up on the courtyard recently, suggesting (as they did) further changes.

Stepping forward with desire, that job and that place – and the lifestyle that came along with it – had represented a whole new chapter for Kevin: one that cannot be underestimated, however humble the beginnings.

Recruited simultaneously on a Youth Training Scheme, Kevin and Nicky Mathers were the first of the new employees through the door. They had introduced themselves on the courtyard out front, while waiting to be admitted, both of them – wondering at the seeming lack of life inside – checking their letters of introduction to make sure of the address.

'Are you here for the welfare advice service?' Nicky asked first, looking Kevin over and already reckoning, after that cursory glance, that – with his baby-smooth face and his mop of mossy hair – he would, no doubt, be her assistant, though neither her age (nineteen), nor her education (thin), suggested any such privilege. 'I wonder what my office will be like?' she mused aloud.

A car – fortunately – pulled onto the path then and Geoff Grimes emerged.

'Sorry, sorry,' he called, clambering out with a weathered briefcase under his arm. 'Up to my ears… Oh, I'm Geoff, by the way,' offering a hand, his tie flapping in the breeze, 'Senior Social Worker for the Deaf,' before taking them inside.

It felt official now, and Kevin had the sense that he had landed on his feet and was finally making progress.

'Kevin Donnellon,' he answered keenly, as Geoff stooped down to take up the mail, Nicky deigning barely a nod, with the air of someone who had seen it all before – *maybe she will be the boss, after all,* Kevin considered.

'Is this it?' she enquired peevishly, while they made their inspection of the open-plan office, a sizeable space taking up half the ground floor, with several doors leading off to other rooms.

'Yep, guess so – it's a pretty tight ship,' Geoff replied jovially.

Noting the desks – a half dozen or so, with stacked chairs – and the typing machines (still under cover), and feeling rather proud to be a part, Kevin wondered what she had been expecting. *This has got potential,* he thought, weaving between the furniture.

'Well, I'll leave you to get familiar with… everything,' Geoff suddenly cut in, turning towards the door, 'but don't worry, I'll be back soon to see how you're getting on.'

Nicky scowled, but only voiced her concerns when they were alone.

'It's a fucking shithole.'

Kevin didn't deny it. There was barely room to spin his chair – and he had twice had to back himself out of a tight corner (his new colleague clearing a path) – yet he couldn't deny the sense of belonging.

'Kev – get the lights!' Nicky bawled, having already settled on the truncated form of address.

She was reapplying her make-up, but with the windows barred shut, despite recent refurbishments, it was hard to make anything out. Flapping his arms, with a helpless smile to indicate his incapacity, Kevin was eventually able to locate the switch and bump his head to depress it, bringing the flickering strip lights to life.

'Ta,' Nicky cried, as she finished off.

'There's a kitchen, in here,' Kevin called back, pushing through one of the doors.

The four fat steps that led down to the annex precluded further investigation, though the kitchen could also be accessed by following the building round from the front. The inconvenience of such an admittedly long-cut didn't trouble Nicky – an equal-opportunities employer – when she figured it was Kevin's turn to go.

'Get your skates on, Donnellon,' she would cackle, 'I'm parched!'

Returning half an hour later, with a grin of near-inebriation – and a tray of drinks balanced on his lap – Kevin welcomed the chance to escape.

Those premises also contained a private office, a depressingly-carpeted lounge and a games room. Permanently full of smoke, once there were more staff in place, this latter featured a pool table and a dartboard, while the lounge provided a view from its grilled window onto the brick face of the neighbouring British Legion.

In the summer, when the greater part of their day would be spent fanning one another with whatever magazine was to hand, the rooms were all too hot, while the autumn brought a chill that was hard to shift. When they discovered that they had access to the warmer rooms at the front, too – these housed the undermanned

Deaf Centre – the two new colleagues would often spend the day there instead.

Kevin was usually first to the intercom when the bell sounded in that neighbouring office, the clients quickly familiar with his bright bolt of enthusiasm.

'Good morning! Come in!'

With Junes Hales and Geoff Grimes, who ran the Deaf Centre, rarely in attendance, Kevin had been shown the ropes and entrusted with a set of keys.

'Make sure everything's written up,' Geoff instructed, gesturing towards the official ledger.

Ever punctilious, Kevin would usually fill out Nicky's entries, too.

Picking cautiously through the cupboards and the cabinets, to acquaint themselves with the various hearing aids and batteries – pilfering as they went – they had quickly made themselves at home.

'Can you hear me now?' Kevin would charge each new client – as he checked the levels – having fitted the batteries.

'Oh yes, that's marvellous!' rheumy eyes showing delight.

'Okay, Mr Davies – thanks,' Kevin would modestly return.

Neither use nor ornament, Nicky was fixing her lipstick, again.

'Stupid old codger,' she muttered maliciously, just below the range of the device, Kevin unwilling to admit to the pleasure of being put to use.

Until a manager came to take charge, the two new employees were at a loose end.

'Should we tidy up?' Kevin suggested, on day two, prying open one of the drawers of the desk he had sequestered. 'It's not like there's anything else to do…'

'What's the point?' Nicky hissed, while Kevin went through the drawers. She was up on her feet again, pacing the floor in her steep, round-toed heels, declaring at regular intervals, 'I'm bored!'

'Well, we haven't started yet, have we?' Kevin told her. 'Once we know what we're doing, we'll be fine.'

Nicky glared across; peeling off her shoes – pink heels, today – to reveal the corns and blisters within, she held her tongue.

'I'm breaking them in,' she explained, offhandedly.

Kevin gave no comment on the fact that she had arrived in a different pair every day so far – at least she was back in her seat again.

'Read that,' she broke in, hurling across a magazine, 'you might learn something.'

Struggling to flip it about on his chest, Kevin read the title back to her.

'*Social Work Today*?' he queried, Nicky's face cracking into a smile at his apparent gullibility.

'Well, one of us needs to know what's going on!' she crowed.

By day three, having already got a feel for the place, Nicky arrived in a miniskirt that left little to the imagination.

'Shows off my tan,' she explained, noting how – his eyes drawn to the uncovered flesh (there was enough of it) – Kevin was inevitably looking her over. When she gave a flamboyant twirl, Kevin found himself looking again. 'Like what you see?' she crooned, stooping low to give a gap-toothed grin – 'Cheeky sod!' He could hardly deny it, but with a lacy red bra showing through a tight satin top – as she thrust out her chest – and a skirt that barely reached her thighs, he was as appalled as he was attracted. 'You can look, but you can't touch!' she added, with a giggle, as Kevin shuffled disconsolately away.

'Rubbish! Garbage!' he was soon crying out, as he launched various papers (from a pile stacked against the far wall) across the room, rattling them off the rim of the bin.

'I think you're finally getting the hang of this, Kev, my love,' Nicky cackled. 'We'll make a proper little worker of you yet!' and he felt her soften – there hadn't been a single expletive.

He turned, sharing a smile – figured that they would probably get on okay. There were rough edges, undoubtedly, but Nicky was pretty and her freckled, heart-shaped face held an undeniable charm, even if it was hard to tell its tone beneath the thick warpaint that she insisted on.

Her fat lips dripped with Russian Red, while Love's Baby Soft – applied liberally to wrist and throat – wafted from her blouse whenever she moved. She was quite a package, though – far from his usual range – she was hard to quantify.

They wouldn't be alone for long, with Ruth Hayden Jones arriving – to take charge – the following week.

'Can I help you?' Nicky barked, with narrowed eyes, when the stranger stepped in from the rain, holding her umbrella at arm's length, looking like she had taken a wrong turn. 'You must have confused the address, love,' Nicky added, shooing her away.

'No, this is the place,' Miss Jones replied with authority. 'Is there somewhere to hang my coat?'

Kevin pointed out the hooks drilled to the wall below the clock, though there were no coats as yet. She thanked him, unbuttoning as she made her way across, only then returning to explain her presence.

Tall, grey-haired – with a fussy rectitude redolent of some other era – Miss Jones reminded Kevin of his head teacher at Highfield Comprehensive; her stilted fashion sense and clipped tone of voice exhausted the similarities.

'Who the fuck's she?' Nicky mouthed, catching his eye.

Welcoming the reinforcements, Kevin gave a shrug.

'I'll take a look around, to get my bearings, first,' Miss Jones resumed, drawing out a pen and a pad, smiling – for the first time – when she caught the look that passed between the baffled employees (who thought she couldn't see).

Kevin gave a smile back, while Nicky scowled in defiance.

'She's a right cow,' she spat, when Miss Jones left, to take an inventory in the stock room – and Kevin wondered, innocently enough, how she could have come to such a conclusion, when they had barely been introduced.

He nodded – the path of least resistance – considering Nicky more like a child than any adult he had yet met.

The next morning, they found Miss Jones already in place ahead of them – she had been no figment of their imagination – with a pile of files laid out on an otherwise empty desk.

'I had a rather late night,' she explained, 'but it was time well spent, given that I was able to put together a list of every charity that has ever operated, at one time or another, within Sefton, or the surrounding boroughs.' She paused, allowing them the chance to respond. 'We've not really been offering much of a service here yet, have we? I don't suppose that anybody even knows we exist, much less what we have to offer.'

Rocking impatiently on her heels, Nicky gave an audible yawn. Sensing that the game was up – the empty days with just the photocopier for company, the prank calls (through tittering fits) – Kevin struggled not to laugh right along with her.

'Our first task is to let people know who we are and what we're about… to let everyone know we're here,' Miss Jones continued enthusiastically, another quick look passing between the junior colleagues.

It wasn't until she was out of earshot that Nicky ventured an opinion – 'she's a bloody slave driver' – before stomping off to the stock room, as instructed (already regretting the heels).

Kevin looked sympathetic, though he was keen to get on with the task he had been assigned, which was to go through the aforementioned list to see which of those charities were still in operation.

'Check the addresses; how many staff they employ… and anything else you think might be relevant.'

'Sounds good,' he returned.

Appreciating the fact that he was to make his own decisions, Kevin would wheel himself through to Miss Jones whenever he had something to report, even though most of the entries – including the rather baffling 'phenylketonuria' – were already more than twenty years out of date.

'You're a bloody *suck*,' Nicky sneered, when he bounded past after one such trip; taking the phone up from his desk to make another call, Kevin, who was learning, ignored her.

Though the majority of those calls would prove to be wrong numbers, or else ring out unanswered, Kevin was growing more confident and professional with each new attempt.

'Good morning, this is Mr Donnellon, from the welfare advisory service for the disabled,' he would begin. Making faces and flashing obscene gestures from the opposite desk, Nicky did her best to derail him. Kevin was unperturbed. 'I was wondering if I could speak to…' scratching a pen through any defunct entry, with only a rare affirmation bringing him to question two: 'Oh hello, yes, I was ringing to find out if you are still active in Sefton?' his pen scraping hurried notes over the page.

'You sound like a divvie on the phone,' Nicky said, having noted Kevin's instinctive suppression of his natural accent.

'Fuck off,' he replied (giving it back in Scouse).

It was left to Miss Jones to take Kevin aside and explain that 'hon.' was an abbreviated form of 'honorary' – in respect of the Secretaries of various Societies – rather than 'honourable,' and had nothing to do with the House of Lords. Knowing the fun Nicky would have had with such an oversight, he was relieved she hadn't noticed. He didn't set his mother, who had started to look on his job in a more favourable light, right either.

'You actually speak to lords and ladies?' Agnes gasped, hardly daring to believe; piling up his spuds, Kevin repeated the claim right back at her, without dropping a single 'h'.

Happy to be treated as any of the other employees, who were now arriving in dribs and drabs – to be judged on his own merits – Kevin asked no favours. He was capable, too, with Miss Jones having no hesitation in entrusting him with work of a higher grade.

'I don't know why they put that stupid bitch in charge,' Nicky would snipe, refusing to let her grievances go, and it was like being back at school (smoking in the bike sheds, while maligning the teachers). Yet, they weren't children anymore and Miss Jones didn't deserve such approbation.

'I think she's alright,' Kevin returned soberly.

The expected eruption never came, with Nicky stalking off to the kitchen instead, where he could hear her getting her teeth into John Gannon.

'There's a ghost up there,' she was saying – in reference to the building's still-untenanted second floor – 'Leslie saw it.'

As the ground shifted and new alliances formed, Kevin was glad to be excluded from such discussions.

In Leslie Kavanagh, who worked for the Sefton Narrowboat Committee (on the first floor) – along with her brother, Liam – Nicky had found a friend, and her ever more frequent visits provided a welcome respite.

'We've got a barge,' Leslie had stuttered – in introduction – 'the 'Pride of Sefton'... and,' her eyes wide, 'we take handicapped people out for trips on the canal.' Nicky was already cackling even before Leslie added – helplessly – 'it has wheelchair access.'

An accessible barge seemed an odd conceit, while the sight of Mr Johnson – the 'captain' who ran the scheme – in his double-breasted suit, was enough to give pause.

Given the undeniably incestuous nature of Ellesmere House, it was no surprise that their next recruit, tapping his way with a white stick – though he could still make out faces, at that point – should be yet another sibling, Miss Jones introducing him, with just the hint of a smile.

'This is Andrew Kavanagh,' the name no coincidence, 'I trust you'll make him welcome.'

Six months later and – ghost, or no ghost – the second floor finally had an occupant, too, in the form of a Sefton-based dial-a-ride service that provided accessible transportation for the physically disabled.

'He's well fit,' Nicky declared of Steve Sampson, its youthful manager, after passing him in the hall. 'I'd definitely do him,' she added, with a leer.

She certainly tried and, developing a second sense – to pick out the soft thrum of his Saab, against the drill of the traffic – she would rush out to meet him every morning, drooling over every inch of his shiny silver suit and his clicking Cuban heels.

'I'm Nicky – are you married?' she had asked, in presenting herself, before declaiming that 'he must be gay' when she was unexpectedly rejected.

There were snorts of laughter at that.

'It's a real beauty, isn't it?' Steve continued – the fingers of his left hand (no ring) drumming lovingly on the glimmering bonnet – adding knowledgeably, 'The engines are made by the same people who supply the Swedish Air Force.'

Nicky nodded blandly, feeling stupid.

'Really?' she replied, inching closer, though it was clear from the start that Steve's interest in her was as thin as her interest in cars.

It would take Kevin more than a year to make his first proper friend at Ellesmere House. With a self-confident, ready wit and a keen sartorial eye, Kevin had considered Mark Cameron a 'like mind' from the start.

'Comrades!' the young buck would greet the office each morning, his tight pants running into narrow winkle-pickers, the reed-thin tie – laid across the broad chest of a button-down shirt – the briefest concession to a dress code.

He even had Miss Jones's careworn face breaking into a smile.

'I think she likes you,' Kevin teased.

With his tall, wiry frame and wavy King Charles hair, Mark Cameron combined the landed entitlements of a public school alumni, with the easy insouciance of left-field bohemia.

When, over their first lunch together – at the Old Bank – with Kevin keeping close watch, his new colleague drew a crumpled copy of *The Guardian* from his faded leather valise, our hero was won.

'Are you a socialist?' Kevin asked, before he could stop himself, the answer coming with just as little pause.

'Yeah – *you*?'

Kevin gave a wide-eyed nod and it seemed they had a pact, with the younger, necessarily, in thrall to the more experienced man.

A month later, taking a detour back from the pub to the flat of one of Mark's friends, Kevin would discover a more sinister side – watching, in horror, as Mark wrapped a leather strap round one of his arms and stabbed in a needle bearing a syringe.

Kevin had only ever seen it done in films.

'Do you want some?' he was asked casually, and – his eyes turning fretfully about the small room – he shook his head.

It was Kevin who got Mark safely back to the office, when they were done; Kevin who loyally fielded the questions he figured his friend was in no state to supply.

'One too many,' he mumbled to their colleagues.

Troubled by the gradual deterioration, Kevin kept the secret, though his loyalty was increasingly uneasy, with Mark even shooting up during office hours at the height of his addiction (taking up temporary residence in the cramped office bathroom when everyone else went for lunch).

'Out on the lash?' Nicky would taunt, on seeing him strung out on his desk again, dark rings circling his eyes, putting his dismissive manner down to his education (if not, to his class).

Anxiously following his wavering progress, Kevin was surprised by how well Mark managed to function, though the relationship he started up with one of the cleaners seemed a step too far.

'She's cool,' Mark had declared, pulling up a chair and giving notice.

'But she's married,' Kevin cautioned, thinking nothing more of the matter, until Mark – who had always been one of the first to leave – was suddenly staying late.

'I'm going to ask her out,' he confessed over a pint, and – before

Kevin could even think of dissuading him – he had already gone and done it.

'But she's married,' Kevin reiterated more forcefully, 'and she's a Jehovah's Witness…'

'She's said I've got to get clean,' Mark resumed, ignoring him.

'And, she's right…'

'She says she loves me – and she'll leave her husband – but I have to stop using.'

True to whatever compelled him, Mark sought help (and quit) and the doting couple were married by the following spring.

Following an extended lunch, involving liberal libations of liquor, the afternoons at Ellesmere House would drag, with the fidgety staff having to keep to their desks until whatever boss they had at the time saw fit to release them. It was like pulling teeth, with the workers seeking various distractions to make the clock move quicker.

On one occasion, the boys returned worse for wear to find Nicky in hysterics.

'Oh my God!' she shrieked – pulling them in – 'Ruth's lost the plot!'

The story – of how Miss Jones had set up the projector, to show one of her home movies to Mike Travers, the Assistant Director of Social Services (who was invited over for the privilege) – came in fits and starts.

'Home movies?' Kevin sought to clarify.

'Yeah… and she was wetting her knickers!' Nicky rejoined.

'Who cares?' Mark grunted, as he slumped into his seat.

'You've got to see this,' Nicky insisted, dragging him up again, before leading them into the back office, which was serving as a dark room, the whirr of the projector playing into a studied silence.

Nicky whispered something that they didn't hear, and Mike Travers – his sharp features caught in the light of the closing door – turned at the sound of it. He looked confused, irritable; straightening their shirts and ties, the boys nodded casually across.

They were already regretting having trusted to Nicky, when they could have been seeing the afternoon out in peace. Kevin felt physically sick, the tension turning his bloated stomach.

'Watch this,' Nicky whispered, and they heard her this time, as the first slide – a lopsided barge on an inky canal – hove into view.

It was followed, almost immediately, to their increasing bewilderment – with no comment made – by another slide, showing just the prow of a similar looking barge (on a similar looking canal). All three were already stifling laughter, even before Miss Jones started up on her handwritten commentary, reading in earnest from a sheet of paper held to her chest. Kevin gave an involuntary shudder on her behalf.

'If the oak before the ash,' Miss Jones declared, nodding her head gravely towards the next – translucent rain playing against a grey sky – 'then we'll only have a splash. If the ash before the oak,' pausing for emphasis, before finishing with a shy smile, 'then we'll surely have a soak.'

She looked triumphant, though with Nicky now openly giggling and Mark dropping to a crouch, there was a growing restlessness. Turning from the screen, while seeking to avoid Mark's wandering eye, Kevin had no way to cover his mouth, as laughter forced its way out.

He was praying for the show to end, but another click brought another slide and another barge; then, in quick succession, an aerial shot of a red wherry (cleaving through evasive ducks), followed by a lock in motion, around which a small crowd had gathered, the water rushing up to meet them.

Perspiring in the heat of the projector, as she waved the images through, Ruth Hayden Jones was beaming.

'I told you she'd lost it,' Nicky crowed, when Miss Jones finally stepped back to the projector to shut it down.

Kevin glanced across to the Assistant Director of Social Services, who was standing, ramrod straight, with his arms tight about his chest and a frown creasing his implacable brow. He had clearly seen enough.

Darkness descended, with Kevin wondering at a woman who had always seemed so stable, so *professional.* Calling, hoarsely, for the lights, Miss Jones seemed to finally see it too, her voice faltering as she led the guest away.

'I really need to be going,' they heard him telling her, with no evident humour; her head bowed in contrition, Miss Jones suddenly seemed very old.

'She'll get the sack,' Nicky speculated eagerly, once they were alone.

Numb – and still feeling the effects of the alcohol – the boys were silent. Kevin edged towards the door, with an odd sense of loss, but catching sight of Mark's face the two of them were almost immediately laughing again.

Miss Jones was trembling when she returned and quietly packed away. Kevin gave an understanding smile, before turning his chair to give her some privacy.

'I suppose you two have been drinking again?' Miss Jones asked (in a rare flash of anger) when they reached the door.

'Just a couple,' Mark returned nonchalantly.

'Well, it's not good enough,' Ruth snapped, cutting him short in a way she had never done before, her hands shaking.

'Daft bitch,' Nicky gloated, misreading the mood.

'For fuck's sake, put a sock in it will you?' Mark hissed, his colour rising.

When Geoff Grimes made a surprise visit the next day, they all – quite naturally – presumed that there were to be consequences.

'I hear Ruth had a go at you lads, for having a couple of drinks at lunch?' he started brusquely.

Meeting his eye with a shrug, Mark answered for the two of them. 'She did mention something, yeah…'

Looking over to Geoff, Kevin felt another tinge of regret, but Geoff had already broken into a smile.

'Well, don't you boys take any notice – it's none of her bloody business!'

Kevin flushed, with sudden shame, while Nicky could hardly contain her delight.

'She's a waste of bloody space that one,' she chirruped, 'thinks she's better than everyone else… could do with going down a peg or two.' There was a celebratory air to the office now, that Kevin wanted no part of. '… And I don't know what gives her the right to order us around,' Nicky ran on, as Kevin wheeled away, frustrated to find no one else taking Ruth's side.

Miss Jones had always treated her subordinates with respect, yet here was Nicky sprawled over her desk and holding court. Still just nineteen years of age, Kevin's education had already begun.

There were more indignities to follow, when Nicky clattered into the office after lunch to find a pile of carrier bags lined up at the door.

'Take a look at this lot!' she shrieked, picking at the items that had come loose. 'They must be Ruth's, the daft cow.'

Returning to their desks, her colleagues barely raised their heads to look, even when Nicky started to drag those same bags out into the middle of the room, pulling them apart in a public show.

'They're fucking undies!' she roared, tossing a pair to Mark. 'Damart knickers!'

'Give it a rest,' Mark spat, sending them back.

'Oh my God, that woman's from another fucking century!' Nicky resumed, as she tore through the bags, launching a set of bloomers and then a cantilevered bra up into the air.

Mark stepped reluctantly across.

'What the hell are these?' he asked, brandishing a pair of frilly knickers, which he strapped to his head, before setting off on an improvised catwalk.

He had bloomers over his jeans (and cowboy boots) for his second run, giving a flamboyant twirl – to whistles and catcalls – as the office rose feverishly to its feet.

'Miss Jones is *laughing with the cold*!' Nicky spluttered – in reference to a recent run of adverts – tears running her mascara, as she fell to the floor, with a lacy bra strapped to her waist. 'Oh, Miss Jones, Miss Jones!' she cried, in strict RP, kicking her feet into the air.

She hadn't laughed so much in her whole, short life... and was, in fact, enjoying herself so much that – carousing for a whole minute longer than anyone else – she failed to notice the silence that suddenly fell around them, or that Miss Jones had arrived (bringing the room to a standstill).

Nothing was said on either side, as Nicky picked herself up and extricated the bra that was caught around her neck, while Mark helped to gather up the bags.

Kevin evokes that anarchic period – 'it was mad!' about as clear as he can tell it – with genuine warmth, recalling the fun he had and the friends he made. He hadn't expected it, arriving – in some trepidation – with the feeling that, having just left college, he wasn't ready for such responsibility.

He would discover, in time – his relief tinged with regret – that he was actually one of the more mature members of their staff.

'It was a farce, really,' he admits, with a typical morning taking in a dozen futile calls (and the accompanying paperwork) to clients who didn't even exist, while something approaching a carnival atmosphere raged around them.

Lunch was a ninety-minute affair and then they were in the home stretch, with the majority of the staff knocking off by four.

'It was a liquid lunch, most of the time,' Kevin clarifies, his smile closer to a grimace, remembering how the room would seem to spin when he staggered back in for the afternoon.

Ellesmere House was boisterous, tiresome and *surreal* – some kind of a dream – but it couldn't last. When Kevin popped his head into the manager's office to find Miss Hayden Jones slumped over her desk in tears, the spell was broken. If she hadn't already seen him, he might well have walked out again.

'They're letting me go,' she explained. 'They've given me a week's notice.'

'Why? What's happened?' Kevin asked in shock.

'They said that we've not made sufficient progress... that we've not taken the service to where they had envisaged.' Kevin could hardly deny the truth of that, but couldn't see how Miss Jones was to blame. 'They said I can't control the staff,' she added stiffly.

'It's not right...' Kevin interjected, his heart turning at the way Nicky and the others had treated her, 'you've done a brilliant job... we just need more time, that's all.'

Miss Jones gave a rueful smile, but it was clear that she had nothing more to say, so Kevin backed out again, determined not to breathe a word.

They would all hear soon enough, with Nicky hardly able to contain herself.

'I always said she wasn't up to it,' she crowed, at a pitch he had no doubt would carry through to Miss Jones.

Kevin wheeled across to pull the door.

'What's eating you?' Nicky barked contemptuously.

Kevin didn't answer until he had calmed down; then, he was forthright in a manner he couldn't have mustered just six months before.

'Miss Jones has always been good to me,' he said, 'and she deserves some respect,' not venturing into his contention that Nicky had, no doubt, played her part in getting her fired (she certainly had Geoff's ear by now).

'She's had her time,' Nicky retorted without remorse, 'and, if you think I'm going to shed any tears for that old cow, then you're mistaken.'

Kevin hated her, right then, but – learning, now – he let the comment go.

Life, inevitably, moved on, with Mark Cameron stepping into the breach, just as soon as Miss Jones had cleared her desk, his Politics degree – and general air of competency – giving him a natural seniority over Nicky, despite her noisy claims.

'I don't know why they've promoted you, instead of me,' she quibbled, careful not to swear. 'It's sexist, that's what it is.'

Mark wasn't in the mood, so he told her straight.

'It's not sexist, I'm just better qualified than you.'

Touchy about that lack, Nicky blushed down to her roots.

'I wouldn't want it, anyway,' she told Kevin later, 'I'm happier on the factory floor, with the rest of you… actually getting stuff done.'

The idea of Nicky doing work, of any sort, was laughable, though – shuffle the personnel as they liked – very little would ever change. It was Mark Cameron, for instance – as manager, then – who discovered the deckchairs.

'I've got a surprise, when you get back,' he had told the gang, as they headed out to lunch.

Having forgotten the promise, they returned to find striped recliners lined up at the front, with Mark kitted out in t-shirt and shorts.

'It's too hot to do any work,' he declared, his thick shades reflecting the light, 'so I've made an executive decision… we're having the afternoon off!'

There were no arguments, with Nicky glad of the opportunity to top up her tan.

'Keep an eye out for Geoff,' Mark cautioned, still very much a part despite the responsibilities of his promotion.

While able to acknowledge the absurdity of their working day, Mark Cameron showed no desire to fix it.

'The welfare advisory service is bullshit,' he would admit, adding his voice to the general complaints, before tipping a pile of papers to the floor and sitting himself up on a desk. 'A complete waste of time – no one even knows we're here, for fuck's sake.'

He was right, and it was as true two years in as it had been at their inception (with no one, any longer, fooled).

'We're only here to make the council look good,' Andrew opined.

'And to get the knock-backs from Europe,' Kevin added, with a sneer.

'Who gives a shit?' Nicky spat, as she applied another coat to her nails, 'as long as we get paid.'

Silence followed that last remark; they were all implicated, with Kevin, for one, still on the payroll a good five years in.

Wondering again why he was even there, Mark looked briefly chastened.

'Time for lunch,' he declared with a shrug, glancing up to the clock (that showed five past eleven).

Recognising the redundancy of the service they purported to provide, Kevin regretted the way Miss Jones had been treated from the start, by both her employees and her employers. She had been operating with one hand tied behind her back, and Kevin only wished that he had taken some kind of stand, given that she was actually trying to do her job. With neither the energy, nor the desire, to start over, her successor – Mark Cameron – was already looking to move on. Kevin increasingly felt like he was being left behind.

By year two, with the volume of calls (and genuine clients) on the rise, extra staff would be taken on to meet the demand. These new arrivals were generally bounced in off the back of a Job Creation and Enterprise Scheme – with the unemployment rate reaching its historic peak (of 11.9%) in April 1984 – and arrived lacking both experience and ambition. They would depart just as soon as they came, for the most part, though Jane Simmonds, Martin Waterhouse and Paula Harrison – all still to make their entrance (to varying fanfares) – would end up working there for the duration.

'I made loads of friends at Ellesmere House,' Kevin concedes, each new intake welcomed into the fold via a series of initiations (with more deckchairs added to the makeshift terrace).

The boredom, especially during the first twelve months, had been stifling, with the staff forever seeking out diversions and distractions. Kevin can't quite recall how it began, but – when they realised the fun to be had – it was quickly established as part of their routine to fill out and file bogus referral forms (in lieu of actual clients).

To the unaccustomed eye, walking in on them, they would seem hard at work, a veritable hive of activity – jabbing at their typewriters and phones. It was a pretence that Kevin was to take to ever-greater heights. He wrote:

Caller:	*Donald Duck*
Reason for Call:	*Required money for new hat.*
Action:	*Advised client to put in a request with social services for an emergency loan.*

Taking pleasure where they could, the completed form would be sent around the room, laughter following its slow passage, while Kevin, his head bowed to the page once more, was already scrawling out the next.

Caller:	*The Joker*
Reason for Call:	*Enquired whether he was entitled to claim income support, having left his last position voluntarily.*
Action:	*Advised to contact local Job Centre (given number).*

There were classical composers and authors, politicians and superheroes – the themes ranging from high culture to low. Mark took the prize, on this occasion, Nicky giving a baffled frown to Kevin's nod of appreciation:

Caller:	*Karl Marx*
Reason for Call:	*Questioned the validity of the welfare state within a free market economy.*
Action:	*Advised to attend 'back to work' interview, as previously agreed.*

They were soon sending letters, too, which they posted out to a series of increasingly contrived addresses.

'Mail!' Kevin would bellow, before skimming his latest creation across the room.

'Should I frank it?' Andrew asked, as he squinted to make out the address, chuckling when he saw that Kevin had written to the Queen.

'I asked if she was 'at liberty' to attend the official opening of the welfare advisory service,' Kevin explained, this despite the fact that they had already been up and running for over a year.

The reply – in which Her Majesty had declared herself, 'too busy to attend at this time, unfortunately', while wishing them 'every success in your future ventures' – came in an envelope bearing the royal crest and would somehow find its way to Geoff Grimes who, still puzzling at it the following day, decided to pay them a visit.

'You lot been busy?' he began.

'Yeah, you know us, Geoff,' Mark winked, 'had a couple of calls come through this morning – we're knackered!'

Geoff wasn't smiling.

'Well, it's not good enough,' he said, the blank faces all still suspecting some kind of a joke. 'And, I'm warning you now, if you don't buck up, you'll all be out on the dole,' he continued, his greying rug of hair wagging, as he wafted the letter back and forth.

He stood where he was for a moment more, marvelling at the typewriters and the phones and the filing cabinets, before remembering again why he had come (and asking outright).

'Oh, yes, and does anyone know anything about this?' A pause – he had their full attention now. 'Did one of you numbskulls actually have the gall to write to the Queen?'

It was hard not to see the funny side and, once he had gone, they were laughing again, the tension released.

'He's right though, isn't he?' Mark admitted. 'We don't really do anything.'

'Well, you're the boss,' Nicky noted indignantly, 'so, it's your fault, if it's anyone's…'

He knew that but, despite the residual guilt, had never thought to address such failings and he never would (in the time that remained to him) – leaving Nicky to her hollow victory.

In an office with such a quick turnover of youthful recruits, it was almost inevitable that relationships, of various kinds, would blossom (and fall). Nicky, who was usually to the fore in such matters, had set her eyes after Leslie's brother, Liam, within the first week.

'He's gorgeous,' she had declared, fairly drooling as she introduced herself with a dainty bow. 'Hi, I'm Nicky… *charmed* to meet you.' Sensing the danger, Liam was already casting about for help. 'Are you Italian?' she asked, before he could escape, brushing a hand through her crisp fringe.

'Lancastrian,' Liam answered drily.

Looking admiringly on, Nicky judged him an indisputable 'catch'.

'Tall, dark and handsome,' she would quip and she wasn't the only one to cast admiring looks his way, whenever he ventured down – the newly-arrived Mr Black was soon in raptures, too.

When Nicky eventually prevailed, Andrew Kavanagh – who had stayed in for lunch – was witness for the prosecution.

'They're in there,' he whispered, when the others returned, with a nod to the games room, 'I heard them go in about half an hour ago…'

With no desire to elaborate, he left the rest to the imagination (glad that he didn't have the eyes to see).

They were all back at their desks and their phones by the time Nicky emerged, staggering forth in her bare feet, with her blouse trailing.

'What the fuck do you lot want?' she hissed, red-faced.

When Liam stumbled out after her – tucking in his shirt and fixing his belt – the office duly erupted.

'Afternoon,' Liam mumbled, offering a cordial acknowledgement, before slipping back up the stairs.

After smoothing down her skirt and running a comb through her bedraggled hair, Nicky was almost immediately back to her old self and keen to divulge. Skipping excitedly about, waiting for what she considered the inevitable questions, she found the lack of interest galling.

'Oh my God!' she sallied forth, calling them to attention when her impatience finally gave. 'You're never going to guess what just happened!' They could do more than guess, but had no desire to hear. Nicky pushed on, regardless. 'We had the place to ourselves – with you lot out at lunch – so we thought we'd make the most of it… We were only supposed to be having a game of pool,' – here she dipped her head towards the windowless room at her back (the door still inching shut) – 'but… oh my God, the next thing we knew, we were ripping each other's clothes off!' Adjusting the strap of her bra, while her heels pattered at the floor, Nicky gave a shriek. 'I'm still shaking – look!' she said, holding out her hands.

They had hoped that was the end of it, but Nicky wasn't finished. 'He ripped my skirt clean off,' she said, turning to show the hem, 'and, then, he had my knickers down…' Pacing the floor, with her arms flapping, there was nothing they could do to stop her. 'He's really strong,' she added whimsically. 'Before I knew it, he had me on the snooker table,' – the six by four green baize – 'and was fucking me all over the place,' the *à* la carte lovers hanging on to the corner pockets for a better purchase. 'It was amazing,' she gasped at last, dropping exhaustedly to her seat.

There was silence then, with no one yet daring to take up a phone, or tap at a typewriter. Nicky looked vulnerable, more like a girl than they would ever have expected. There were tears in her eyes.

'Anyone want a cup of tea?' Kevin cut in (though it wasn't his turn), with a wilfulness that grew with each passing day.

Everyone, it seemed – excluding Nicky – wanted one.

'I'll give you a hand,' Andrew said quickly, the party well and truly done.

A caricature, Nicky Mathers nevertheless serves as a vivid reminder of former times and the life they shared. Kevin wouldn't forget her, just as – starting out on his professional path – he would always remember the short shrift given to disability rights at Ellesmere House. Going forward, he would meet with those same attitudes, in any number of organisations.

It was probably the making of Kevin that he was offered an escape before he grew too settled, and too accepting of malpractice, with Geoff Grimes pulling him aside one day to tell him that they were moving him on.

'You're wasted here,' he said, and Kevin, who had never dared to voice his disillusionment, took him at his word.

He accepted the promotion too (with open arms), leaving all those friends at what felt like the right time, satisfying ambitions that might otherwise have been forgotten.

'I'd still pop in, now and again,' he admits, 'if I needed something written up, or just for a chat,' his memories of those anarchic days stirred afresh by my continuing questions, hardly able to believe they had got away with it for so long.

'It's too bloody hot!' Nicky moaned, as the air con rattled redundantly on, pushing her chair away from the desk, the precedent having been set months ago.

Her colleagues were almost immediately up on their feet too, though – despite giving the call – Nicky was the last to join them on a deckchair out front, emerging in a polka-dot bikini and flip-flops, her glass fully charged. Leslie had saved her a place.

'Open day?' Nicky muttered in confusion, her eye drawn to the fire station across the road and the sign pinned to a board out front. 'What the fuck?'

'And, we've got front row seats!' Leslie giggled.

Bubbling with excitement, Nicky angled her chair for a better view.

'Get a look at that lot!' she drawled, pointing to a group of bare-chested firefighters (whistling through her teeth).

Leslie mumbled something in response, but Nicky, who was already up on her feet, calling out in appreciation, didn't hear her. Several heads were turned at once, though it was noticeable that, of those who looked across, most – knowing Nicky of old – were already putting their tops back on and seemed set on ignoring her.

'Kevin, my love,' Nicky intoned slyly, as she slid back down to her chair, 'would you mind putting a bit of this lotion on for me?'

While acknowledging the pleasure he had once taken in working his small fingers over Nicky's smooth skin, from her hands to her shoulders (then down to her waist), Kevin now wheeled across with reluctance.

When, playing to the gallery, her voice carrying clear across the street, Nicky started to cry out in audible pleasure, Kevin backed away again.

'You're mad!' Leslie squawked in delight.

His eyes passing quickly over Leslie's shapely legs (showing beneath her denim skirt), Kevin recalled the night he had recently spent in her bed.

Leslie had – sadly – been in another room at the time.

'So near, but so far!' Kevin chuckled, giving the punch line.

I waited for him to continue, but there was nothing more to tell, except for the fact that, after driving Leslie back to work the next day, her perfume would remain a pleasing fixture in his car for the rest of the week.

Nicky was now rubbing ostentatiously at her thighs, smearing on the sun cream, with moans and groans. When the men gave no reaction, with some of them even turning the other way, Nicky clambered up on her deckchair and set about hollering.

'Open day! Open day!' she shrieked, giving crude gestures. 'Why don't you come over here and put *my* fire out?'

They had heard it all before, but Nicky had never been quite so explicit; they expected some response. It never came. Instead, Nicky could only watch, in disbelief, as the firefighters packed away the benches and chairs.

'Stupid bitch,' Mark hissed in passing, as he led the retreat, with Kevin and the others not too far behind.

'Not one of you is a proper man!' Nicky bawled, in the disappointed throes of hysteria, as the courtyard cleared.

'You're crazy!' Leslie simpered, with misplaced admiration.

Shaking at the ice in her drink, which was flat, Nicky turned to her friend with a generous smile, as the sun was driven temporarily behind a cloud (and they found themselves in shade).

Goosebumps rising on their skin, the girls grabbed at their belongings with fearful squeals and headed back inside.

Chapter 7

August 12 1982 would provide a rite of passage that Kevin had no reason to expect. A staging post that could – quite naturally – never happen for the first time (again), it was a date he could hardly forget.

It began as any other day – blustery, as Kevin recalls – with the scattered cloud outside doing little to temper the heat within and the afternoon dragging on.

'I'm bored,' Nicky sniped aimlessly.

She lacked the humour of earlier years, and – preferring the peace and quiet of an empty office to the trials of extended company – Kevin was relieved to see her stalking out to lunch with the rest.

Taking advantage of their absence, Jane Simmonds, Ellesmere House's latest recruit, slipped in from behind.

'What you doing?' she asked, pushing up onto his cluttered desk, as (blushing and flustered) Kevin turned to face her.

'Nothing much,' he admitted, indicating a half-eaten sandwich and offering it up; blinking down at him through her pageboy fringe, Jane declined.

'Not hungry, thanks.'

Given her slender build, and the fact that he had already taken a couple of juicy bites, Kevin was hardly surprised. Her size was a topic that Nicky had recently weighed in on, taking Jane's angular frame as something to question; Kevin could only wonder what his mother – a natural feeder – would have thought.

'I'm not that hungry, either,' he said, with a sympathetic shrug.

Despite her reputation as a dour soulmate – 'she's plain Jane,' Nicky had cackled, in a malicious christening – Jane was one of the few people in the office that Kevin actually liked and he welcomed their infrequent conversations. She had much to recommend her, with Nicky's premature rush to judgement a matter of jealousy as much as ignorance.

'She's cool,' he maintained, no longer willing to let such idle judgements stand and, given the gossip that Jane provided for her under-employed colleagues, they could hardly complain.

'She's a *dyke*?' Nicky had spluttered, very nearly speechless, when she discovered that Jane was cohabiting with a woman.

Kevin was quick to inform his mother and Jim, too, seeing something of a kindred spirit in his new friend (who played by her own rules).

'I was hoping to slip out early,' Kevin confessed, pushing his chair away from the table, 'if I can get past Tom,' both of them instinctively casting a glance towards the manager's office, the door, as ever, ajar.

Mr Black was on the phone, a stream of innuendoes followed by a high-pitched whinny of a laugh. Their eyes met, smiling into the silence that lay between them.

'I was wondering if you'd like to come over for dinner later…' Jane cut in, taking him unawares, 'I could cook something?'

'I'd have to ring my mum,' Kevin replied, his eyes raised, waiting for an explanation.

'Well, ring your mum then,' Jane clipped back, taking up the phone and placing the receiver into the crook of his small hand.

Kevin made the call straight away, in a show of independence.

'Hi, Mum,' he began, continuing before she could interrupt, 'I just wanted to let you know that I won't be home for tea, because I'm eating at Jane's,' – casually dropping the name – 'so don't wait up.'

'As long as you're okay,' his mother returned, after a sharp intake of breath.

'Yes, Mother, I'm fine,' Kevin returned hurriedly, dashing down the phone as Nicky crashed in (having already heard her thumping up the stairs).

With Mr Black firmly in situ for the rest of the day, there was to be no early dart. Kevin lingered instead, so that they would be the last to leave and no one would see Jane getting into his car.

'Nice motor,' she smirked, running a hand down the tailgate spoiler.

'It's an XR3,' Kevin declared – a lie – hoping she wouldn't notice the scratches.

Jane didn't drive, but directed him back to her flat, which Kevin was relieved to find was sparse and open-plan. More importantly, it was situated on the ground floor, which he hadn't even considered (giving him a free run).

Having parked his chair, Kevin hopped confidently onto the sofa, as directed.

'Nice pad,' he said, echoing Jane's phrase, as he turned his head to take in both ends of the room, his words seeming slightly foolish (wondering, suddenly, why he had come). 'I like the way you've done it out,' he added, reading at the spines of her books, curious to see what they might have in common.

'Thanks, but it was like this when I moved in,' Jane replied, bringing glasses and a bottle of wine in from the kitchen. 'I just put a couple of pictures up,' she added, Kevin's eye drawn to the large photo-prints lining most of the walls.

Turning back to Jane, he was glad to see that, as the conversation started to flow, the relationship they had in the office had survived the relocation.

'And, then I got the job at Ellesmere House,' Jane concluded the potted history of her life thus far – Kevin surprised to hear no mention of Sandra (her partner) – 'and the rest you know.' She smiled, pouring him another glass, before stepping through to the kitchen. 'And, what about you?' she called back. 'You must have some stories to tell?'

At his ease, after a glass of wine, Kevin was soon regaling her with the more interesting, or comic, of his established routines, noting that most of his anecdotes still revolved around his friends from school. His relative youth was an embarrassment – a lack of experience, rather than years.

'It must be great to have your own place,' he mused, observing the markers of maturity that littered Jane's flat, while he still lived at home (in a room he had decorated as a teenager).

Back on the sofa, Jane charged his glass again.

'Dinner will be about ten minutes,' she said, and he nodded, sipping at the wine, so that it wouldn't spill, suddenly feeling out of his depth.

'The pictures are cool,' he offered eventually, while Jane fixed him with an ironic smile.

'I took them,' she replied, 'they were part of my final submission.'

'Wow, *really*?' Kevin gasped, shuffling around, his eyes skipping from one to the next.

'I can show you the dark room later, if you like?' Jane added, stepping up to lay the table, while Kevin took a closer look. 'I work freelance,' she continued, 'hire a room and professional models.'

'What – and sell them?' Kevin asked quickly.

'Yeah, sometimes,' Jane returned, as she served the food, 'agencies pay for the whole set… I get a bonus if anything's published.'

Nodding in earnest admiration, Kevin could hardly believe that 'plain Jane' had this whole other life. Somewhat subdued, he was still processing what he had heard as Jane manoeuvred his chair into place at the table.

'Thanks, cheers,' he said, and – his preconceptions subtly shifted – he found his eye involuntarily wandering when, her short skirt skipping up her thighs to expose the flesh beneath it, Jane took the seat beside him.

'Tuck in,' she said, filling his glass, and Kevin reflected on the contrast to his mother (who was virtually teetotal) and her annual Christmas sherry.

There was grated parmesan in a small bowl – he had to ask – a cruet for the oil and a tall wooden pepper grinder; not for the first time, Kevin was following Jane's lead.

Once the plates had been cleared and Kevin invited back to the sofa, Jane emerged from one of the other rooms with an oversized leather folder.

'These are some of my other pieces,' she said, displaying her first touch of pride – that Kevin was quick to second – as she opened it across his lap.

Thinking, instinctively, of the photo albums his mother would bring out at Christmas, that showed him trussed up in an improvised nappy, or else playing with his sisters' dolls (to their general amusement), Kevin was prepared for the worst, with a fixed smile on his flaccid lips.

Presented with a succession of nudes, in contrasting black and white, he was pleasantly surprised.

'Shit, these are good,' he declared. 'You've got a really good eye,' he added, affecting to a knowledge that he didn't have, as he sipped more quickly at his wine.

They lapsed into silence and it seemed that the evening had finally caught up with them; Kevin considered that he should probably be making a move. He didn't get the chance, with Jane jumping promptly to her feet and urging him to follow.

'I'll show you the dark room,' she said, leading him through, Kevin picking out the smell of lavender as he went thumping after, his eyes gradually adjusting.

'Jane?' he called, stepping cautiously in.

He heard movement, over his left shoulder, then laughter.

'Over here,' Jane said, before flipping on the bedside lamp. 'Don't be shy, I won't bite.'

Kevin squinted across, in confusion, though it was only when Jane drew down her skirt that he saw that her blouse was already unbuttoned (showing the cotton bra below). Dumbstruck, Kevin didn't move another inch, as Jane – now stripped to her underwear – stepped towards him. She came to a halt less than a foot away, her bare thighs nearly making contact with his flushed face.

'Don't worry,' she whispered, leaning in to ease him down to the floor, before dropping to her knees, 'I'll be careful.'

Bewildered, Kevin could only watch in silence when she set about the zip on his pants, which she wrestled over his rigid feet.

'And, what have we got here?' Jane chuckled, when she had them off, meeting Kevin's eye with a reassuring smile, as she brushed her fingers down his penis, which was now thrusting out of his checked boxers.

She had his shirt off next – he didn't complain – lifting his hands out of the way so that she could get it over his shoulders, her fingers stroking in circles at his chest and his stomach (and then down again).

They proceeded to fuck, Jane working her way cautiously up on top and then guiding Kevin inside, before rocking herself back and forth with gentle, lilting moans. Too frightened to look at her, Kevin lay perfectly still at first, but – quickly growing into the role – he was soon bouncing along in rhythm, calling out encouragement each time Jane paused to check he was alright.

'Bloody marvellous!' he cried, while Jane, with no thighs to straddle – and, breaking into laughter – struggled to keep her balance.

As the rhythm increased, it was all Kevin could do to keep up; the commentary – fortunately – dropped away.

Panting heavily, their hearts beating in unison, Jane – her skin now coated in a fine dew – rode him hard, bouncing the two of them up and down for a further ten minutes, leaving Kevin bruised and bruited beneath her, to no ultimate climax (for either).

It had all been so quick... and, then, it was over, Jane rolling off to the side, and then onto her back, her breaths staggered. Ever loquacious, Kevin was already grasping for words.

'That was amazing!' he gushed, blushing at the sight of his engorged penis, before turning back to Jane, her small breasts parted on her chest, chestnut hair between her legs.

'Not bad, for your first time!' she declared.

Stretched out on the floor, as naked as the day he was born, Kevin cast his eyes up to the ceiling with a smile that wouldn't leave – and, in that moment, he had fallen in love.

Jane was quickly up on her feet again, and – hearing a shower hissing into life in the next room – Kevin was brought to his senses, recalling suddenly everything his mother had once said… and the clumsy prosthetics he had once worn… and the way Jim had liked to push him about in his chair. He didn't feel like apologising anymore – they could all go to hell.

By the time Jane had returned, dressing quite openly in front of him – and that was something he had never seen before – Kevin was already back in his clothes and back on his feet.

'I said we'd meet a couple of friends in the pub, if you fancy it?' Jane told him, scanning her reflection as she fitted herself into a beige jacket. Kevin nodded. 'I'll call a cab,' she added, just like that.

Still trying to understand what had happened, Kevin was happily compliant, with one adventure leading naturally to the next. He had already climbed into his chair, from which perch he kicked out his pants, before combing down his hair with a dab of spittle.

They waited for the taxi in silence and were silent when they went out to meet it, too, though once they had clambered aboard and spread themselves across the back seat, the tension broke and they were giggling like children.

'The Royal,' Jane managed, with a smirk, and it only really struck him then – as it hadn't before – that he had just lost his virginity: that Jane, who he had never even considered before (in that way), had just initiated sex and was now sitting beside him like nothing had happened.

It was only a short drive; giddy and in high spirits – and still fairly drunk – it was probably the most beautiful ride he would ever take.

'You okay?' Jane asked, with gentle solicitude.

Grinning foolishly, Kevin was – for once – utterly lost for words.

He took it in his stride though, and when they arrived to find Sandra, Jane's flatmate – and supposed partner – already stationed at the bar ahead of them, along with three other friends, he wasn't in the least perturbed, shaking hands with each of them, before offering to go for drinks.

Apart from the occasional glance and sidelong smile, Kevin and Jane had almost immediately reverted to the way they were in the office – with no suggestion of anything untoward – and that somehow felt appropriate.

'You must come out with us again,' Sandra said, and Kevin blushed, even this seeming a delight on a night like this.

The jukebox ran through Kevin's unconventional choices – he had thrust in a fistful of coins – and the drinks went on flowing, while Kevin puffed regally away on the cigarettes that were passed his way.

Hardly even aware of the steps that took him there, Kevin very nearly floated home; waiting at the door, with his usual petitions, Jim was like a douse of salt.

'Have you been drinking?' he asked, sniffing at the air.

'What if I have?' Kevin sneered. 'I'm nineteen years old!'

'Your mother's been worried sick,' Jim persisted, 'we waited up.'

'Well, you needn't have bothered – I'm not a child.'

'Then don't bloody act like one,' the testy reply.

Wanting only to be left in peace, Kevin dropped down from his chair and hopped onto the first step, finding an unexpected spurt of energy as he bounded up the stairs. On the landing, he turned to find that Jim was still standing in the hall below (his mother yet to emerge).

'I'm nineteen years old,' he repeated with a slur, 'and I can stay out as late as I want – and *see* whoever I want.'

Hearing his words carry, stark in the otherwise silent house, Kevin was almost sober again.

'While you're living in our house, you'll live by our rules,' Jim decried dryly – glad of another round – 'and you'll come home at a decent hour and, most importantly, you'll show your mother some respect.'

'Fuck off,' Kevin muttered, out of range, wondering if he would ever escape.

He had said too much and he knew it – even in his intoxicated state – slamming the door with a finality he wished was more final, Jim's tone having sent him to bed with sudden doubts.

Jane had asked him not to tell anyone in the office, but – rising surprisingly early the next day, and the first to his desk – Kevin wasted little time in informing his colleagues, taking to the floor just as soon as they arrived (and running them through the details).

'We were both up for it,' he explained, with flaming cheeks (still half-cut), 'and one thing led to another,' adding – while confusion could be read on every face – 'and we don't see any reason why we can't make a go of it.'

'Because, Jane's a lesbian,' Andrew pointed out, 'and, she's already seeing someone else.'

'Well, she's not anymore!' Kevin returned with aplomb, spinning his chair.

It took Jane – who arrived for her afternoon shift, just as the others were leaving for lunch (with smirks, in passing) – all of five minutes to explain the misunderstanding, pointing out that, though she had loved every minute, and genuinely *liked* him, she was happy with the partner she already had.

'If I wasn't a lesbian, you'd be my first choice,' she added, 'but… the simple fact is, I'm more interested in women. Last night was just a one-off.'

Kevin didn't argue and was actually relieved to be free of the engagement, having never even started to fancy plain old Jane, while his heart beat with glee at the fact that he had proved, beyond all doubt, that everything 'worked' downstairs: that he was a man like any other (an equivalence that was no moot point).

Chapter 8

'Cruelty' wasn't the word: schadenfreude, perhaps – or, possibly, Lebensraum. For, having long commanded the field, Kevin was now forced to share.

'I need to go,' Karen said, with a glance to her watch, her thoughts drifting back to Dan and the house they had recently set up.

Kevin offered to drive.

'Why don't you come in? Dan would love to see you…' Karen said, when they pulled up outside.

'Thanks,' Kevin replied, 'but I need to make a start on that essay.'

He was lying, and had only a limited interest in his course now, with Karen his one fixed point and all he required. Breaking a carefully curated balance, Dan's arrival had shown Kevin that, after the pain of the preceding years, Edge Hill had been as much an escape as a destination.

'Come in,' he said, releasing the catch, with a brisk nod at my approach, before turning back to the screen, spitting:

'He's a retard.'

'Who is?' I asked, already knowing.

'Who the hell do you think?'

'Well, *you* introduced them,' I teased.

Kevin glared, only softening when he saw my smile.

'Yes, yes, but that was a mistake… Karen's worth a dozen of him.'

'I suppose that's up to Karen,' I countered, treading a well-worn path.

'She doesn't love him,' he assured me, tipping his glasses to the table, 'and it's only a matter of time.'

For what? I thought, figuring that Karen had merely been letting off steam in voicing such concerns.

Nestling closer as she whispered into his cupped ear, Kevin could hardly be expected to make an informed judgement with his heart beating at such a pace. Karen asked too much and took too little account.

Thirty-eight years old, Kevin sounded like a child when he reported back to me, slurring words in his unalloyed joy.

'I wish he could be more like you,' Karen had said – he told me – laying her head on his chest after another row.

'She's lovely,' he cooed, and the way he picked at Dan had to be seen through that prism, Kevin pushing at the limits of what could be said, while struggling to keep pace – his cruel barbs misdirection, rather than malice.

The ease Karen exhibited in his company – the clear lack of restraint – rested on a prejudice that neither could acknowledge: how else could Karen think it appropriate to smother Kevin with kisses, or to take him so regularly into her arms?

The wheelchair that got Kevin close was the defining condition that took him utterly out of play, with Karen no more able to imagine that Kevin could have designs on her – and think that she would reciprocate – than that she could have taken up with her own brother.

'I still love him,' Karen conceded, and Kevin felt the ground go. While initially resigned to losing her, when the whirlwind romance started to cool – and Karen was calling up late at night to express her frustration – it had seemed like they had reached another stage. 'Though, it's mostly just physical now,' Karen added, with a smile.

'I don't know why she stays with him,' Kevin sniffed, 'she doesn't even like him.'

I refused to answer.

Karen had hardly believed the speed and simplicity of those first few weeks, and it had only been as a joke that, sharing a cigarette as they lay side by side on the bed (after making love), she had put the proposal.

'We should get a place of our own.'

'Do you think?' Dan had returned, without pause, kissing down on her temple, as their eyes met. 'Where would we go?' he added, and, as easy as that, Dan had agreed to uproot his life.

Within a month, they had found a flat – with Kevin providing the removal van – and we were all invited to the housewarming, where Karen held tight to Dan's arm and everything looked to have fallen into place.

'To the happy couple,' Kevin cried, delivering the toast with genuine affection.

Proud of his part in bringing them together, Kevin had watched, in something close to tears, as Karen skipped joyfully about the room, introducing Dan to the rest of her friends. He knew there would be changes, but had no real regrets, and though he would, inevitably, see less of Karen over the proceeding weeks, they were no less close, and when problems arose, she would still come to him first.

'He's always going out… never tells me where he's going,' she complained, while still trying to get to grips with a man she thought she knew.

'He's probably just missing his friends,' Kevin would offer in her beau's defence.

There were other issues: Dan's drug use (that she hadn't thought so pronounced); the way he would trail his muddy boots around the house (after work); his increasing hostility towards her university friends (after the initial rush of sociability).

Kevin answered each fresh charge with a genial shrug that suggested she was making too much of what were the usual teething problems.

'You were always saying that the students you went out with were drips,' he reminded her, 'that Dan was different…'

'He is,' Karen agreed, doubt playing in her voice as she pulled Kevin close.

As the resentments grew and she increasingly came looking for advice, Kevin took satisfaction from the value she put on his opinion (in the sway of his judgements). When he heard her slam the door, before leaving the house and striding across to the van, he knew what to expect.

'He's a wanker,' Karen snapped, yanking at the belt, 'an idiot.'

'Why – what's he done now?' Kevin asked, with a smirk, not reading too much into curses that would just as quickly turn to talk of their sex life (and their nights of passion).

A welcome guest and a friend to both sides, Kevin did his best to keep the peace.

'I'll make you a cup of tea, once I've got my boots off,' Dan would call, from the porch, when he returned from work to find Kevin already there ahead of him.

'We've got drinks, thanks,' Karen snapped, with unaccountable belligerence, as Dan headed sheepishly up the stairs. 'He'll have left a right mess,' she hissed, going out to check.

She returned to her seat with an air of irritation, no longer at ease.

'I know it's his house, too,' she confessed, 'but I prefer when it's just the two of us.' Kevin blushed. 'Dan's always getting under my feet,' she added, before he had the chance to reply.

Excepting for the intermittent highs and the drunken moments of bliss, the coming weeks showed no improvement and Kevin was no longer offering excuses.

'You should dump him,' he spat suddenly, after three full glasses of wine, the tone and force of his words bringing silence.

'I know – you're right,' Karen admitted, 'and, I'm sorry.'

'Sorry, for what?'

'For getting you involved, when you've got your own life. For being selfish and thoughtless – for saying things I don't mean… I do still love him.'

Those words caught him short and Kevin stumbled out again, with no clear idea of where he stood.

We were friends, too, until you took the relationship on, but I was never sure where the divide lay: what was love – and, what merely affection, admiration… *pity*. Seeing Kevin splayed out on the floor, like this – and begging my indulgence – I noted the similarities, with both of us wondering at the next step.

'He doesn't deserve her,' he resumed.

'Well, I'm sure Karen's capable of making her own decisions,' I said.

'He doesn't love her,' he added, teasing out the truth.

'And, you do, I suppose?'

The question was an unnecessary slight – perhaps he did love her: and, she loved him (and I loved you)…

'He said he doesn't want to have children.'

Karen was crying – and that was the point when Kevin knew it couldn't last.

Offering what consolation he could, he suggested that Dan might change his mind given time (not believing it); on the drive home, he considered the fact that *he* would have given Karen whatever she wanted.

She was standing at the side of his van, in tears.

'I honestly don't know what I'd do without you,' she said, before reluctantly waving him away.

He watched her trudged walk back to the house, finding it inconceivable that she would be spending the night with Dan (and could still love him).

They returned to the subject the next day, after their lectures, in what felt like a crisis point.

Kevin defended Dan, saying he'd probably come round to the idea, eventually. The brief light of hope in her eyes – flashing with their old fire – was worth the sophistry.

'If there's anything I can do,' he said again, holding her gaze.

'You're lovely,' she sniffed, leaning in to embrace him. 'I wish Dan was more like you.'

As the tensions grew, her disillusionment would turn to anger. There were still moments when (as she would confess) 'we were fucking like bunnies', but such reprises were increasingly less frequent, and more desperate, too.

'You're an idiot,' Karen would curse, not caring who was around.

'What would you know,' Dan hissed in return.

'More than you,' Karen sneered, picking at the insecurities of his limited education.

Seeing that vulnerability, as his eyes fell and his face darkened, Karen would feel sympathetic again and want to make up. But Dan didn't take his lessons, or give her any choice.

'Fifty-three emails,' Kevin declared, tapping at the mouse, 'and I must have written just as many in reply.'

'I don't know how you've got the time,' I said.

'And, we speak on the phone nearly every night,' he added.

'I can't see what you could possibly have to talk about, when you've already spent the whole day together.'

'Oh... *everything*,' Kevin sighed, undeterred.

I was smiling now, with indulgence, knowing such infatuations first-hand, though in 1999 – before social media had properly taken hold – fifty-three emails was excessive.

'Look,' he said, starting in on the text before I could excuse myself. 'Had a lovely time last night,' he read – editing along the way – 'and it was such a beautiful film... thanks so much for sharing...' He looked across, knowing how I liked to question his taste in films and music. 'I was thinking about the story all the next day... and I genuinely believe that everyone has a soulmate, somewhere.' I stood up, zipping my coat; determined to keep my attention, Kevin raised his voice. 'I just hope that one day I can find my soulmate too – he must be out there, somewhere!'

His eyes were shining, in triumph, and I wanted to be wrong.

'I need to go,' I said.

'Have I played you the tape?' he asked.

'Yes,' I said.

'Oh, well, it's *marvellous*... and, did I tell you I'm going to her parents, next weekend?' I had no choice but to wait for an explanation; he was pleased to have news. 'She wants to bring some of her stuff back from home, so I said I'd drive her... thought we'd make a weekend of it.'

'Good,' I replied, testily.

'I've reserved a table at an Italian restaurant, in Worcester – because Karen loves Italian food – and we're going there on Friday night,' he ran on, breathless (needing to say it). 'I'm staying in a room on the ground floor... her dad's built a ramp for the chair.'

The day was already getting away from me, so – ending the conversation – I stepped purposefully through to the hall.

I checked my phone and there were two missed calls (your name a siren).

I would learn, later, that the film that had turned their heads was *When Harry Met Sally*. The reference was piteously transparent, but I had problems enough of my own.

◊

There's a photo, somewhere.

We're sitting side by side, leaning purposefully into the camera we have given someone else to take our picture with (though I don't remember who), squeezed between that other couple, our legs and arms touching.

Pitched forward with a smirk, the bright lights reflecting off the circular panes that shade his eyes, Will is on the right, while his girlfriend – whose name I don't recall – is sitting on the opposite flank.

You're pressed close, in a flared dress that barely reaches your thighs, with milk-white arms emerging from abbreviated sleeves. You're shy, but comfortable in your own skin, and I am full of admiration – flushed with a love I didn't expect.

We're young, that's what I see when I look at that picture now – with no idea of what is to come… Will and his girlfriend – their eyes wide with incredulity at the fact of our coming together, like this – are only playing though, as they blink with confusion into the lights: we are the stooges here.

Will and I had briefly been friends four years before, but with no idea where he even lived now, I hadn't seen him since.

We had met at Hugh Baird, having signed up for a parallel class, falling into conversation one night, in a break between sessions, and going on to become friends. The speed and depth of that connection had surprised me: with his leather pants and his self-assurance, Will was not the sort of person I would usually take up with, but we were soon meeting up every week, discovering that – as outsiders – we had much in common.

Later that summer, after the end of our courses, Will would be in the audience at the first gig I ever played, cheering and applauding between songs. When I ripped the microphone from the stand it was taped to, he jumped up to recover it, leaving me free to continue; when I stumbled off the stage at the end of the set, he was generous in his praise. I was glad to know him.

The band had split up within a week and Will and I had somehow found ourselves rehearsing together. Technically limited, we had taken great pleasure from ad-libbing a series of impromptu comic songs (that would have us doubled up on the floor).

That happy interlude had proved too brief.

After leaving for university that autumn, I hadn't seen or heard from Will until this moment – four years on – when he was suddenly sitting before me, grinning ear to ear.

'I knew it'd be you,' he cried, taking my arm. 'When Caroline said she'd met someone from Crosby, called Colin – who was in a band – I knew it'd be you!'

He was beaming, as the two girls shared a long-suffering look, and it felt like fate. It was then that we took the photograph and, catching Caroline's eye, there was a joy there that we never quite approached again. We were in our own world – the only two people in the room.

I have that photo somewhere, though I am no longer in touch with any of its principles and will likely never see them again.

We had met at Brian's Diner – where I had taken one of my friends (who had come up for the gig) – earlier in the day and with everything still so new, and nothing yet said, I was nervous about how to proceed.

Since we had kissed and then spent the next day together – walking, mostly – you had returned to your family home (for work) and, though we had spoken on the phone, nothing was decided. I wanted to see you, to put a face to the voice suggesting that crooked, bashful smile.

Glancing both ways before stepping in, and almost tripping as you headed across, you looked uncertain, though you were smiling that shy smile and I knew, then, that there was no mistake.

While you forged through the mismatched sofas and chairs, I

felt my pride rising at the fact that you had come here to see me. I was glad of the chance to show you off, but immediately recognised that it was a wasted opportunity, when all I really wanted was to get you alone.

Stepping out in front of us, you were just as I had remembered, your pale skin drawn with the occasional pimple, beneath that vivid shock of frizzy blonde hair. There were dark rings under your eyes – you looked like you hadn't slept.

'Hi,' you said, with a bright uplift, extending a hand to my friend, while turning a confirmatory smile to me, our eyes meeting with a subtle flicker of acknowledgement.

You shuffled awkwardly in place before taking a seat, your face conveying warmth and goodwill. I knew then for sure, even if it was a feeling I couldn't put into words, or express. You were a discovery – untouched.

Too scared to ask outright, I had invited you over to make music instead, meeting you at the station (running up, late, to find you waiting on a bench with your guitar). Back at the house, where I had set up a couple of amps so that we could play through each other's songs, the styles and methods didn't really fit, and had provided no opening.

Strumming with a discordant brio and that startling voice, you had gone on alone, while I made the drinks (glad to find you right beside me, when you stopped). I rolled a joint then, and suggested we go for a walk, taking you to the pub first, and then down to the beach, drawing everything out.

Having talked ourselves to a standstill, after playing through nearly every record I owned, you decided to stay over, taking the bed, while I laid my head down on the desk in the corner.

I couldn't sleep like that and had hoped that you would call me across, but you didn't; up again, at first light, and worn down by the previous day, we finally kissed. There had been no more than that – a mere introduction… yet, the whole world had changed.

We parted on the street, with a sense of anticlimax. I didn't want you to leave, like this – retracing tentative steps – but could take comfort from the fact that I would be seeing you again later. There were seagulls cawing carelessly overhead and I had never felt happier.

We would play at Brian's Diner six months later, though – after that gig – I would never go again. Turning, through heavy rain, onto Stanley Street (five years hence), I would find a strip club standing in its place.

Our drummer had called (from Leeds) to announce that he no longer wanted to play, so we would perform for the first time, that night, with a drummer from one of the other bands.

Sitting at the top of the Municipal Building steps, each lost in our own thoughts – as the wind picked up in vibrant squalls – my mind would repeatedly drift back to you (and it didn't matter).

I thought of the soft, yielding mouth, the sloping smile and the scent of your hair, that I still seek out now, in old shampoos (when I need reminding).

Ray stamped his cigarette to the floor, before striding in ahead of us.

She tapped at my shoulder from behind before dropping into a crouch.

'Hi,' she said, in a quick, brittle tone – her skewed mouth forming words I could barely hear – and the whole world shifted.

She had changed since the morning and was now wearing a short cotton dress with black tights, her knees knocking together.

She was lovely, and I had almost forgotten – her face, now just centimetres from mine, in dizzying sharp focus: the button nose lifted coquettishly (and that smile). I was light – joyous – and could have stayed like that for the rest of my life.

Remembering that she was a musician, too, and would know what I was going through, I tried to make conversation, but it was hopeless, when all I wanted to do was hold her.

'We're at the back,' she said, pointing over her hunched shoulder, and I found myself nodding, as I turned to follow. (I think she took my hand.)

Her friends were waiting up ahead, with expectant smiles… and, that was when I saw Will, and that was when the photo was taken, though so much else – from that scene and that whole period – is now lost, and irretrievable.

Once the equipment had been loaded into the van, we had cleared out, the crowd dispersing in twos and threes, with the clink of bottles and skunk fumes filling the narrow side street. There were hugs and handshakes, laughter and shouts, as the night settled around us.

I was holding Caroline close, now – didn't want to lose her, or to give her up – running my fingers over the skin under her thin dress, as we staggered into a phone box.

It was the first time we had been alone all night and, shutting over the door and stepping inside – to shelter from the elements – I had everything I could ever want. Pushed up tight, in the sudden silence of that enclosed space, we were immediately kissing, while our arms and legs and hands explored.

Within minutes, there were people banging on the door, giving whoops and cheers. We turned, in shy acknowledgement, only then remembering where we were.

Digging out some coins, which I dropped into the slot, I listened for the tone – that my buzzing ears had difficulty picking out – all the time aware of that body next to mine, as I made the call, testing my palm against her hip, stroking down her lower back, nuzzling into her hair.

We were alone again, with just the patter of rain at the glass, as I gave the instructions, though we stepped out to find Phil, waiting on the kerb. He offered his congratulations and shook my hand warmly, before leaning in, with a low stoop – he was well over six foot – to kiss at your cheek; said he'd call soon.

There's a photo, somewhere.

Chapter 9

When she called, to demand his number, Kevin thought she was playing a joke. When she cried out, in delight – at the fact that Dan was single – Kevin felt cold inside

'An average sort of a bloke,' he told her, wanting no part.

'And, he lives with his sister?'

'Think so,' he replied casually, before shuffling off to his room, where he took the three short steps up to his chair.

Turning, in silence, to the floor-length mirror, Kevin noted the wiry, silver-flecked hair and the grey-blue asymmetric eyes (wondering at his vanity). *She's still just a girl*, he counselled, giving a closer examination to the lines that marked his face, such a contrast to Karen's softly-rounded cheeks.

While Kevin was a lively and energetic presence, next to Dan he undoubtedly felt his age. Kicking his jeans out from where they had caught beneath him – flipping his shoulder to straighten his shirt – he took another look. *Not bad*, he thought, with a sardonic snort (knowing such judgements weren't his call).

Kevin shuffled up in his chair, recognising how foolish he had been to give such weight to their supposed intimacy – already wishing he had made greater use of their time.

'Hurry up, bug-a-lugs – we need to leave!' Karen shouted through, an all too typical catcall that had him grinning once more.

Answering her remaining questions with a note of impatience, the short drive to Edge Hill had dragged, for the first time.

'He's alright, I suppose,' he concluded, flapping at an indicator, before qualifying, 'he's a bit mad, but nice enough.'

'And, you're sure he's not seeing anyone?' Karen asked, again, as Kevin broke – rather abruptly – at a set of lights, the indicator keeping time.

'Don't think so,' he replied.

'And, he hasn't got any kids?' Karen resumed, breaking the silence.

'Course not,' Kevin returned, tapping his foot to the pedal, as Karen drummed a rhythm on the dash. Despite his reservations, he was already smiling when Karen erupted into a high-pitched squeal: 'Yes!'

There were no further questions and, exiting the seminar into bright sunlight an hour later, the subject seemed, thankfully, closed. When he dropped her home, it was a relief to be invited in, as per routine, even if the atmosphere had shifted.

Karen was distracted when she brought the tea through.

'I'm going to call him – right now!' she cried, and there was little Kevin could do but offer his support, when – uncharacteristically hesitant – she finally took up the phone.

'We're meeting at the Brooke, later,' she announced, her eyes blinking as she dropped the receiver. 'Bloody hell,' she added, with a nervous laugh.

Kevin offered to take her – of course – and to pick her up again (if necessary); Karen thanked him, tipsily, before darting up the stairs.

'I need to work out what I'm going to wear,' she called down, sounding like a stranger.

Taking up the remote, Kevin flicked carelessly through the channels, but could still hear Karen clattering through her wardrobe in the room above. His stomach was turning; then, Karen was down again and giving a twirl.

'What do you think?' she asked. 'I just need to fix my face, and then I'm done.'

'You look fine,' Kevin snapped, thrown by this sudden regard for her appearance, for the idea of her wanting to impress a man.

'The thing is,' she explained, presenting herself with a shy tilt of the head, 'I want him to know I'm interested, without looking desperate.'

Kevin's face dropped, but he nodded back.

Bounding down the stairs again, with her scented hair beaten into shape and her modest chest pushed up against a tight blouse, Karen looked amazing. If this was a joke, she was taking it too far.

Dropping her off at the pub, Kevin watched Karen step gingerly in through the double doors – in the ungainly heels she had chosen for the occasion – feeling like he really ought to stop her. It seemed impossible that she would go to such lengths, and – hoping that it was some mistake – he sat on for the best part of an hour, in case she reconsidered, or needed his help.

There was to be no reprieve, with Karen phoning the following night, in a state of elation. They had hit it off straight away, she crowed, and gone back to Dan's flat, after last orders.

'We were all over each other,' she gasped. 'It was unbelievable!'

'I said you'd make a great couple,' Kevin stuttered, laying his claim with a sadness he struggled to conceal.

Karen barely heard him, running on.

'We just kind of fitted, you know…'

The sharing of intimate details was hardly new – they had always been explicit before – but the tone marked a change, with this encounter already seeming more substantial.

Kevin turned on the speakerphone before shuffling across to his bedroom.

'He's an absolute stud,' he heard, Karen's words – thankfully – softened by the span of the hall. 'I thought we were going to wake the whole bloody house!'

When I saw Dan again, the following week, he would also declare his love, in a triangulation that tied the noose.

Tumbling down the stairs in a borrowed t-shirt and with matted hair, Karen gave a sheepish grin to Tina and Anne, before being introduced and offered a seat.

Breakfast was a more elaborate affair than she had expected, with Dan making a fuss, when all she wanted was to take back up with her new man. Despite her natural affability, Karen was oddly restrained, and when it came time to leave – she was taking Dan home with her – she had snatched up his hand before they were even out the door.

Sunday provided for an empty carriage – neither of them could yet drive – with each station they alighted at allowing them to nestle closer. Lost in one another's company, they almost missed their connection, with Dan hurrying them out as the doors drew shut.

'Twelve minutes,' he read from the display.

Her face beaming, Karen tapped at the metallic bench.

'Come here, you,' she said.

By Old Roan, her head was down on his lap and Dan was stroking his fingers through the knots in her hair. It was only an inspector, boarding at Aughton Park, who stopped them going further.

While Dan was shifting hurriedly through his pockets for their tickets, Karen took the opportunity to have another look at him (she had been too wrapped up before): the broad shoulders and muscular chest; the bronzed skin held to gaunt cheeks – drawn, once more, to the thin line of his pink lips. *He's gorgeous,* she thought, giddily.

The fields – the yellows of rape and wheat – flashed by, in a blaze of colour, as their arms found one another once more. It was a journey they didn't want to end; theirs a language that had yet to be codified.

They practically jogged back from the station, Karen calling 'hello' into the empty house – to check her flatmates were still away – before throwing off her coat. There was no tour of the lodgings… nor did they linger on the ground floor. Instead, dragging him by the belly of his shirt – in an inversion of the tradition – Karen directed Dan straight up to her room, without once relinquishing her grip.

'Come here, you,' she caroused.

She didn't need to ask.

They fucked in the bedroom first, she told Kevin, that night, after a quick shower (in a voice that ran to delirium). Then, sufficiently recovered – finding the thread again (and it seemed to have no end) – they did it on the couch, and finally – pawing at each other, in near exhaustion – down on the living room floor.

'I got carpet burns,' Karen admitted, 'but, it was worth it,' Kevin's silence inviting her to describe what he had no desire to hear. 'We were absolutely buggered,' she continued, giggling, '— spent the rest of the day in bed!'

Karen stopped now, catching her breath, before thanking Kevin for the part he had played – 'for making it happen' – her words a further cause of regret. He had wanted her to be happy, but not like this.

'I'm really happy for you,' he said.

It was the same story from Dan, too.

'I'm in love!' he enthused, just as he had so often before.

Kevin would be forced to hear it all again, the next day, on the way to Edge Hill, his thin – *false* – interest drawing still more confessions. It was the first time he had ever wanted to cut Karen short and, at the end of his lecture, he declined her invitation home.

'Thanks for everything,' she said – leaning in for a hug – 'you're amazing… and, I'll be eternally in your debt!'

'Yes, yes,' Kevin returned brusquely.

'I introduced them, remember?' he explained, when I called unannounced, for my second ever visit.

He had been asking after Karen and Dan.

'When Dan meets someone new, we usually don't see him for a couple of months,' I explained; seemingly satisfied, Kevin asked after my brother, instead.

Those first few weeks were trying, with Karen's thoughtful assurances only making the situation worse. There was an air of condescension now, when she invited him back, still singing his praises as though nothing had changed and everything could be just the same.

The honeymoon – fortunately – didn't last. For, despite moving in with Karen within a week, and then trawling through the classifieds for a place of their own – which they had soon secured – the fault lines would appear before they had even settled on the furniture. Dan was coming out with us again, which told its own story.

Bringing her concerns to Kevin, with stuttering vulnerability, they would talk through the issues on the way to college (and on the return), with their conversations often being taken up on the phone later. Kevin hadn't realised how much he cared until this moment of crisis – if he had felt like he had been left behind in those first few weeks, there was clarity in his concern now.

Watching Karen edge away from the kerb, he would still be thinking about her when he reached home. He loved her – he was sure of it – without ever quite conceiving what that meant.

Chapter 10

In setting out the meanings and varieties of love – and its attendant pleasures – Shakespeare maintains that the objects of our affections do not fade, or decline – as might a summer's day – nor carry within them the canker-blooms that bring their destruction (as a headily-scented rose). Love has substance, even if its definitions are opaque, with the qualities we admire in any individual often inaccessible to another.

Kevin had reason to wax lyrical over Karen. She was young and pretty, with an easy charm – that was clear – but, where Kevin saw poetry, I could only ever see prose. Despite a repeatedly stated ambivalence, Kevin – who had no one else to tell – would tell *me*, and he would always reach for the details.

He was early, he explained, and – as Karen strode, obliviously, past his parked van – he had welcomed the chance to observe her in her natural state, watching as she picked feverishly through her bag – for cigarettes – which she then struggled to light (brushing the hair from her face to check at her watch).

Kevin was sitting in rapt silence, when she spotted him – lifting up her sunglasses for a better view – with the pleasure he felt in the discovery hard to justify.

It was only when they were stretched out on the couch, back at her flat, that he noticed the shoes.

'What the hell are you wearing?' he spluttered.

'Why? What's wrong?' Karen returned, with a quick look down to her feet.

They were the DMs she had bought at the weekend and she puzzled over them for several seconds before, finally, breaking into a smile.

'You're wearing odd shoes!' Kevin howled.

'So, what – who cares?' Karen snapped, turning them to remove a price tag still tacked to the sole.

She didn't return those shoes, but continued to wear them just the same.

In the search for telling details, Kevin would usually call over earlier than arranged, so that – with Karen generally running late – he would be invited in and have the chance to investigate.

Smirking, at the sound of her banging about in the room above, Kevin's eye would scan through the familiar objects of the living room, seeking out the clues of her existence: the scrunched up tights (caught up in his wheel), the hairdryer hanging over the arm of the settee, the blotched banana skin squatting in a wilted pot plant.

'Can we go, now?' Kevin barked, with seeming impatience, when – with a great puffing out of her cheeks – Karen finally made it down again, but the truth was he didn't care.

'Soz,' Karen replied, as she patted at her coat for the reassuring rattle of keys, grabbing at one or two other last-minute items as she followed him out.

There was much to admire in the breathless pace of her life – those departures such a contrast to Kevin's more regimented style – and her influence would grow over that first summer (with Dan yet to arrive).

Skipping on ahead of him at the end of the lecture, Karen lit a cigarette from beneath the bridge of her elegantly cupped hand.

'Let's get the hell out of here!' she cried, rallying weary legs.

Kevin was glad to go, having lost much of his interest in academia. By the end of that first year, it was only Karen's presence and encouragement that kept him on track. Kevin, who would have been happy to give it all up, only completed the essays he was set because Karen insisted on it, just as – swinging his chair in triumph – she was the only one who took pleasure from a good

grade. In all such praise, Kevin was grudging, at best.
'Not bad,' he might allow.
'Quite the little professor,' Karen would tease in reply, diving headfirst at his chest, blowing bubbles with her cheeks.
'Alright, alright,' Kevin blustered, batting her away.
He would have eaten her, given the chance.

The months passed and they hardly noticed them, with Kevin already well into his second year before he appreciated the strength of that attachment. University had initially been a means of escape, with no great expectation, though Karen had been familiar from the start, so when she invited him over for dinner – for the first time – Kevin ironed a shirt and took a shave (thinking it a date).
He had taken a bottle of wine, too, giddy at the thought of having her all to himself (with her flatmates out for the night).
'Ah – rosé!' Karen squealed with delight, pouring them each a glass, before directing him to the couch, while she returned to the kitchen.
The sound of the bell came as a surprise, Karen rushing in answer; he was even more surprised when a man's voice was followed by heavy steps, and Scott Humphries – a fellow Politics student – stumbled in.
'Good to see you, mate!' his classmate blundered, with a gormless grin, forcing Kevin to shift up.
Turning to Karen for an explanation she couldn't supply – she had already gone – Kevin felt claustrophobic, even as he made conversation (bringing up an essay that was due and the modules on offer for the final year). Already bored, dinner came as a relief, with the three of them squeezed in around the kitchen table and Kevin able to take cover behind his plate of food.
After serving the dessert, Karen excused herself and Scott immediately leaned across.
'I'm thinking of making a move,' he said. Kevin was blushing, as he edged away. 'I've liked her for ages, so would you mind giving us some space…'

'Yeah, sure…' Kevin forced out, feeling relief at Karen's return, as – grinning impishly – Scott advised caution, with an admonishing finger.

'Dutch courage,' he whispered, taking up another can.

Karen's quick eyes passed between them, sensing some change, especially when Kevin moved across to his wheelchair. She narrowed her eyes, but made no comment.

Scott was already up on his feet.

'Do you need some help?' he belched, his eyes flitting to Karen.

'No – I'm fine,' Kevin hissed, through his teeth.

Rolling irritably out of bed and scrambling across the polished floor to the phone, Kevin answered brusquely.

'Yes.'

'Oh my God – it was absolutely disgusting!' Karen blurted, without introduction.

'What was?' Kevin asked.

'Scott,' Karen returned, before running, in detail, through the 'torrid' evening she had been forced to endure, following Kevin's departure. 'He was all over me,' she said. 'Started off by stroking my hair – then he tried to kiss me… ugh!' Fearing to break her rhythm, Kevin didn't even move. 'He must have been waiting for you to leave, before making a move,' she resumed. 'I can't believe he actually thought he had a chance.'

Kevin could feel his heart thumping at his chest, as Karen rounded mercilessly on her admirer.

'When I told him that I wasn't looking for a relationship right now, he said he loved me and begged me to give him a chance – said he thought I was gorgeous!'

'Shit,' Kevin muttered.

'I know – it's mad… but, he begged me not to say anything, so – please – don't tell anyone else.'

'I won't,' Kevin assured her, thinking of the pleasure he had originally taken from such an invitation (and how glad he had been to have Karen all alone).

The brisk rejection of those advances was a warning that Kevin would heed, even if events were to overtake him. For, the intimacies would continue – despite Dan's arrival (the following summer) – and the boundaries fall away.

'I'm hungry,' Karen declared, into the library's stultifying hush, as they packed up their books, 'I'd kill for some chocolate…'

Such random suggestions were typical; Kevin looked on with affection.

'We could pick a pack of biscuits up on the way home?' he suggested, seeking restraint, but she was already on him, leaning over his chair, her head on his shoulder.

She smelt lovely.

'Imagine if we got locked in here, tonight,' she resumed, 'just the two of us; or, if we had to spend the whole night together in the staff common room. What do you think?'

Uncomprehending, Kevin looked on in bewilderment.

'As long as we had a kettle,' he chuckled, as Karen pushed him out.

She was irrepressible, and – the days passing, at pace – it was all so easy… red lights giving way to green, as Karen drew closer and Kevin's jumbled feelings coalesced.

The following December, in what Kevin took to be the defining part of the process – giving final *carte blanche* – Karen clapped her hands together at a sudden thought and suggested, with an intemperate slur, that they should spend Christmas together.

'I know you hate going to your mum's,' she added mischievously, 'and we'd absolutely love to have you!'

'What about Dan?' Kevin found himself asking, without thinking, knowing even as he said it, that such a comment implied that he could be considered a threat – a suitor – but the words were already out.

'Oh, sod him,' Karen returned blithely, 'I'd much rather spend Christmas with you!'

Chapter 11

Learning to drive was a further, facilitating step towards the sort of independence Kevin had always craved, those four wheels offering him wide-ranging physical mobility for the first time in his short life. After his previous struggles to beat a path across a single room, Kevin could now beat a hasty retreat across a city, with an equality and equivalence he had never met with in any other field: a driver on the road is simply a 'driver on the road' – all born equal before traffic sign and signal.

Prior to this spectacular new finding of his feet, Kevin had been at the mercy of an underfunded public transportation system and prone to the wayward vicissitudes of operatives who retained a freedom of discretion that would be gone within a decade. There were drivers who would encourage him aboard and others who would decline him outright, just as there were vehicles fitted with ramps to give access, while others offered nothing.

'Sorry mate,' the driver would say, with a diffident shake of the head from his high perch, the doors drawn shut before Kevin could respond.

To travel had been a trial, with no redress in law: if it rained, it rained…

From the moment that he saw Pamela Jones – one year (and one month) older than he was, and born with the same condition – racing past him *in a car*, while he trundled down the hill in his rickety chair, Kevin knew that one day he would be driving, too: that he would be mobile and independent in a similar fashion.

With her red hair turned out in fat curls and her face awash with freckles, Pamela – then seventeen – had passed her driving test (at the second attempt) that same week and, raiding the coffers of the

Thalidomide Trust, had gone and bought a set of wheels.

Parked skew-whiff on the Donnellon drive, announcing her arrival with a furious revving of the engine, she had watched, with a smirk, as mother, father, sister and son all emerged for a tour of inspection.

'How *marvellous,*' Agnes beamed, her bemused face pushing into the cab, her quick eyes taking account of the workings. 'It's amazing,' she added, wondering at the waist-high pedals that Pamela showed could be operated by hand and the elevated seat that gave an unrestricted view of the road.

'These are the lights,' Pamela said, showing them, 'and, these are the wipers,' flipping an indolent finger, to set them flapping (against a clear sky).

'Well, who'd have thought?' Agnes marvelled, with continued incredulity, as Pamela reversed nonchalantly out again. 'And, she makes it look so easy!'

Rooted to the spot, with an admiration already bordering on obsession – at what proved an epiphany of sorts – Kevin had, eventually, to be dragged back inside.

The electrifying jolt that the sudden appearance of Pamela Jones's maiden auto occasioned wasn't the first fixation to strike, nor the last. Kevin's political allegiances over the years have proved as varied as they are sincere, his religious conversions as misguided as they were heartfelt (taking him full circle from the ennobling firesides of the Bahá'ís, to the chill of the picket line).

His relationships were no less fickle and tied him in no fewer knots, with Kevin as quick to fall for the foreign in 'American Mary', as he was the homespun in Karen (his West Country girl).

That moment, with Kevin sitting open-mouthed on his parent's block-paved path, could have been lifted straight from Kenneth Grahame.

'Poop, poop,' Toad mouths in wonderment, from his summarily over-turned carriage, while the car that upended him races blithely away.

Gazing, glass-eyed, after Pamela, Kevin knew – without any shadow of doubt – that this was the life for him, too.

His mother, of course, had other ideas.

'Oh no, absolutely not; you'll get yourself killed,' she declared, when her son skipped back into the house to announce his intentions.

It was already too late, the seed being sown the moment he set eyes on that spanking new machine, his imagination stirred into ferment. Kevin didn't deign to respond, knowing only that he would be taking steps to get himself on the road, too.

The firing gun had been sounded on Kevin's motoring career many years before that fateful encounter, when he had returned home from school – on his eighth birthday – to find a four-wheel battery-powered scooter waiting on his front step.

'Can you drive it?' he asked, as he was helped aboard.

'Fully operational,' his father told him, before giving a run-through of the controls.

Kevin soon had it moving, and was soon taking his first turn of the garden, too, following the cobbled paving that bordered the lawn, with the family dog, Cindy – a West Highland terrier – in tow.

'Heel!' Kevin would call down, when Cindy started to flag, and up she would hop, Kevin as happy to ferry that sole passenger about, as he was his friends and colleagues in later life.

'It was red,' he recalls, 'with a rubber bumper running round the base… a bit like a dodgem from the fair.'

More suited to the elderly and the infirm than the flamboyant figure that Kevin generally cut, he was describing a mobility scooter.

Within easy reach of his small fingers, the accelerator, brakes and steering stick could all be operated by hand. Straddling the padded seat with casual aplomb, Kevin lacked only the full-fingered leather gloves and quilted driving cap.

Once adjudged old enough to venture beyond the restrictive tramlines of the home grounds, Kevin would propel himself along the public promenades too, chasing round the block at a fair old clip of four miles per hour, until the battery ran flat. Then, having made no allowance for such an eventuality, our hero – temporarily stranded – would have to wait, with restless impatience and a careful smile, for an obliging passer-by: *Vorsprung durch Technik*.

The scooter was fitted with indicators and headlights, which Kevin would flash at imaginary road users, engaging the rudimentary gears on corners and full beam when dusk descended. He couldn't have asked for more and certainly wasn't expecting the next addition made to their freeway, returning from school one afternoon to find white street lines running down the centre of the path, his father having spent the afternoon, after a funeral, painstakingly painting them out.

'They're brilliant!' Kevin panted, after completing a circuit under his father's genial gaze.

They were just the start, with a zebra crossing (and flanking yellow posts) added next, though his sister, Joan, was the only pedestrian who ever ventured out (when calling Kevin in for tea).

'Give way' signs completed the autobahn, and – despite having the road to himself – Kevin, who had memorised the Highway Code by the age of twelve, was a scrupulous driver, who would correct his father's cursory readings of the road whenever they ventured out.

'Would you give it a rest please, Kevin,' his mother would complain, 'your father needs to concentrate.'

Meeting Kevin's eye in the rear-view mirror, Mr Donnellon was more sanguine.

'He's quite right though, love… without Kevin, we'd end up getting a ticket.'

Kevin was grinning, counting that a victory, though it was only with Pamela's triumphant arrival, all those years later, that everything fell into place.

The first thing Kevin did when he left home, for good – at the age of twenty-one (in April of 1983) – was to put in a request to his local authority for a car, assuming joyful command of his maiden motor, a sky-blue Ford Escort Mark II, in October of that same year.

'I'm not waiting two bloody days!' he declared, in reference to his first scheduled lesson, 'I'm not waiting another bloody minute!'

'You'd be better off with a professional instructor,' his sister tried, in vain.

Bouncing excitedly about as she helped him out of his chair and into the car, tangling himself up in the seat belt in his impatience, Kevin had forced her round within the hour.

'Come on, let's go!' he exhorted, tapping eagerly at the controls, savouring the thrumming purr of the engine beneath his crooked thumb, testing the brakes and gears.

He was in a world of his own and Joan was already concerned at the all-too-familiar lack of restraint – it was typical of her brother to overreach. Kevin, of course, considered his confidence justified; he had studied the *Motorists' Handbook* – didn't imagine that practise had anything to teach.

Mimicking the instructor who had once taught her, Joan sought to keep it formal.

'If you could put the car into first gear, to begin,' she said – with no idea how – 'and, then: mirror, signal, manoeuvre.'

Having confidently engaged first, Kevin was revving the engine before she had finished, releasing the handbrake as he jigged into second and the car edged haltingly away from the kerb.

A mask of concentration, Kevin quickly built up speed, before bringing the vehicle to rest again. They had reached the end of the road, where – figuring he had passed whatever test had been set – Kevin reapplied the handbrake with an undeniable swagger.

'Where next?' he asked, turning to Joan for direction, his eyes already picking holes in the traffic ahead.

'Take the next left onto Sterrix Lane, please, Mr Donnellon,' she told him, with a wink.

Kevin was almost immediately feeding the wheel through his stubby fingers, delighted to see the pedals set freely in motion, the gears aligning (without stutter or drawl).

It was all so easy, the car responding to every touch, the wheel – spinning, *slipping* – so light, and it seemed he was born to it… even as he lost control, and over-steered, and felt the rudder go breathlessly slack.

'Fuck! Fuck! Fuck!' he cried, in a panic.

'The brake – press the bloody brake!' Joan squealed, her hands flapping aimlessly at controls she could make no sense of, with Kevin batting down on them too (after his initial confusion).

In the aftermath, it was all too clear.

'I'd never even heard of power steering,' Kevin explained, of what proved a black swan, with the wheel yielding too freely.

He hadn't expected such power, and – losing the wheel as he took the corner – had sent the car careening off the side of the road and into a privet hedge (spluttering and squawking through any number of nests).

The landing was, fortunately, a soft one: Joan jerked with force against the restraints of her belt (and back again), while Kevin – his stomach tight to the steering column – felt his ribs crack at the forward thrust, his head rattling back and forth as he fought for breath. No other vehicle was involved.

To Kevin's irritation, a number of his neighbours were already piling across to right the car.

'We'll have you out in a jiffy, little man!' Big Eric assured him.

Kevin shook his head and waved his fist – as if to send them away – glad to find that he wasn't injured, while lamenting his error.

His chin on the wheel, Kevin, who had been dissuaded from trying the engine – which had thick smoke hissing from the bonnet – could only steer as he was pushed unceremoniously home.

Bringing the car to rest outside his flat, Kevin disembarked from the driver's side, for once, anonymous hands taking him up (a further indignity), before dropping him down on his hastily assembled chair. There were cheers and words of encouragement, as Kevin wheeled tortuously through the sympathetic cavalcade of his leering neighbours. His mother was among them.

'Joan said you had an accident, you poor thing…' she cooed, forcing her way through.

Hoots of derision followed Kevin back to the house, though it was only when he was free of his chair – and settled against the sofa – that the shock of the day's events hit, with Kevin growing suddenly pale (the cup of tea he was offered rattling lamely at his chest).

'I did say it would be better to wait,' Joan reminded him.

Kevin nodded dejectedly, wondering whether having a car was really such a good idea.

Those steps were mere beginnings, however, with Kevin passing his test first time, even if the bossy and condescending instructor from BSM proved just as powerless to train caution into his youthful charge as his sister.

'Feed the wheel!' Malcolm, a pungent mix of Old Spice and perspiration, would bark, as – deaf to the world – Kevin took a hairpin, one-handed.

There was no emergency brake in Kevin's car, and – sensing the influence of moonlighting sessions – Malcolm was no fool.

'You've clearly been going out on your own time,' he adduced – after a particularly fraught session – 'and picking up bad habits.'

Kevin denied the accusation, but he *had* been out – at every opportunity – putting in dozens of poorly-supervised miles. Having long since developed his own inimitable style, Kevin was in a hurry, too, and didn't care for advice.

'You do know how to drive?' Kevin only thought to ask Gary when they were already halfway through their first session.

'Course I do,' Gary replied scornfully, though he had never driven a car in his life (and his scooter hadn't even required a test).

The restrictive L-plates had already been removed, so it was too late for such technicalities, with Gary deciding on a scenic route, with no consideration given to the tight turns and blind corners.

Next up was a trip to Blackpool.

'It'll be a laugh,' Kevin explained, 'and give us a proper run…'

There were no complaints from Gary, though this was their first evening trip and neither knew how to work the headlights.

'Too bright,' Gary declared, with a squint, of the first, 'they must be the hazards…'

Kevin tried again, Gary eventually giving the thumbs up, and off they set, following the coast road (where they could) – all 49.4 twisty miles – to see the recently illuminated lights (the temperature dropping all the way).

It was only when – a portion of chips later – they turned back around that they discovered that they had driven the first leg with little more than their sidelights for company. Their chatter a combustible constant – the blind leading the blind – they hadn't even noticed.

Driving proved a curiously emotional experience for Kevin, who was free in a way he had never thought possible, and he was soon a regular – and recognisable – fixture in the local area, the sight of his bobbing head begging questions.

'How the fuck do you drive?' Big Eric asked, in astonishment.

'Same as you,' Kevin answered with a grin, guiding him generously through the pedals – tapping at the metal rods that ran from his chest to the floor (and the original levers).

'Boss, lad,' Eric said, as he squeezed into the passenger side, where Kevin's chair now resided, shaking his head at the vertical post that rose up from the removed seat belt panel.

'It's a hydraulic arm,' Kevin told him, explaining how he would hop back across, as the engine shut down, and – sitting side-saddle – set the arm (that was attached to the chair) in motion, ducking his head as he passed below the window frame.

'It was bloody useless,' Kevin says, of the 'car chair system' – unreliable at best – and would often leave him swinging in the breeze while he struggled to align the wheels.

He can laugh about it now, but I can only imagine how it must have felt to be marooned in such a way – Kevin flapping his hands, in desperation, for assistance. It was a design fault, and even back on safe ground the chair would sometimes collapse under his weight.

I had never really considered the difficulties of those long-winded procedures – Kevin never complained and made it look easy – but I can understand now why he might have felt compelled to drive at such terrible speeds (taking his chances while the going was good).

Once safely ashore – in later years, he would exit via a retractable ramp – Kevin rarely set the alarm, or bothered with the locks (and I was starting to understand).

'I hate to feel trapped, or hemmed in,' he told me, and thus – pressed tight to the wheel – he never used a seat belt either (taking advantage of a legal exemption).

Speaking to Kevin's niece, at a party in her uncle's honour – some thirty years later – corroboration would be provided.

'He was crazy!' she gushed, recalling those youthful trips and how recklessly Kevin would corner, his passengers crying out in alarm, as the vehicle seemed set to tip. 'Sometimes, he would steer with his stomach,' she added, 'holding a cigarette in one hand and a can of beer in the other!'

When Kevin did finally have the accident he had always threatened, skidding sideways over sodden leaves (on a wet night in the Lakes) and coming to ground against the staring blank trunk of a sycamore, he was lucky: he was still there, in one piece – his big head, tiny legs, stubby claws.

The car was a different matter, however, with the engine taking a terminal hit.

'What the fuck have you done?' Paula cried, already rubbing at her shoulder, 'I think my neck's broke.'

'Don't be daft,' Kevin retorted, 'there's nothing wrong with you,' though, typically insistent, the patient demanded to be taken into

A & E.

The scans proved inconclusive – Paula unable to locate the pain, despite the doctor's prompts. Having put in a sizeable claim on Kevin's mounting insurance, she would continue to wear the neck brace she had been given, as a precaution, for the best part of a month.

Once all the legally required, and practical, adaptions were complete, Kevin's attention turned to design, with the visual features of the car a close match for his colourful personality. Following the advice of the automobile magazines, to which he now subscribed, Kevin would insist on fourteen-inch clover-leaf alloy wheels, with rear spats and a whale-tail spoiler, while the body panels were finished in a lime green wash and the upholstery a resplendent two-tone.

Kevin had the Mark III, a bustle-back rear hatch – the Escort's latest iteration – in mind, and though the brash body addenda was mostly for show, and added little to the functionality, those superficial changes proved vivid enough to seduce the uninitiated.

'The engine was a beast,' Kevin recalls, with the extended steel exhaust providing for a distinctive growl, and – with the internal limiter removed – Kevin able to reach speeds of up to 120 miles per hour on the open road.

The final extravagance took the form of an impromptu paint job, with one of Kevin's neighbours applying a pot of blue emulsion to the tread of his tyres, making a car already renowned for its low-fiction threshold, livelier still.

The erratic braking style was well-suited to a 'boy racer', with Kevin riding the clutch at every opportunity, his eyes pinned to the road ahead – seeking out advantage – as he steeled through a red light, or cruised through an amber, the whole idea to keep moving.

'Bloody lights!' he would bawl, throwing up his hands at rules he imagined shouldn't apply, believing that he should – possibly – be given his own lane.

Waiting at a red light, offering a disdaining appraisal of the vehicles around him, sneering at the lack of horsepower and the dull-seeming drivers slouched over their wheels, Kevin would push impatiently at the accelerator. Then – green, again – he would throw the gearstick into Drive and, hissing out of a grinding wheel-spin, belch away in a plume of smoke.

Executing doughnuts and three-points whenever the mood took him – his abrupt 180 degree turns producing magnificent arcs of burnt rubber (in charred tarmac arabesques) – Kevin drove like his life depended on it, the two-spoke steering wheel the perfect fit, and diameter, for small hands, the 'cripple hook' coming naturally.

Time was finally called on that unfettered freedom, when a police car pulled up alongside, at another set of lights.

'Is this your vehicle?' one of the officers called across, having indicated that he wanted a word.

'Yes, officer,' Kevin returned politely.

'Not nicked it, then?' he was asked, and Kevin shook his head, with a tight smile.

Trafficking his car to the kerb ahead of them, in regulation style, Kevin didn't over-rev, or block-shift through the gears. Asked for ID, he shuffled in his seat, to get at his wallet and, recoiling at the sight of those small hands emerging from abbreviated sleeves (in the vicinity of his shoulders), his inquisitors saw their error.

'He's thalidomide,' one of his companions broke in, pushing proprietarily through, 'handicapped, like,' he added proudly, 'but he's alright.'

Kevin welcomed the cheerful recommendation – Cheshire grins spread across smudged faces – while the officers merely took down the registration: 'thalidomide' proving, as ever, an answer and explanation to every question.

Flicking the switches and flipping the clutch, before pulling away from the kerb, Kevin was free to go, the two dumbfounded constables waving him off.

'Drive safe,' he was advised.

Safety was hardly a priority for Kevin, who liked nothing more than to take his loose-end neighbours (unemployed to a man) out on random drives. Packing them in, front and back – the car awash with the strains of marijuana – Kevin would readily admit to a genuine sense of belonging in their questionable company.

For, from the stonewashed jeans, to the tight-fitting Fred Perry – the clipped moustache, to the thickset mullet – Kevin was a man, now, and he knew it in every bone. With his pungent pomade dabbed liberally to bull neck and ruddy chin, Kevin pulled into Crosby Marina, tipping back his seat to take in his apparent domain.

He turned, reluctantly, at the sound of a horn – to his left – while his trigger-happy comrades pushed their snouts up to the glass.

'What the fuck?' they snarled, working down the windows.

'Eh, soft lad,' their neighbour called back, 'what's that piece of shit you're driving?'

Snapping his bucket roll-top upright, as the car rocked back and forth under the weight and invective of his friends, Kevin shifted round to his accuser. Noting the nature of the opposing car – with its black radiator grille, quad spotlights and teledial wheels – Kevin blushed: for, this was the fabled (and much coveted) XR3.

Recognising that this was now boy racer territory, he accepted the challenge nonetheless, with both cars skidding out of their respective bays, in parallel, before tearing away, in tandem.

'Skin the fucker!' Lathom roared, his voice lost to the rumble of the twin engine (that had pedestrians turning, in fright).

His keen eyes seeking out the road ahead, Kevin didn't hear him, or have need of encouragement. When they, briefly, drew level – on Hall Road East – Micky, hanging by his legs from the window, reached across to the other vehicle.

'Ram the fucking knob!' he cried, as he was wrestled back aboard, his head hitting the dash.

The aggressor's coral beige XR3 took the corner first, barely breaking stride – on a blind turn – with Kevin close behind, neither driver caring for what was on the other side. At the roundabout, they bore left, Kevin cutting across the oncoming traffic – to keep pace – horns blaring feverishly at his back. Barrelling on – headless, heedless – his eyes fixed on his adversary's personalised plates, Kevin couldn't have cared less.

He got his first sense that something was wrong when, turning off the Hightown bends, they headed – cross-country – out to Lydiate and Maghull. There was smoke coming from somewhere, and the smell of rubber… One corner, then the next, where the car seemed to slide… and then a third, where – his distinctive blue tyres now bleeding over the road – Kevin lost control of the wheel and clipped off the kerb, and through a hedge, into the adjacent field (dropping several feet on the other side).

Miraculously, no one was hurt.

'Where are we?' Kevin asked, in momentary confusion.

There was no reply, though – with the tall stems of the surrounding crops towering above them – they were more concerned with how they were going to get out again. Kevin tried the engine and was gratified to hear it coughing back into life.

'We need a fucking periscope!' Lathom cackled, before forcing the window down and staggering out.

He was the first onto the roof.

'You can see from up here,' he called back down and, joined by another of their troupe – one on either side – they set off through the swaying crop, the two friends sending intermittent instructions into the blind-sided driver, as the battered car rumbled on.

'Left… no, no, *right,*' they cried, hammering at the roof, while Kevin – with thumps returned, in answer – did his best to follow.

Crunching up onto a dirt track that led to a slip road, they eventually found their way.

'Mind the seats,' Kevin advised, when the boys jumped back in, setting off with a new-found caution, not that the car was in any state to do anything else.

Their swagger would return in full later (in the telling).

Kevin mistreated every vehicle he ever owned – from his first, to his last – and could often be found racing, late at night, down the M62 (breaking records, to make up time).

His first car, a second-hand Escort Mark II, had issues from the start, and – by its fifth year – it was breaking down every couple of weeks, with the head gasket blowing out on three separate occasions. Kevin was thankful for his Ellesmere House colleague (and friend), the self-professed 'automobile geek' John Carr, who was usually on hand to bail him out.

'Can you fix it?' Kevin would ask, bearing gifts (a six-pack of beer, or a carton of cigarettes).

Following him out, to the car – parked, as ever, at a rakish angle – John would shake his head, teasing, 'I don't know how you get them into such bad shape,' before checking the water and the oil.

It was by John's good grace that Kevin's varied conveyances were kept on the road for so long, though even he couldn't work miracles, and time would eventually be called.

'It's finished,' John said, reading the rites on Kevin's first car – having been tasked with getting the thing moving again – 'but, if you give me some idea of your budget, I'll see what I can do.'

John returned, the following week, with the offer of another Escort, that one of his friends could do him a deal on: it was basic, he said, but in 'good nick', with low mileage.

'I'll take it,' Kevin declared, forgoing an inspection.

The new vehicle, a sober azure – with none of the previous car's bodywork – was distinctly underwhelming, though Kevin recognised that he was hardly the man of five years before. He was mature, now, and drove with greater care. Driving, as a result, was no longer so much fun, with Kevin finding his kicks elsewhere.

When Andrew suggested fitting a phone, Kevin was initially cautious – the cost was exorbitant – but eventually persuaded to make his case to the Thalidomide Trust.

'I'm usually out on my own,' he explained, 'and I'm always breaking down.' He paused, gauging the reaction. 'I don't know what I would do if there wasn't someone around to help.'

The Trust stumped up, Kevin having them wrapped around his little finger, by this point, and – within a week – he was driving across to the BT warehouse (more a hangar than a showroom) to have one fitted.

Given his pick, Kevin chose the weightier box-style phone, which – fixed to the right of the steering column – was within easy reach, watching with curiosity as the wires and the circuitry were tucked beneath the upholstery.

Ten minutes later, and – the switch flicked – Kevin was the proud owner of an early model Motorola (with green, oversized buttons) and, a hundred yards up the road, he was already pulling over to try it out.

'You'll never guess where I'm calling from,' he gushed into the headset.

'I'm on nights – I don't care...' Neil returned, gruffly.

'I'm in my car – ringing from a car phone!' Kevin cried. 'Can you call me back,' he said – giving the number – 'so I can make sure everything works?'

'I bet it costs a bomb,' Neil noted, when his call was connected, and that was the extent of it, with Kevin making very little use of that latest toy (in a long line).

While appreciating the reliability of his second car, it was only with his *third* pick – a red Ford Transit 3.0 V6 – that, like Goldilocks, Kevin found his match. He had never considered a van before, but once he had experienced the play of such a powerful engine – 125 horsepower – he would never consider anything else again.

'It's amazing!' he declared, circling, in something like awe. 'I'll take it!'

There was no thought to the practicalities, of course, and the adaptions would prove problematic, with the only garage willing to take the work being more than a hundred miles away, in Driffield (East Riding).

Kevin's solitary test drive would involve a no-way comparable, left-hand drive American Chrysler, which – unversed in a beast of such scale – he had merely shunted (uneasily) around the ex-military concourse.

'If you could ease your hand off the accelerator now,' the sales representative had had call to caution.

Returning to his familiar car, Kevin had been justifiably shaken, and he was already harbouring doubts about making it back over the Snake Pass, when Gary agreed to accompany him. Clinging, precariously, to the craggy hillside (through the gathering dusk) – giving the occasional warning, while fearful of breaking the driver's concentration – he proved all but redundant.

Driving at a snail's pace, the light was already gone by the time they reached home; that didn't stop Kevin's neighbours from crowding round, under the glare of the streetlights, to run a suspicious rule over this bright new thing (leaving smudged prints on the freshly lacquered hood), while Kevin beamed back from behind the wheel.

Brand spanking new, it didn't belong there.

'The engine's 125 horsepower,' Kevin preened, stepping on the gas, before releasing the ramp, with a chuckle, as his audience clamoured to get out of the way. 'Listen,' he urged, working the near-silent electric windows up, then down again. 'Forty-watt stereo,' he resumed, shoving a tape into the cassette deck to set the van bouncing to Steve Harley.

'That's boss, lad!' Big Eric declared, breaking the reverential tone, before hoisting himself up (and pulling Gary out). 'You'll be able to take the whole lot of us to the pub in this thing!'

That last comment was met with cries of assent, while Eric gave a disarming smile. Glad to be the centre of attention, Kevin immediately took him up on the request – the first of many such excursions.

They had driven back from Driffield on a full tank; it wasn't until he ventured into a petrol station to fill up again that Kevin discovered that this new van, which had been fitted with an early catalytic converter, ran on unleaded and, likewise, that there were a paucity of garages to supply it.

All of a sudden, the gauge would be flashing red again and Kevin chasing off in search of replenishment.

'Wasn't there a garage a couple of blocks back?' Gary would chip in, looking up from his book – or the rolling countryside – before stubbing out his cigarette with something like decision.

'No good,' Kevin snapped. 'Didn't do unleaded.'

He made a U-turn, just in case.

Ultimately unfit for the muscular purpose to which Kevin put it, the Transit van was a whole other proposition, with just as much to go wrong as there was to go right – a crack here, a rattle there, as they rumbled warily on.

'It was a real gas-guzzler,' Kevin ruefully admits. 'We'd be out in the country somewhere, bombing along, when suddenly we'd be all out of fuel!'

He had – inevitably – loved every minute, with this latest vehicle the best match yet for his vigorous and vibrant nature. More reliable than those earlier Escorts, it was more easily accessed by chair and offered better visibility by dint of the additional height – Kevin afforded a weight and weft that his own two legs had never given.

'People get out of your way when you're in a van!' he crowed, happy to turn heads as a result of the 1.65 tonnes of amalgamated steel he was now carrying, rather than for those other, all too obvious, reasons.

For, the judgements and estimations made in respect to Kevin were all too often selective, paying neither due regard, nor taking fair account, of the fact of his disability, except on their own prejudiced terms.

Hurrying back to the van, after a visit to the theatre – taking shivering steps through the frosty air – we were dismayed to find ourselves boxed in from behind.

'Can't they bloody read?' Kevin spat, in scornful reference to the wheelchair signs appended to the double doors at the rear, with the notice 'Please do not park within 2 metres' printed out in stark capitals. '*You'll* have to drive,' he decided, when we first faced that situation together, while I was stood looking on, only now realising the importance of that two-and-a-half metre clearance.

Kevin had already whizzed round to the front.

'Get in,' he called, delighting in my discomfort – as I took his seat in the front (and faced those unfamiliar controls) – 'I'll direct you.'

At the time, I didn't even know how to drive.

The precedence had been set for Kevin several years before, when he had skipped, chuckling, out of an Alan B'stard concert (in Manchester Apollo), to find a silver BMW slotted into the space he had been careful to leave at the back of his van. *Shit,* he muttered, casting about for assistance in the lashing rain, wondering how he would ever get home.

He welcomed the stoop of a traffic warden, for once, his white knight calling up the traffic police, who ordered a pick-up truck, to have the 'obstruction' removed.

'The green one, first,' he instructed, once I had the keys in, 'then, the black button at the top.'

'This one?' I asked, making sure.

'Yes, *yes*,' his impatience showing, '—just *press* the bloody thing!'

Having fixed the gearstick into Drive, I released the handbrake, as Kevin directed me to the accelerator pedal, through which I started the van forward, feeling its heft creep in stop-start jolts. Seeming set to lurch out of control, I released the pedal (in a panic), before quickly reapplying the brake.

'Forward! Forward!' Kevin cried, urging me on, until I had finally made enough room for the ramp and was instructed to stop.

Taking me through the same steps in reverse, I shut the engine down, before sliding happily back across to the passenger side.

Kevin's first Transit van was a revelation and would serve his transportation needs for over eight years, with the majority of its faults a result of the adaptions rather than the vehicle itself. For, over time, the tall, attenuated levers, that were such a liberation, had started to stick – despite liberal applications of WD-40 – while the ramp refused to drop and the brakes to grip… until it was all simply untenable.

'I sold it to Lawrence Clarke, for £500,' he told me – grinning – though he hadn't mentioned Lawrence Clarke before and I knew nothing of their relationship. 'He's got cerebral palsy,' he added, for clarification.

Those were happy days, with Kevin's most memorable drives being the ones he took with Gary – to Sellafield, North Wales… the Lakes – yet, the two of them haven't spoken in years.

It seems a waste, when – with their lives laid out before them – they had once been so free. There would be music and the wind in their hair, and Gary would even – on occasion – call a sudden halt, to go racing off across a field, to pick impetuously at the wild flowers he had seen from the window, the music pouring all the while from the stereo, their voices lifted in ecstatic rendition.

Chapter 12

It was Innocent Fate, the band that Gary had recently put together with friends, that was playing on the stereo; oddly characteristic of a fractious decade, that carefully chosen sobriquet could not have been settled on at any other point.

When Kevin suggested that he could manage them, the band – knowing his drive and enthusiasm – was quick to agree, with Kevin proving both a proficient promoter and an impassioned impresario.

They took a rehearsal room at Vulcan Studios, a converted warehouse at the end of one of the pockmarked side streets leading back from Derby Road (to what remained of the old docks), the whole gang seeing only elegance in the surrounding desolation.

After hauling out the heavy equipment, they stepped briefly out of the rain – lighting up cigarettes from beneath sodden fringes – before applying themselves back to the instruments and the amps.

'Give us a hand,' Liam called, drawing Gary from his reverie, and off they set, shuffling the cumbersome Fender Vibrolux up the solid stone steps that marked the entrance.

Kevin's more sedate approach – four strong arms hoisting his chair into the air (as directed) before depositing him back down on the other side – was a source of unexpected mirth.

'Would you like some grapes?' Neil teased.

'Nah, not hungry,' Kevin returned jovially, 'but the least you could do is open the bloody door!' he added, his chair now hemmed into the small corridor that led to the foyer.

They could hear music – juts and spurts of bass and guitar, the rasp of a snare drum, the judder of a tom – as they turned in from the hissing rain, Gary spitting out one last time.

Nodding casually to Aussie John, parked behind glass (in a small room to the side), they dragged the equipment through, leaving

Kevin to his own devices.

'One-two; one-two…' Gary mumbled into the SM58 to test the volume, a squall of feedback sending him skipping back to the PA, where he turned the dials to strike a better balance.

Strumming with a 0.6 millimetre pick on muted strings, Neil Hardaker's second-hand Fender Telecaster was slung over his right shoulder, each calculated stroke returning a wash of sound. When he hit upon a familiar run of chords – the drummer tapping unconsciously at the kick pedal, while tightening a bolt on the high-hat – there was a sudden air of expectancy. Miming through his rewrites, trying out various rhythms and rhymes, Gary was crouched against a wall.

After settling up with Aussie John, Kevin made another booking before following his protégés through, looking on their preparations with pride, quite genuinely believing that Innocent Fate had something that all the other bands, in all the other rooms – running up to the third floor – lacked.

After taking up their positions, Liam gave a count of four and Neil struck the opening chord.

'I feel isolated,' Gary sang, in a rich tenor, 'an island of ideas. Put me on a pedestal… you are a Mills and Boon.'

Kevin had typed out a set list for their upcoming gig and they ran through the songs in order, imagining that they were playing for real. The Firehouse was a small venue – Kevin had gone to look – and, as the band hit their stride, he could already picture the audience. *We'll blow them away*, he thought, with renewed certainty.

They're improving, too, he thought, both technically and in terms of performance. Once reluctant to take centre stage, Gary was now hanging over the microphone with a sense of purpose, enunciating his words with relish. Drawing on a cigarette, leaning into the mic, there was no denying the star quality. The guitarists strutted back and forth on either flank, spinning melodies around the vocal lines, their fingers racing over the fretboards, while the drums beat unerringly on.

'Yeah, yeah, I *like* it, but...' Kevin would presage any minor criticism – sure to keep their feet on the ground – but he rarely went further than suggesting a change to the running order, or that the bass was too low in the mix.

Kevin knew his limits, while believing that he knew enough about music to be able to adjudge that Innocent Fate had something. He never tired of hearing the songs either, even on their fifth or sixth run-through, and was always trying to pick out the words that Gary was so secretive of. Kevin was teased for the optimism that helped to drive them on.

Their first gig, the following weekend, was loud, brash and inspirational – everything a first gig *should* be – even if, in their wild exuberance (at the roar of the crowd), the tempo was too quick, which significantly reduced the length of the set.

Spitting out his words, Gary led the charge, while Liam sought to rein them in.

'We're Innocent Fate,' the singer announced, at the end of the first song (and they were already onto the next).

Playing in front of an audience changed everything, with the songs taking on a life of their own and the band now able to see – where they couldn't before – when a verse dragged, or the solo was overindulgent.

'This one's called Suburbia's Child,' Gary introduced another, the sweat pouring down his face, and a disjointed cheer went up.

A wall of sound swirled around them, and they were already halfway through, their authority growing. Liam concluded the set with a kick to the snare that sent the kit spinning.

It was only when they had stumbled off the low stage and were pacing a deserted back corridor, that they truly appreciated that the last twenty minutes had been the most exciting of their lives – that all they wanted to do was to get back on again. There were to be no encores, however.

'Leave them wanting more,' Kevin had advised, remembering something he had read about Joy Division.

Gazing over the shining faces of the crowd – necks beating in time to the music, bright eyes transfixed – Kevin had tried to gauge the mood, noting how the dozen or so girls, who made up the front row, already seemed to know the words. *This is it,* he thought, swept up in a fever of emotion, knowing now – if he had ever doubted it – that Innocent Fate was a proper band (and he an integral part).

Ten minutes later, Kevin was stood in the back office, discussing – through the muffled throb of the PA– the possibility of remittance. It was no conversation. This gig had been a 'trial', he was told; if they played again, and brought similar numbers, then they might get paid.

'We'll be packing this place out, when word gets round,' Kevin declared, cheerfully saving face.

'That was brilliant, lads!' he enthused backstage – seeing no reason to break the illusion – 'and the manager was singing your praises, too.'

Taking the five-pound note that was handed them (from Kevin's own pocket), it was nothing less than the band expected.

After such an exhilarating night, the everyday grind of continued rehearsals proved a disappointment. They had hoped for some kind of reaction – A & R men, perhaps. Rolling into the rehearsal room with a fat grin working over his face, it was left to Kevin to lift flagging spirits and motivate stalled momentum.

'I've booked us a photo shoot,' he announced.

There was laughter, confusion – cynicism – but they were all there (present and correct) on the day in question, trailing cologne, with coats and jackets slung insouciantly over their narrow shoulders. If Kevin hadn't known better, he'd have thought the attention had gone to their heads.

'Where do you want us?' Gary asked, checking at the collar of his new shirt, combing a hand through his hair.

Having shuffled them into position, the photographer suggested various poses – arms across chests; hands in pockets – adjusting them according to height, with Neil the only one to retain his jacket (over a thin black tie on a white shirt).

Kevin wondered at the change – running his eye from the pigs to the humans (and back again). Recalling his Orwell, he was glad to have no further part.

'Posers,' he called, though the resultant pictures were impressive, with Kevin having decided on a high-resolution finish on glossy photographic paper, with the name – Innocent Fate – running across the foot of the promotional release in a hand-drawn *Brush Script*.

Ripping through the parcel he had gleefully signed for, Kevin's eye was naturally drawn to the small print in the bottom right corner – 'Management, Kevin Donnellon' – and any last reservation fell away.

Having doubled up on rehearsals in preparation, they were booked into Crash, to cut their first demo, the following month. Despite an affected nonchalance – arriving by cab, in regulation shades – they were all struck by the level of professionalism, from the carpeted rooms and soundproofed drum booth, to the complex mixing desk (manned by an engineer).

'I've got my own bloody room!' Liam bawled, nose to the glass, breaking the sombre tone.

He had headphones, too, and would play to a click-track for the first time in his life.

After tuning up, and testing their levels against the desk, each seeing to their own particular instrument, they were finally able to play, and they could no longer pretend. For, after so many months of practising on sub-standard equipment, with the music from the other rooms continually bleeding through, Crash was a revelation.

'It sounds really good,' Gary mumbled, in stupefaction, after the first run-through.

With the drummer keeping precise time (and recorded in

isolation) and the guitarists huddled over their effects, working on overdubs with a freedom they had never known, the resulting sound was another surprise. Spinning joyously around the room in his chair, Kevin was the only person who was able to give physical expression to his emotions.

'That's great, boys,' the engineer called through, after the third take of their second song – 'Painted Portrait'.

'So, this is where the magic's done,' Kevin chuckled, easing the tension as they stepped into the mixing booth, lighting up cigarettes out of habit.

Once the first song had started up and was pouring resplendently from the overhead speakers, the mood was exultant.

'It's fucking brilliant!' Kevin erupted and, hardly able to believe that they could play to such a level (that it wasn't all a trick), they all nodded in agreement.

Gary rode back in the van with Kevin and, though he didn't have much to take (just a microphone and his lyric sheets), he felt like he carried the whole world in the master tape stowed on his lap. They drove in silence, unable to think of anything but what they had produced in those last few hours.

This was finally Kevin's time, and it was with an almost missionary zeal that he ran two hundred copies off from the master (onto C46 cassettes) and sent these out, recorded delivery, to every single record company in the book (and to several of the popular music magazines, for review purposes, too). *This is just the start*, he thought, though they would receive only a handful of acknowledgements in return (all politely demurring).

Disillusionment followed upon their halting progress, and though they kept up regular rehearsals – and played a handful of gigs – the hunger was gone. Undeterred, Kevin secured them their most high-profile show to date.

'We're playing at the International Garden Festival!' he

announced, 'and that means national exposure...'

'I'm away in July,' Liam returned casually.

'I'll need to check the dates, too,' Neil cautioned.

'There'll be hundreds of people there,' Kevin barked back, their apathy an affront. 'Fuck going on holiday!'

Even Gary, who was trying to catch the light as it fell across the rotted window frame, was already hunkering back over his sketchbook. Nothing more was said of that gig, as they ran listlessly through the rest of their set, their interest briefly flickering at the introduction of a new composition ('Inca Tribe').

That gig would prove an end of sorts, with the band having run its course, though there would be one final kick against the inevitable, when Kevin turned to Gary – during a Friday evening transmission of *The Tube* – to suggest that Innocent Fate should be given a chance.

'We're better than that lot,' he sneered.

'We'd blow them off the fucking stage,' Gary concurred.

'We should go down and demand to be put on!' cackling now, at the absurdity of the proposition.

They left early Monday morning, with the drive across to Newcastle – the location of the studios – taking a little over three hours, Gary inserting Style Council's *Café Bleu* into the cassette deck, before he had even considered fitting his seat belt (Mick Talbot's delightful piano composition immediately dancing out at them).

He had a copy of the demo too, and this was on next, Gary wondering if he would ever get used to hearing his voice played back in such a way, while Kevin sang along (word-perfect). Their eyes met on the run-out – their joy, then, an encapsulation of the whole day.

Following the incised line of Hadrian's Wall, a picturesque route through heather-speckled meadows – the van bouncing noisily over every bump – they left the M6 at Carlisle. At Throckley, on the A690, a silence fell between them at the sudden appearance of snow: soft speckles hanging guilelessly in the air, before dropping hesitantly to the ground.

On the outskirts of Newcastle, Kevin pulled to the kerb to ask for directions, with Gary calling out to the first person he saw, a young woman who stepped lightly across. She was beautiful, with smooth, unblemished skin, a button nose, green-blue diamante eyes and long lashes that she flicked, hypnotically, between them. *She's an angel,* they thought simultaneously.

'Weor dyer need te gan?' she asked, leaning in, her eyes drawn naturally to Kevin (her breath, strawberry gum).

'The Tube studios… on City Road,' Gary said quickly, wanting to hold her attention, his words clogging up even as he tried to release them.

When she stepped back to get her bearings, their eyes were drawn along the length of her – from the tottering stack of auburn-flecked hair, to the fingerless gloves pinned to delicate, expressive hands, her legs shadowed by skin-tight yellow and black stretch pants.

'Aye, ah dee knaa, pet,' she replied, a rapid blaze of patter, her eyes crossed in concentration. Then, suddenly, an *epiphany,* remembering – 'Ah, sorree…' – with a smile again, turning on her heels to point them back the way they had come. 'Owa there – doon bi the Quay.'

The world seemed to stop as she skipped away, her small head peeping out from the high ruff of her fur coat, the snow falling around her.

They hadn't been following the instructions, but were happy to leave it to fate as, drifting through the drizzling hinterland at the stray outer edge of Quayside, they negotiated a series of concrete byways (the snow turning to hail).

'I can't see any signs,' Gary muttered, turning his head about (imagining that *The Tube* studios must surely be worth some kind of plaque).

'I think she said it was down here,' Kevin mumbled, though he had been paying no more attention than Gary, 'and then, to keep right...'

They were driving at a crawl, gazing out on the boarded-up shops that faced onto the idling swings in the litter-strewn playgrounds – and on, through to the crumbling rises of Byker, with not a living soul in sight.

'It's pretty bleak,' Gary noted, as Kevin flipped the wipers, fearing an attack.

Turning another corner, they finally saw it, in blue, thirty-metre letters: Tyne Tees Television. Decanting excitedly from the car, they edged reverently around the building – in a form of pilgrimage – noting the stark, whitewashed walls, the sash windows at the front such a contrast to the narrow strips of concrete at the rear. When they reached the iconic arch of plastic 'tube' that gave the show (and the studio) its name, they stopped for a moment's contemplation, before stepping inside, moving with a clear purpose (feeling in their bones that they belonged).

The reception area was glass and chrome, and it was only gradually – the filtered air stilling their enervated nerves – that they started to breathe more regularly, though while they were still taking in their surroundings, a large group of figures in bright, baggy suits floated past, Gary doing a double-take, before nodding towards the man at their centre.

'It's Hank Marvin,' he whispered, Kevin catching a glimpse of the iconic glasses just as the cortège stepped out to the street.

'Don't know why they let those old has-beens on,' Gary hissed, his characteristic rhetorical turn filling Kevin with renewed belief, in consideration of Hank Marvin and those varied hangers-on.

They've had their fucking chance – it's time they buggered off!, he thought, recalling with relish the disdain Gary would show for any band he didn't rate: how he would have to tune the radio to another station, before something was thrown.

'Absolute dross,' Gary had recently declared, of Elton John. 'I'd quite happily hand him to the firing squad.'

'Rod Stewart's absolute shit,' he had insisted, on another occasion. 'I'd like to meet him, just so I could smash his stupid face in!'

The blander the better; the more gaudily-sequinned, the more deserving of ridicule: Thatcher's Britain was a time of division.

'Good afternoon!' Kevin said, rolling bullishly up to the desk. 'I'm the manager of Innocent Fate and I'd like to speak to someone about getting us on *The Tube*... Innocent Fate are one of the best new bands in the country,' he resumed, not waiting for an answer, 'and you'll regret not putting us on if you don't take this opportunity.'

Gary flushed at such a direct approach.

'If you'd just take a seat,' the receptionist advised, 'I'll ring through and get someone to come down.'

They shuffled back from the desk to a grey sofa, where they steadied themselves and ran back through all that they planned to say, believing that their whole career hinged on the next ten minutes.

'Hello, pleased to meet you,' said a man in his mid-twenties, a hairless arm stretching out from a rolled-up checked shirt.

There was no tie, Kevin was pleased to note, and little ceremony.

Opening up the leather portfolio he'd brought along for illustration, and passing over a selection of the band's promotional shots, along with a copy of their recently completed demo, it was Kevin who did the talking.

'We recorded it at Crash Studios last month,' he explained, 'and I think it gives a good idea of what Innocent Fate are all about – we genuinely want to be bigger than The Beatles.'

The rangy researcher smiled right back at him – seemed impressed – though, in the middle of the sales pitch, his pencil tapping away at the pad he had laid across his knee, he suddenly interjected.

'I take it you guys are from Liverpool?'

'Yeah – *Scousers*, if you like…' Kevin returned.

'Then, you know Half Man Half Biscuit?' They didn't, not *personally*, and Kevin regretfully told him, wondering – even as he did – whether he should have embellished the truth. 'Well, that's good,' the researcher resumed, before explaining that Half Man Half Biscuit had been booked to play a couple of weeks ago and pulled out at the last minute. 'Totally unprofessional,' he continued. 'Said they couldn't come because Tranmere were at home… we were still chasing round, trying to find another band, even as we went on air.'

The Tube was now, it seemed, somewhat 'dark' on bands from Liverpool.

'We're a professional outfit,' Kevin told him – already deeming the meeting a success – 'and you can rest assured that we won't let you down.'

'Well, I can't promise anything,' the researcher returned, 'but I'll certainly have a listen to your tape.'

That seemed fair enough and they shook hands on the deal, but returned to the van with a nagging sense of disappointment. They had hoped to meet Jools Holland – or the foxy Paula Yates, perhaps – and had stumbled on a founder member of The Shadows instead.

It was a good story and Kevin a garrulous raconteur – his eyes shining at the telling absurdity. Gary, however, didn't remember seeing Hank Marvin when I asked, but did recall the researcher's frustration over Half Man Half Biscuit (and that had the ring of truth).

Talking over that same incident with my other brother – who had rehearsed in the same studios as Half Man Half Biscuit, for a time – the facts were further confused. For, he had been there on the day that call came, he said, and told of an afternoon spent laughing over the band's refusal to appear.

I wondered, now, whether Andrew had told Gary first, or whether Gary had really learnt of it while over in Newcastle, as he said, rounding off that beautiful day with a final anecdote. No one knows, and there is no one to ask. (Neither brother would give way, when I pointed out the inconsistencies.)

The return journey was slow and passed without incident. The building that once contained The Firehouse now sells PVC windows and doors.

Kevin was twenty-four years of age.

Chapter 13

Martin Waterhouse's brief tenure would bring at least a degree of order to the chaos of Ellesmere House. On his resignation, no one could have guessed at the next chapter.

Ruminating on the stuttering progress of his own career, Kevin didn't see how it could make any difference and, thus, when Tom Black – who he still counted a friend – was given the nod, he welcomed the advancement. Unaware of the round of changes to come, Tom's first directive – that he be henceforth addressed as Mr Black (with all his letters signed off as TAA Black) – brought only amusement.

'I hail, in case any of you were wondering about this beautiful accent of mine, from the royal court of Berkshire,' Thomas Arthur Archibald pointed out – indulging in what he considered humour – before running his new subordinates through an admittedly circuitous résumé.

His thoughts drifting, Kevin couldn't help but wonder at the crummy flat in Walton Vale – a bedsit over a newsagent's – where he had occasionally had reason to drop Tom home (given the airs and graces)... wondering too at the relevance, to disability rights, of the first class doctorate in Italian Studies that he had brought along with him.

'Well, they have *spazzes* in Italy, don't they?' Nicky suggested, in all seriousness, as she tottered back to her desk.

Tall and virtually bald, with grey tombstone teeth and disc-shaped eyeglasses, Mr Black – a high aesthete, with a streak of vulgarity – had the look of Himmler, as Kevin recalls, and was something of an acquired taste.

'Morning, minions!' he would call, to announce his arrival, and the hearts of his staff would sink. 'Gary – kettle!' was the next cry, picking out their most recent conscript for the first order of business.

Gary, who had hated him on sight, would offer a thin drizzle of saliva to the mix, before bringing it through. Watching the exchange from behind his desk, Kevin sensed kinship. He had already noted the precision of the new recruit's wardrobe: the buttoned-up Fred Perry; the folded cuffs on straight-cut jeans; the brushed suede tassel loafers. If he didn't know what the style was exactly, he could see that it was no accident.

'He looked like Paul Weller,' he suggests fondly and I can verify such a characterisation – the flat brown hair, the fishtail parka – with Gary's customised Vespa bringing a touch of glamour to the concrete courtyard out front.

For Kevin, it was just good to have someone else to talk to.

'The Jam,' he was told, unerringly – when he asked – the two of them soon swapping albums, opinions and even books, which was a departure for Kevin, who hadn't seen the point (of reading) since leaving college and entering the world of work.

'André Gide,' Gary answered, under question. 'You can borrow it, when I'm finished…'

Looking over the cover, with an interested eye, Kevin really thought he might.

There were, he learnt, only three years between them but, finding that he had, in that same time, covered considerably more ground, Kevin was naturally protective, especially with Tom so regularly on the warpath.

'Keep your head down,' he advised, recognising – in his friend's forthright nature – an easy target.

'I do,' Gary returned, with a smirk.

They were sharing a cigarette, out back – swapping notes.

'It was a right laugh when Mark Cameron was in charge,' Kevin reminisced, 'but, I suppose, Tom's got his own way.'

'He's a fascist,' Gary spat, unsympathetically.

Bemoaning the luck that had seen him wash up at Ellesmere House, Mr Black had been drawn to Kevin from the start and was quickly sharing confidences. While appreciating the fact that he was the only member of staff on first-name terms, Kevin had little to say in return.

Fortunately, Tom had answers of his own, and – beating against what he considered poor judgement and taste – he was keen to instruct. This had initially consisted of a friendly word, advising Kevin (for instance), by way of introduction, on the deficiencies of denim.

'We're not in the Wild West,' he had declaimed, with a sigh.

It was only after making the jump into management that those suggestions were more onerously applied. Kevin had been flattered to be called into Tom's claustrophobic office, for a lecture on fashion, at first.

'Clothes can make or break a man,' it was explained. 'That shirt, for instance?' querying, with a disparaging flick.

Kevin nodded, with due sobriety – didn't even think to defend a purchase his mother had made. Agnes picked out his toothpaste and aftershave, too, with Kevin never giving such matters any thought. Tom's sudden interest would have him considering not only colours, but styles and fit, too.

After several weeks of what was purely academic advice – that had Kevin pawing in desperation through his wardrobe every morning – Tom finally decided to take him shopping.

Kevin drove into Liverpool city centre, his convenient blue badge allowing them to park in front of one of Tom's favourite shops. While Kevin was waiting for the lift to drop, the pedagogue strode on ahead.

'Now, *this,*' he exulted, in C&A, ladling the sleeve of a shirt over Kevin's chest, 'is perfect for your colouring.'

The item was passed to the shop assistant before Kevin could reply. Tom had him in a jacket next, his protégé – a blank canvas to experimentation – spinning his chair in the floor-length mirror.

'And, one of these, in the young man's size, please,' Tom instructed, indicating a paisley waistcoat. 'You'll have to measure him, my love,' he added, seeing the girl's confusion.

The waistcoat joined the shirt in the basket, Kevin wide-eyed at the pace, precision and sheer pleasure of shopping with Mr Black.

'How much are they?' Kevin finally thought to ask, at the counter, as several more items were piled onto their haul (a scatter of materials, colours and branded labels).

'What does money matter, when it comes to fashion?' Tom decried, Kevin instinctively welcoming a return to the indulgence he had been brought up on, savouring the shock of the new – the smell and feel – just as much as he did the shucking off of old skins (in the form of the clothes he had been wearing since leaving school).

On his first visit to Nunsford Close, Tom had consigned most of those old clothes to the bin (with Kevin dropping them into the Spastics later in the week). It was a liberation – that striking makeover proving that he was no longer a boy.

Once he had him dressed, Tom seemed to think that it was his duty to feed him, too.

'I've no doubt you exist on a steady diet of ready meals,' he supposed.

Examining Kevin's cupboards with an air of disdain, Tom had brought out a single pack of crisps and a dusty tin of beans. With Rhona Brown, Kevin's first Home Help, over on a daily basis, to prepare his evening meal, the supposition was misguided, though Kevin acquiesced.

'We can't have a friend of mine going hungry,' Tom resumed, showing his teeth in a leering smile.

In confusion, Kevin acquiesced once more.

It was only as he was leaving that Tom suggested, on a whim that they call in at the new Sainsbury's, which, he eagerly reported, 'has its own bakery'.

Kevin went along, without expectation, but the trip proved oddly illuminating. Skipping down the aisles, with his trolley packed to the rafters, they drew looks, Kevin as proud of his companion's knowledge as he was of his discrimination.

'Mr Black's coming over for his tea, later,' he gloated to his mother, on their weekly phone call.

'Why?' Agnes returned briskly, wondering at such a hands-on boss.

Kevin did his best to explain, but he wasn't sure why Tom – who had stocked both his wardrobe and his larder – had now decided to teach him how to cook, too.

'Full of E-numbers – gunk, pure and simple,' Tom advised, as he bent over Kevin's fridge, before directing him to empty it out. 'These will have to go,' he whistled, dropping a pack of ice lollies to the bin.

Bristling at the idea of being told what he could and couldn't consume, the new discoveries were ample compensation, with Kevin very quickly developing a sophisticated palate on his own account.

Tom would come over once a week to help his new student prepare a meal: pasta (with a bolognaise sauce), risotto (with prawns), or stir-fried chicken on a bed of noodles. Kevin had never seen an aubergine before he met Tom, or ventured beyond melted cheese on toast, yet here he was grinding peppercorns and adding a dash of Tabasco, his speciality the mayonnaise he could now make from scratch, whisking up the egg yolks with ever-improving proficiency. Laying out the finished dish with a decided flourish, Kevin wasn't always sure whether he was to eat it, or give it a mark out of ten.

The choice of wine was treated with the same exactitude, with Tom showing Kevin what to look for on the label, to guarantee quality, and insisting that they imbibe the wine in the proper manner. There were different glasses for different varieties – small-bowled, for white; wider-bodied, for red – and Tom would fill each to the mid-point, before turning the lambent liquid to intensify the aroma. Encouraged to take just a single discriminating sip – at first – once given license, Kevin would swig down the remainder in one.

'Philistine!' Tom shrieked, with gleeful affection.

The lectures that followed, on the types and qualities of various bouquets, were laborious, but Kevin, who had recently developed a penchant of his own, welcomed the education.

They were a good fit and good company, at first, with Kevin – who was still just finding his feet – looking up to Tom as he would to an older brother. It was only when Tom started to over-reach, when the regularity and force of his visits, and opinions, grew out of all proportion, that Kevin felt anything but grateful for the time and the attention.

Increasingly persuadable, he had accepted – at first – that if Tom called, unannounced, on a Friday night, he should be open to suggestion. Trailing Calvin Klein Obsession, Tom would push at the open door with a bottle of red clasped under his arm.

'Are you decent?' he would call from the hall, and he was in the kitchen next, prising out the cork, before skipping across to the stereo to put on one of the records he had previously recommended (Kevin having added it to his collection).

After the introductory crackle, with the music now pulsing from the speakers, Tom would start to dance, his hands clapping exuberantly to the beat while his shoes squirmed lasciviously over the parquet.

'You spin me right round, baby, right round, like a record baby…'

At the inevitable beep of the pre-ordered taxi out on the street, Kevin would find himself swept along on another night of adventure, his submission providing the barest form of consent. Despite this initial reluctance, however, Kevin certainly knew how to party, and – once the alcohol had taken hold – he would be throwing shapes on the dance floor with a similar abandon.

Turning his throbbing head to the shuttered blinds, Kevin would often find himself on the sofa the next morning, with little recollection of how he had made it home, but figuring that Tom must have stayed over (and taken the bed).

He had, Kevin squinting across to the kitchen, at the hiss of a pan (and the smell of bacon), to find Tom and an additional companion tucking into a full English. He didn't ask who their guest was – it seemed impertinent at this point – but Tom was seldom unaccompanied.

'How do you want your eggs?' Tom called across, as Kevin dropped to the floor.

A social animal, Kevin hardly begrudged such intrusions; he was, in some ways, rather flattered. It was only towards the end – when *he* had grown, too – that the friendship started to feel more like an imposition.

'Who is it?' Kevin asked.

'Tom,' Gary returned, in an undertone, edging away from the window.

'Kevin! Kevin!' they heard. Then, Tom rattling at the letter box, 'Open up – it's an emergency!'

With the Mark II Escort sitting – in full glory – out front, Kevin could hardly deny his presence, though he had plans of his own and would have appreciated prior notice.

Pushing past Gary at the door, Tom dispensed with the pleasantries.

'It's a nightmare!' he bawled. 'The water's down… and I'm going out – so, I need to use your shower.'

Noting the bag slung casually over his shoulder, Kevin waved him off to the bathroom, with Gary sent to show him how everything worked. They could hear Tom from the living room: first kicking off his shoes, then emptying out his toiletries, before – mercilessly – breaking into unaccompanied song.

They were smiling, even if they wanted him gone.

Tom emerged trailing aftershave and the sticky sap of pomade, turning about in the mirror for a full five minutes (trying his thinning hair in various styles), before finally deciding that he was done.

'You have genuinely saved my life!' he called from the hall.

With Mr Black safely off the property, Gary went to check on the bathroom.

'He's left a right mess,' he adjudged.

Kevin was already up on his feet.

'What? Let me see!' he cried, stopping short in the doorway.

Peering through the steam, he could barely make out the floor through the litter of discarded clothes – socks, shirts and underwear – while every surface seemed to be smeared with product of some kind.

Stepping, soberly, back through to the living room, he put a record on – in the hope of forgetting – but the idea of leaving the mess in the bathroom for Rhona to clear in the morning didn't seem right.

'Do you mind?' he asked, sending Gary back for the clothes.

They had finished off a second bottle of wine, and were starting on a third, when Gary brought the bin bag in from the hall.

'All designer, no doubt,' he muttered, picking his way through.

'Only the best for Mr Black… from the royal court of Berkshire,' Kevin adduced.

'He's a knobhead,' Gary returned succinctly, hoisting the bag to his shoulder, before carrying it across to the back door.

A mere witness, Kevin was powerless to intervene when Gary stepped outside and tipped those same clothes to the turf. With a nervous glance towards the other flats, he had followed Gary out, and watched – now – as he lifted up a brightly coloured shirt and twirled it into the air.

'A distinctive little number,' he sneered.

'Why don't we go back in?' Kevin tried, helplessly. 'It's cold.'

'Perhaps we should make a fire, then?' Gary returned, extracting his lighter and, in one smooth motion, setting a flame to that garish shirt.

The fabric hissed, as it caught, and was dropped to the floor, with another item soon joining it, to form a pyre, of sorts.

The rest of the bag went the same way, Kevin remonstrating in vain, before spinning his chair away and wheeling back to the house. There was no talking to Gary, like this, especially when he had been drinking.

Looking out on his friend, his pale face illuminated in the light of the bonfire – his eyes coal-black with concentration – he suddenly understood. *Fuck Tom,* he thought, too – the devil taking him.

Leaving the fire to burn, Gary was uncharacteristically subdued on his return and it was left to Kevin to bend over the record player and start up another disc (Bruce Foxton's familiar bassline breaking an unfamiliar tension).

They drank more quickly, now, with a sense of sobriety hanging over them.

Kevin was already out of bed, and showered, before he looked in on Gary – who had spent the night on the couch – and sought out the scorched silhouette on the grass outside.

'Fuck…' he mumbled.

Nothing more was said until they had taken breakfast. Then, determining that they would have to replace everything they had burned, Gary compiled a list, adding items of his own to Kevin's breathless dictation.

Whittling the search down to just three shops – Burtons, C&A and Wade Smith – and deciding that Gary and Tom were of a similar build, they were rather hopeful, though Kevin was ashamed to admit that he now knew Tom's tastes just as well as his own.

After the extremes of the previous night, Gary was almost surprised to find his scooter still standing, safe and in one piece, outside – Kevin's influence, no doubt – and he turned the engine with relief.

Rhona opened the door to him, on his return; Gary, who would have preferred some privacy, shuffled past with his head bowed.

'I couldn't get everything,' he explained, tipping out the first bag that contained a shirt similar to one Tom had arrived in, along with a familiar-looking pair of slacks.

'What size are they?' Kevin asked, of the shoes he pulled from a box.

'Ten,' Gary answered, expectantly.

'Tom's a nine,' Kevin pointed out, only now considering the difficulty of the task.

'I can go back… change them,' Gary suggested, as a full-throated laugh broke out in the kitchen.

'You're in a right pickle,' Rhona chuckled, unfolding her arms as she stepped across. 'And do you not think Mr Black's going to notice they're all brand new?'

It seemed obvious, now.

'He'll sack us,' Kevin muttered, wondering at a long-forgotten freedom.

'Don't care – he's a prick,' Gary hissed, 'and I hate working there, anyway.'

'Aye, but if he sacks you, you'll lose your dole,' Rhona advised.

Still nursing hangovers, the earlier bravado gone, the very thought of seeing Tom again – first thing Monday morning – brought the boys to silence. Rhona, who had children of her own, was sympathetic.

'Why don't you blame me?' she said. 'Tell him I threw the clothes out, because I thought the bag was rubbish – he'd never know.'

'Are you sure?' Kevin asked, his face smoothing out.

'Ach, it's no skin off my nose,' Rhona said, waving away their gratitude, 'and, if it stops you two moping about, then all's the good…'

Tom looked on Kevin's explanation with suspicion, but accepted the apology and the roll of fives that were handed across in recompense (Kevin claiming they had come from Rhona).

That night should have been warning enough about giving full vent to grievance, but – with Kevin still months away from the antipathy he would eventually come to feel – it was just the start.

Gary, a perceptive observer, could see what was coming, even if Kevin, who had given Tom a set of keys (to go with his credit cards), refused.

'It's convenient,' he explained, of their arrangement, '… means I don't even have to take them out with me anymore.'

When they took a taxi, the fare was generally pre-paid, with Kevin having only to step outside his door and mount. When they went shopping, Kevin had simply to pick out what he wanted, to find that same item already packed up and paid for. The extravagance Tom encouraged was liberating: those spending sprees a good deal lighter now they were hands-free. They carried less guilt, too.

'He was over nearly every night, in the end,' Kevin tells me now, still trying to figure his way through.

'He was manipulative,' Gary corroborates. 'Kevin let him get away with murder.'

The credit cards, that Tom made such use of, draw most of Gary's fire, though Kevin insists that Tom was only ever acting on his behalf, and was generous in his own right – he was always bringing over expensive bottles of wine – with no reason to steal.

It wasn't larceny, he avers – real or imaginary – that ultimately did for their friendship, but the growing strains and demands of an association that extended from the office to the home (and took in all stations between). Even Kevin's easy-going nature had its limits.

'He does my head in,' he was already grumbling, from the couch.

'Ach, what's the man done, now?' Rhona scoffed, taking it for another lovers' tiff.

Kevin would explain, then, that he had been forced out to a nightclub, when he didn't want to go, or that Tom had invited himself round again – that he got no peace – but it was hard to put a finger on the actual complaint.

'Well, you're a grown man, so you need to tell him.'

Kevin glowered across – knowing she was right – yet Tom had helped him, too. It had all happened so quickly; he was still so young…

He remembered the episode only when we were deep into the mnemonic of our ongoing discussions, confessing with genuine surprise.

'I actually tried to kill him, once.' That brought us to silence. 'It was Rhona's idea,' he added quickly, explaining that she had been the one to suggest using the poisonous seeds from her laburnum tree (if it was really so bad).

Not knowing whether it was a joke, or a test, Kevin had found himself stirring the sample Rhona had provided into Tom's share of the mayonnaise (and watching as Mr Black licked his plate clean). The evening ran on, as usual, with no obvious effects; fearing the worst, it was Kevin who was now feeling sick.

He couldn't sleep either, and would roll, bleary-eyed, into Ellesmere House the next day, to find that Tom, usually a stickler for punctuality, hadn't arrived. Kevin's legs went, and he couldn't hear whatever Nicky was trying to say… His eyes pinned to the clock, expecting that at any minute he would be taken in for questioning, he didn't even notice when Tom did – eventually – present himself.

'Sorry I'm late, gang,' he crowed, 'but I had the shits… must have been something I ate,' he added with a smirk, turning to Kevin.

He knows, for fuck's sake, Kevin thought, thanking every God he knew for the vital reprieve. His eyes were wandering, his hands shaking under the table.

I was still processing that murder attempt when, finding what he considered the confirmation, Kevin resumed (reading from the computer).

'Native to the mountains of southern Europe – deciduous, with yellow trifoliate leaves…' He paused, with an air of triumph. 'Lethal, if consumed in excess.'

It was out of character for Kevin to have undercooked in such a way, and fortunate too, but that would be the last time Tom ever came to dinner. He almost seemed to know.

Perpetually casting doubt on his subordinates, Mr Black could hardly believe that Kevin was still seeing Gary, despite the latter's departure from Ellesmere House. He would never come close to understanding a friendship that would endure, when so much else around them proved transitory.

Chapter 14

Kevin had rolled into Hugh Baird the next day, in a state of great excitement.

'Did you see it?' he asked his friends, meeting with apathy and opposition.

'Self-obsessed toffs,' was a put-down that sowed doubt, Kevin creeping away – in disillusionment – with no one to share what would, henceforth, be a guilty pleasure.

It was liberating to learn, in later years, that Gary was also a fan of the series, which Kevin had on tape – with the adverts excised – and, over the next few weeks, they would watch them back through.

Given their politics, it was odd to think that *Brideshead Revisited* had struck such a chord, but there was something in its nostalgic tone – and in Charles Ryder's declared intention of 'leaving behind an illusion' – that had drawn their youthful imaginations.

Trawling through charity shops for clothes that met their requirements, while making running repairs with a matching white thread, the two friends were soon dressing in the style of those screen idols. They wore boaters and blazers, with a teddy bear or a bottle of wine sitting up on the seat between them.

The influence went beyond mimicry, with Gary volunteering, in deference to the mural produced by the fictional Sebastian, to make one of his own.

'I didn't even know you could paint,' Kevin exclaimed, after stepping into the bathroom to check on his progress. 'It's really good.'

Gary nodded shyly.

Rhona was typically abrupt.

'It's obscene,' she declared, when she first chanced upon the naked, writhing bodies now lining the bathroom walls.

Kevin, who had been hoping for such a response – and given no warning – answered her with pompous disdain.

'It's art, Rhona – you wouldn't understand.'

Gary had enrolled on a Fine Art course before the year was out.

Like their heroes, the boys had also taken to wine, with Rhona voicing her doubts here, too. Flicking his fingers dismissively at his bare chest, to comic effect, Kevin explained that what they were drinking was 'fine' wine.

'Imbibed from a tall glass, for better articulation… Oh, but you wouldn't understand.'

'So long as it doesn't get out of hand,' Rhona cautioned, 'and you don't go wasting all your money.'

Something of an expert by this point, Kevin didn't have the patience to explain the finer points, or to try to express the pleasure he found in such evenings (in sessions that passed from the ridiculous to the sublime).

Gary would usually begin.

'This one has a delicate, forbidding flavour,' he would declare, setting the tone.

'With a pungent and invigorating after-taste,' Kevin responded, with a smirk, before moving onto the next.

'This one,' Gary began again, searching for the word, 'is a *wise* wine… like a prophet in a dark cave.'

That had Kevin spluttering.

'And, this one, this one…' he tried, with a straight face, 'has the tang of camel hide… mixed with the gentle aroma of Saharan dung!'

They were in full flow, now, their bellies tight with unrestrained laughter.

There is much to recommend the brief period of their lives that would reach its apotheosis with the trip they took to Oxford (in the summer of 1985).

'It doesn't seem real, somehow,' Gary had said, on arrival, while waiting for the lift to drop.

Kevin could feel that estrangement, too – though they hadn't yet left the car park – recognising that this was a pilgrimage rather than a jolly.

'It's magnificent,' he returned unequivocally, as he led off, with Gary having to break into a dignified trot just to keep up.

Giving wondering glances to left and right, and up to the ornate cornices, as they passed through the campuses and colleges in a sense of rapture, their pace had soon slackened: Magdalen College; Christ Church; the Bodleian Library; Radcliffe Square – and, everywhere they turned, those spires! It was exactly how they had imagined it; even the weather held out.

Coming to a dead end, they were about to turn around and withdraw when Gary spotted an arched doorway, with its heavy, wrought-iron gate pulled back. Peering through, they could see grass on the other side, with students laid across it, and wisteria lining the walls. It looked idyllic.

'All visitors report to the porter,' the sign read, and they puzzled at that, until noting the dark-suited figure who was glaring out at them from some sort of anteroom.

'I suppose we'd better go back,' Gary said, in a low voice.

'No way,' Kevin replied, setting off past the porter, who – adjusting his hat – made as though to stop him, but held back at the sight of the chair.

They were laughing as they rolled out into the bright sunlight, and – the pale stone of the loggia walls a perfect foil for the climbing plants and teeming window boxes – it was like entering another world.

There was birdsong, too – suddenly – with speckles of blossom, from the stunted cherry trees, falling all around. Casting covetous eyes over the students, who looked so at home discussing poetry and philosophy – with all the time in the world – they lacked the words.

'It really is beautiful,' Gary declared, sotto voce.

They stayed for more than an hour, until the sun had passed behind the slate roof and the students were starting to disperse – stumbling out by some other door to escape detection.

'I love it here,' Kevin sighed; there was no argument.

Caught up in the ravages of modernity, when they stepped out onto the crowded High Street, it all seemed like a mirage.

'It's a fucking disgrace, to allow such a monstrosity…' Gary hissed, balking at the affront of a McDonald's.

He was striding away before Kevin could answer, forcing his way through the idling pedestrians, as Kevin set off in chase, his chair straining at the limits of its battery.

'I could do with a cup of coffee for the way home,' Kevin called after his friend, pointing out a vegetarian café, 'and maybe a bit of cake?'

Gary nodded his consent, recognising that this was a fitting conclusion; they had seen more than enough and now needed to let their impressions breathe. They left an hour later, in silence, a sorrow settling over them as they hit the motorway, dusk falling on the horizon.

Chapter 15

University was no panacea – he was under no illusions – and, at times, keeping company with students barely half his age, Kevin would feel all of his thirty-six years.

Seeking to bridge the gap, on Karen's advice, Kevin would tune in to *This Life* on Thursday nights, just to be able to give an opinion when it was up for discussion the next day. He tried the music she suggested, too, listening through gritted teeth to the latest Terence Trent D'Arby, just so that he could hit the high notes of the chorus in the union bar.

Despite such adjustments, Kevin would still frequently wander off-piste, before Karen had the time or the notion to correct him. Naturally headstrong, he would struggle to find the right register – his broad accent out of step with the soft surrounding tones, his values out of time – and he would frequently miss the mark.

With Karen, however, he had sensed a connection from the start; free in her company, he trusted her to help him make the right calls.

'What are they talking about?' he would whisper frantically, whenever he found himself out of the loop, and she would chuckle, playfully, before offering her advice.

'You know what Dave Johnson told me?' he started up, kicking against boredom. 'Well, apparently, Edge Hill now enrols students with grade E at A-level,' he continued, with a look of astonishment, when he had their attention. 'This college will let absolutely anyone in!'

'It's true,' one of their party piped up. 'I mean, that's all *I* got, and I couldn't believe when they accepted me!'

Well versed in the art of retraction, Kevin was already back-pedalling.

'That's why Edge Hill is so unique,' he said, 'the range of social backgrounds and the… the diversity.'

Kevin glanced across at Karen, who had turned away, stifling laughter, as they grabbed their coats and headed out again.

The girl who had spoken up was another Karen, who had arrived from Coventry the previous week, to find herself temporarily displaced, after the digs she had arranged had unexpectedly fallen through.

'I'm a bit scared, to be honest,' she admitted, lifting her shy eyes. 'I've been staying on a friend's couch, but it's pretty stressful not knowing where I'll end up… and not being able to get settled.'

Kevin was troubled by the thought of her leaving home under such circumstances, though – almost embarrassed by the attention – Karen had already returned to her drink. Her features weren't even fixed, yet; there were pimples on the side of her neck.

'You can come and stay with me, if you want?' Kevin broke in. 'I've got loads of room and wouldn't mind the company,' suddenly imagining what it would be like to have a young woman around the house.

'Are you serious?' the girl asked, her face lit with hope.

'Yeah, I could put a bed in the room at the front,' Kevin continued. 'Why don't you come and have a look?'

Karen came for a tour the next day, Kevin beaming resplendently as he led her – first – into the bright room at the front (which he said would be hers if the tenancy went ahead). He showed her the kitchen next, pointing out the fixtures and fittings as they went, and then the two alternate bathrooms, explaining how the Clos-o-mat had changed his life.

After walking Karen into his bedroom, where he parked the chair, Kevin led her through to the lounge, which he said they would share, though he'd get her a television of her own.

Pushing at the back door, Kevin rather proudly presented the garden.

'I'm getting it landscaped,' he explained, 'with a ramp up to the door.'

Not bad at all, he thought, following Karen's eyes, as they were drawn to the ornaments and paintings scattered liberally through each of the rooms – the suit of armour, the bats…

'Well – what do you think?' he asked, when they were sitting down to tea, after he had explained the workings of the kitchen.

'It's brilliant – I love it!' Karen cried, her enthusiasm settling the matter.

'You can move in whenever you want,' Kevin said, but it was only as he drove her home that he considered how far he had let his imagination run, and only in the following months that he would see how *this* Karen had served as a forerunner for the next – testing the water for what was to come.

The move never materialised, with Karen soon being offered somewhere closer to home. Having barely stepped foot in his life, she had already left it for good by the following afternoon.

'The one that got away,' Kevin chuckles, only able to discern the pattern when it was already too late (and the die cast).

Chapter 16

Turning in circles, Kevin never thought to upset the rhythm, or to question the direction of travel. Utterly immersed, his feelings were confused – his desires and expectations a blind spot he would have done well to heed.

Off and on, off and on – how does it ever begin?

The process had been gradual, with love a mere conversation, at first. Karen could concede it casually enough, with regard to Kevin, but never with the force of emotion that she applied to Dan. It was hard to know where he stood, when – lending a willing ear – he would bear witness to the latest accounts of their fraught relationship, which showed passion even in denunciation.

Mary Becker, who hailed from Clinton (Iowa), and arrived at Edge Hill in the autumn of 1998, was a welcome distraction from the approaching, and seemingly inevitable, danger (that he didn't yet see): an antecedent that proved a precedent.

It was the university's disability supervisor, Hazel Delacroix, who would introduce Mary to Dave Johnson, a senior lecturer (and mutual friend), and Dave who would eventually introduce Mary to Kevin.

'Roster's jam-packed,' the professor complained, throwing up his hands, 'what with work and family commitments.' He simply 'hadn't the time' to help her settle. He was referring to Mary, though Kevin didn't yet make the connection. 'And, there's quite a resemblance, too,' he added. 'It's uncanny… and immediately put me in mind of you.'

Kevin nodded distractedly. He would only consider the apparent resemblance later, in averring that Mary was actually the more attractive of the two.

'I'm guessing you've got more free time than I have?' Mr Johnson pursued. 'So, I was wondering if you might be able to show her round...'

After accepting the proposal, without much thought, Kevin was ushered to the door.

They met in Dave Johnson's cluttered office the following week, and – seeing the likeness for himself – Kevin was instinctively drawn. While the dark irises of her caramel eyes held steady, Kevin's gaze ran in admiration over the slim figure and stooped gait. The long chestnut hair that fell in waves across her thin shoulders, clinched it.

Bright and unabashed, smiling all the while, Mary looked Kevin over, too, before stepping forward to shake his hand, with a firm grip (showing no concern for the logistics). Kevin drew the squat fingers of his right hand from the trailing denim sleeve, to return the greeting.

'Pleased to meet you!' he exclaimed, his busy eyes flipping from David to Hazel (and back again), as though seeking approval.

'Likewise!' Mary returned, lickety-split.

The tone was careless and languid – Kevin already won – and, as they stood facing one another, he sensed an attraction and wondered if Mary could feel it, too. *She's lovely,* he mused, taken with the casual attire – the shorts and the sandals – as much as her engaging, off-the-cuff informality. There was definitely *something* about Mary.

It was left to the adults in the room to snap them out of it, reminding them of the need to exchange details if they were ever to meet up again.

'Got them printed last week,' Kevin explained, of the business card he handed across, taking the note, of a surprisingly elegant hand, that Mary passed him in return.

'See? Told you!' Hazel whispered, when she had him alone. 'They could be sisters!'

The recognition felt providential.

'It's uncanny,' he gushed to Karen, in his breathless report.

Karen was sceptical and, when she eventually saw Mary for herself, denied any such resemblance, insisting, 'She looks nothing like me – I don't know what you're talking about.'

Whatever the veracity of the claims, Mary would provide an engaging distraction from their increasingly confused relationship, with many of their friends already considering them too hands-on (and Andrew teasing about wedding bells).

Pawing at the air for her scent long after dropping her home – the van permeated – Kevin knew, too, that at thirty-six years of age (and, as her employer), he had no right to be thinking in such terms. If he understood that it was inappropriate, he never stopped to consider exactly why.

Mary – *immaculate* Mary – came with no strings and no such complications. This was a relationship founded on an equal footing, with the fact that she was single just an added fillip.

'Where do you want to go?' he would ask, with no other thought but to show her a good time.

'Surprise me,' Mary would return, with touching simplicity.

On their first trip, Kevin drove them out to the Albert Dock, insouciantly flashing his disabled badge at the yellow-clad security guard to secure them a free parking space right outside the trendy bar (which he then steered them into).

Over brunch – Kevin took a coffee and a cake; Mary, a salad and an 'English' tea – he started up on history, dropping his tone respectfully as he outlined Liverpool's links to the slave trade and the city's more recent fall from grace.

'It was like a ghost town in the eighties,' he concluded. 'The Tories didn't give a shit.'

'The Tories?' Mary asked, thrilled at the new phrase.

'Yeah, the Tories,' Kevin answered quickly, 'they're like the Republican Party in the US, but worse…'

Mary was smiling again – her new friend was engaging company.

When they turned off the dual carriageway, onto a wide, pock-marked road, they found themselves alone.

'Where are we?' Mary asked, frowning through the clouded windscreen.

'Dock Road,' Kevin said, pulling off to the side to explain how the dilapidated area around them, and the huge stone buildings, had once been buzzing with life. 'It was the most productive dock in Europe, at one time,' he continued, shutting down the engine before suggesting that they go for a closer look, the two of them scrambling over the rubble of miscellaneous debris until they reached the edge – the murky Mersey lapping at the sandstone walls below.

'It's awesome – so… *morbid*,' Mary giggled, 'and I never would have seen it if it wasn't for you.'

'It's a pleasure,' Kevin returned with a bow, hiding his smile, while Mary – with so much still to learn – wondered again at his accent. 'Shall we go?' he said, more softly, as though appreciating the fact.

'That would be a most splendid idea,' Mary replied, in her best Queen's English.

By the time he had dropped her home, they had already arranged to meet up again, Mary happily bobbing her head as she took Kevin's small fingers into her own and gave a brisk shake.

'I'm so glad we met!' she affirmed, to Kevin's obvious satisfaction.

For their next excursion, deciding on a trail closer to home, Kevin picked Mary up from her halls of residence and they headed off into the surrounding countryside, where fields of beet and barley lay spread over the horizon: the tight, winding lanes offering the chance to show off his driving skills.

They came back along the coast road, Kevin giving descriptions as they went.

'Formby pinewoods,' he declared, with a nod over his shoulder, 'famous for its red squirrels.' Mary gave a confused smile, as he continued. 'The recent arrival of the larger, American squirrel has

– of course – severely depleted their numbers.'

There seemed an irony here – Mary being American, after all – but they were already gone, chasing through a red light, Kevin pointing out St Mary's Church on the corner – and the large wooden cross fixed to the wall – before giving a potted history of the Blundell family (whose estate they were chasing past). 'And this,' he announced finally – with a sigh – driving those all-too-familiar streets on autopilot, 'is Crosby, for its sins…'

Pulling to a halt before his sister's modest terrace, with the engine still running, Kevin pumped on the horn to bring his nephew rushing out. Then, just as quickly, he spun around and took a left, before barrelling up over the train line, the setting sun – to the west – a blaze of fire.

They stopped when they ran out of road, scrambling through the sand and shale – Kevin skirting the dusty dunes – towards the beach and the dramatic twilight. The rising currents picked through Mary's hair and she struggled to set it straight, both of them laughing unheard into the whistling wind, before returning red and breathless to the van and its heaters (the temperature dropping). They ended their outing with a meal at the Punch Bowl, where – sat, in quaint relief, beside an old, spired church – Kevin was once more the master of ceremonies.

There would be more trips over the coming weeks, and – sharing references and confidences – they were soon wholly at ease in each other's company. Surprised at how quickly it had all come about – at how fond he had grown – Kevin was already looking to take the next step.

'I think I'm in love,' he told Karen – after doing the math – pointing out that Mary was not only single, but also had no plans to return to America.

'Be careful,' Karen said, 'I'm not sure I trust her.'

She caught his eye then, with a gently furrowed brow; the intervention came as a surprise.

'Why not? She's lovely.'

'I can't really put my finger on it,' Karen said. 'I just wouldn't want you to get hurt.'

'Why would I get hurt?' Kevin bristled. 'We get on brilliantly and Mary's great, she really is…'

Karen smiled then; couldn't help herself.

'Don't mind me,' she said, 'I'm sure she's very nice.'

'She is,' Kevin replied, 'and we really should all go out together, sometime.'

It was the first time he had considered it, and it was perfect, Kevin now arriving with a companion of his own, rather than sitting awkwardly between his two friends. The symmetry was pleasing; Kevin welcomed the assumptions. It was left to Karen to put Dan straight in private – when he said he thought they made a cute couple – delivering her rebuttal with unexpected force.

Believing that he had no choice but to act on the progress they had made, Karen's birthday – when they would all be out together – seemed the perfect opportunity. Looking back from the bar to the two girls, who were now friends, he knew he had to tell her.

Mary gave a wave, before continuing with her conversation.

'He's a post-grad, in his early thirties,' she said, '—and he's *gorgeous*…'

Karen dropped her drink to the table, edging closer.

'Since when?' she asked.

'About a month, or so,' Mary replied, with a grin. 'Hazel introduced us – he's her nephew.'

'And, does Kevin know?' Karen asked.

'Don't think so – why?' Mary returned, casually.

I was there that night too, but – when the decision was made to drive on into town – I asked to be let out and, acting on a recent invitation, headed over to my cousin's house instead. I still don't know why I went there, when I should have been with you, and I regret the fact.

Eventually accepting a lift that was going the same way, I already lamented the loss of that evening (as so many before it). When the driver set about showing off the capabilities of his ostentatious two-seater, reaching speeds of a hundred miles per hour on the dual carriageway, I turned to the window.

He dropped me a mile from home – had no intention of making a detour – and I was only glad that I would never have to see him again. There was frost on the ground, and – passing Dan's old flat (where we had spent many such nights together) – I looked in, hoping to find someone up… but the lights were out and the heavy curtains drawn against the cold.

I quickened my pace.

'It's all fucked up,' Kevin cried, when I stepped through to the lounge the next day, only briefly describing where they had gone (after I had left them) – two different nightclubs – and the state they had all been in, before moving on to the journey home.

He had dropped Mary off first, he said, pulling up outside her halls and cutting the engine. The moment had 'felt right', he told me, so – forgoing all caution – he had reached across, in one quick motion, and kissed her square on the mouth. He was breathing hard when he pulled away, could feel the beat of his pulse.

Mary hadn't moved, had barely shifted position. Kevin wondered, briefly, whether she was too drunk to even notice (and whether he should try again). When Karen dropped down to the kerb, to let her out, Mary shouldered her bag and the cool breeze seemed to revive her.

Kevin looked on with wide eyes when she turned.

'I'm sorry, Kevin,' she began, in a brittle tone, 'but you need to know that this isn't the way we do things in the US.'

'It was only a kiss,' Kevin replied.

'No, Kevin, it was more than that,' Mary snapped back, 'and, in America, we would never kiss anyone like that, especially not in public, unless we were going steady…'

Kevin could hardly look at her, but wasn't ready to give way.

'I thought we *were* going steady,' he said – returning her phrase (giving way to his anger) – 'I mean, we've been out enough bloody times…'

The derisive snort that followed told him everything he needed to know and he did well not to react, as the van fell silent.

'We're friends, Kevin, *good* friends,' Mary resumed, 'but, that's all we can ever be – and I'm sorry if I gave you any other impression.' He hated her – and that dumb American accent. 'Besides, I already have a boyfriend,' she said, adding insult to injury, and he no longer cared if he ever saw her again.

The rest of the drive, as he set about dropping the other passengers home, and the night – running through to a dull, grey morning – was an insensate blur. It was only Karen's calming presence that got him through. Letting Dan go into the house ahead of her, she finally turned to him.

'You don't have to say anything,' she said, and that was when the tears came.

It was three in the morning by the time Kevin reached home; the evening's events playing on, he could only sleep in snatches. By dawn, he was already out of bed and sat before his computer, working on an email of apology, glad that he wouldn't have to speak to Mary in person, that the internet offered such a direct form of communication.

His behaviour had been an aberration, 'a mistake', he wrote, after 'such a fabulous night' – he had misread the signs and regretted having let his emotions get away with him. He was sorry.

'I just hope we can go back to how we were before,' he concluded, shuddering at the hypocrisy of those grovelling words, '—that our friendship doesn't suffer.'

When Mary phoned – finding him at Karen's (where he had taken refuge) – she was calm and businesslike.

'It was probably just a cultural thing,' she allowed, and Kevin accepted the compromise, without believing it. 'I'll be going back to America soon, anyway,' she added. 'I'd hate to think of us parting on bad terms.'

'I thought you had a boyfriend?' Kevin snapped, wondering if she had ever considered him at all.

'Oh, well, yes,' Mary returned blithely. 'He'll probably come, too – we haven't decided.' Kevin's breath was tight, his head bobbing, as Karen rubbed a consolatory hand over his back. 'But, anyway, I was thinking we could maybe go out for a drink somewhere, later… to clear the air?'

Turning sheepishly to Karen, who showed her displeasure, Kevin ended the call.

'After the way she treated you, I can't believe…'

Kevin nodded, knowing only that he had to see it through.

'She's been good to me,' he explained, 'and I shouldn't have presumed…'

'But, she lied – she's had a boyfriend all this time.'

While valuing her friendship and opinion – and the way she had immediately taken his side – Kevin knew he had no choice.

'I just want to hear her out,' he said.

'Well, call me as soon as you get home,' Karen said, as Kevin turned his wheels, 'and, I swear, if she hurts you again, I'll knock her bloody block off!'

Crouching down to his chair to take his two hands into her own, such overindulgence set the tone, with Mary laughing along with Kevin's jokes and encouraging him to draw out stories that he no longer had any desire to tell. They were to go on as they had before, it seemed, except that now Mary was uncharacteristically affectionate.

Lost in the rush of conversation, and already slightly tipsy, it wasn't until Mary told him that she wasn't going back to America after all, but moving in with her boyfriend, James, that he saw the evening for the whitewash it was. *She's using me*, he thought, and it was all he could do to get through the next interminable hour, before claiming – then – that he had an essay to complete and needed to leave. There was no attempt at a kiss when he dropped her off, on this occasion. He felt nothing but disgust.

His anger grew as he drove away, imagining what that couple would be saying behind his back – how stupid he must have looked. *Bitch,* he muttered, as he rolled into his flat and retrieved the phone. The drive had sobered him; he could have no excuse.

'You've no right to see Mary behind my back,' he slurred – after finding James' number (in the telephone directory) and explaining who he was – 'and, she's a slut, anyway, so you're welcome to the bitch!'

He was shaking when he dropped the receiver and wrenched the cable from the wall. *Fuck,* he thought, knowing there would be consequences (but not caring).

He didn't reconnect the phone until the following afternoon and, when he did, it immediately started to ring. It was Dave Johnson, who suggested – in a sombre tone – that he needed to come in, first thing, to try to make amends.

'Calling James up like that was totally unacceptable… you're just lucky that Mary's been so understanding… that she's such a kind girl.'

Bowing his head in contrition the next day, Kevin admitted his fault on all counts, before offering an unreserved apology to all concerned.

'We were very disappointed,' Hazel put in, soberly, and he bowed his head again, wondering suddenly what any of it had to do with her, resenting such an intrusion into his personal affairs.

He hated both of them, but hid his contempt as he rolled out of the office. If his card had been marked, at least he now knew where he stood – and he welcomed the stipulation that he was to have no further contact with Mary, or any of her friends.

Running Karen through his trial and acquittal, later – after he had given himself some time to take it in – there was laughter on both sides.

'It was like being back at school,' he sneered, feeling free again, and regretting the way he had neglected the one person he could rely on. 'I mean, what the hell's it got to do with them?'

'Sod all!' Karen snorted, with laughter in her eyes.

Mary would call Kevin up again, three months later, to let him know that she was going back to America.

'I'd like to say goodbye, properly, if I can,' she said, 'because you were always very generous.'

Kevin agreed, out of sheer curiosity.

'I don't know why you'd give her the satisfaction, after the way she treated you,' Karen hissed, clearly irritated. Kevin was smiling, but didn't answer. 'And, I suppose you'll be expected to pick her up and drive her home again?'

Kevin nodded, recognising – even through his amusement – just how far Karen had his back (and moved by such support).

Kevin had suggested going for dinner, and he arrived in his best shirt, though as soon as he saw Mary – who slipped across, with tears in her eyes – he was pleased to find that he harboured neither resentment nor affection.

He ordered the most expensive bottle of wine and settled back in his chair, content to hear Mary rattling on about her various projects. He didn't care, and it was a relief to know that he genuinely had no desire to see her again. When she told him she'd write, he couldn't imagine what she could possibly have to say, but he nodded along and didn't contradict her.

He was exhausted by the time he dropped her home and utterly unmoved by her tears when she leaned in for a kiss, before hugging him close. He didn't turn to watch as she fitted her key in the door, before waving him blindly away. She was no longer of any concern.

Chapter 17

Kevin had not seen Shirley for the best part of six years by the time he had found a place of his own and moved out for good, though he had never quite lost hope that one day they would be friends again; believing too that, whatever else might transpire, there would always be a connection.

Thus, less than a week after arriving in his new residence – and impatient for the natural turns of fate – Kevin took up the phone.

'Thought it was about time we touched base,' he tried casually, reining in the delight of hearing her voice again, after all those years, encouraged by the fact that she seemed to welcome the call.

Interested to see how they would get on now that he was a fully-grown man – with his own flat (and a car) – he invited her over. He was getting ahead of himself, of course, though it all felt perfectly natural, until Shirley cut him short to ask, in all innocence, 'Can I bring my boyfriend?'

'Course,' Kevin dissembled, stumbling into a sorrow that surprised him, forcing the words, 'I'd like to meet him,' as though that was what he had intended all along.

Surely, when she sees me... he mused helplessly, considering that whatever she felt for her boyfriend couldn't compare with what they had once had – that no one could know Shirley like he did. The fact that he was now an adult, with a full and varied life, would surely put them on a new footing.

When Shirley – smiling warmly, as she bent over him – arrived with a very visible pregnancy, Kevin could have cried.

'You must be the boyfriend?' he said instead, offering a hand.

After sitting them down, Kevin stepped away to make the tea, glad of the chance to hide his face and settle his features. Spooning in the milk and the sugars with a casual air, he ripped into a pack of biscuits with his teeth.

'Tuck in,' he said, composing himself for what he expected would be a tortuous evening (hoping only that it wouldn't drag on).

He could hardly bear to look and, catching Shirley's eye, he had the impression that she could see right through him.

'How come you ended up here?' she asked, turning her head about the room.

'Moved in about a week ago,' Kevin replied, wondering at his earlier pride, blustering through his embarrassment. 'Told Geoff I couldn't stand it at home… that he needed to find me a flat, or I'd be moving into his office.' He was answering his own questions, holding off the inevitable. 'I didn't give him a choice, so here I am!' he concluded, with a chuckle.

He didn't think to explain who Geoff actually was, hoping that the confusion would muddy the waters. Sipping slowly at his tea, he momentarily imagined that he had the upper hand; *they don't know a thing,* he was assured, meeting Shirley's questioning smile with one of his own, watching as she cast about for something to say.

'I'm glad you've got your own place,' she offered eventually, 'but your mum must miss having you at home?'

Shirley, he remembered, was always thinking of others.

'Probably glad of the peace and quiet,' he bluffed – not about to elaborate – forcing enthusiasm, 'and, now that I'm working for the Welfare Advisory Service, I need my own space…'

He left it to Shirley to ask, as he knew she would, what this job actually entailed, and he drew it out, willing the time to pass.

'I always knew you'd be a success,' Shirley said, stroking at his shoulder as she took another biscuit and – though he tried to look pleased – Kevin understood and wondered why he was pretending (with the person he had once known such truth with). 'Kevin was always so clever,' Shirley told her boyfriend, 'and was always into the best music.'

'Still am,' Kevin shot back, recognising – for the first time – just how inappropriate it was to be reaching out to Shirley now, when he was finally making his way.

Trying for distraction, feigning an interest, Kevin eventually saw fit to ask about the bump.

'I'm due in about a month,' Shirley told him, laying a hand over her engorged waist; Kevin nodded back, as though this was something he could know.

'Do you live together?' he asked, seeking to make sense of the situation, his eyes flicking between the two guests, knowing that if he didn't ask now he never would.

'Not yet,' Shirley replied. 'We're still at my mum's… but we're saving up for a flat… for when the baby comes.'

Kevin understood, then, just how lonely he was.

'You'll need your own place, I suppose,' he acknowledged fatuously, lacking anything else to say: the reunion – he had held such hopes for – an excruciation.

Yet, paying respects to what had once been, he dragged it out, running through the changes made in the intervening years.

'It's strange how things move on,' Shirley conceded, cutting through the rest of their chatter, and – for a moment – she was Shirley Duggan and they were listening to music in his room again.

Catching his breath at those memories, Kevin nodded across, trying in vain to recall the girl he had once known. Pitched proudly beside her lover, with her waxy, red cheeks and swollen, blue lips, she was almost unrecognisable, and – in that moment – Kevin suddenly understood the falsehood he had been perpetuating all these years. *How could I have imagined Briar Moss would make any difference?*

'It's just temporary,' he found himself explaining, '—this place, I mean… until I find something better.'

Shirley's relieved look told him all he needed to know.

He had wanted them out from the moment they arrived, but – hiding his discomfort – he went on with it, seeming cheerful throughout. When his visitors started to talk as a 'couple', he was actually rather relieved, and led them on with open-ended questions.

'Shirley said you were independent, but I never imagined this,' the boy – and he really was a boy – interjected at one point, sweeping his hand about the room.

Kevin turned to Shirley, to confirm what he deemed a breach of trust; she didn't notice.

'It can get quite noisy at night,' Kevin conceded, a deft change of subject, making light of the high-pitched cry that sounded on the corridor.

'You're okay, though?' Shirley asked at last and – sensing her disappointment – Kevin nodded back, before reiterating that it was 'only temporary', as Shirley climbed carefully up to her feet and tendered a final, tentative smile.

She's lovely, he thought, as he led them out, her thick blonde hair in contrast to her boyfriend's bullish crop; remembering the pregnancy, he questioned how such a boy could possibly be the father.

'You must come again,' he rattled off politely (the past another country).

Eight months pregnant and already too many years late, Shirley turned to wave as she climbed into her car. Automatically flicking up his hands, Kevin held his smile. He never saw either of them again.

Stretched out on his already-made bed, Kevin groaned as he played back through the evening he had just endured. He was ashamed – humiliated.

Listening to the shouts and cries of the residents in the other rooms, the padded tread of the auxiliary staff and the doors pulled shut with a resounding clank, Kevin wondered – suddenly – what he was doing in such a place.

A sharp knock at his outer door brought him round.

'Hello?' he called firmly.

'It's me,' Barbara said, pushing in. 'I was wondering if your friends...' she continued, her eyes darting about the room.

'They left about an hour ago,' Kevin told her, propping himself up on a pillow.

Barbara Atkins, who had been the manager at Briar Moss for over two years, dropped into the armchair opposite.

'Would you like some?' she asked, indicating a bottle of wine.

'Why not?' Kevin replied, reviving.

Pressing a glass into the three fingers of his stronger right hand, he shuffled into position to take delivery.

'I've had a head start,' Barbara conceded, pulling a tumbler from one of her pockets, before pouring him a full measure.

'More?' she asked, when Kevin emptied it, and he nodded, his silence inviting the question he knew was coming. 'Who were your friends?'

'Well, I suppose you could say Shirley was the first girlfriend I ever had,' Kevin answered, with a darting glance.

'She seemed nice,' Barbara noted, 'and she was pregnant, wasn't she?'

'Eight months,' Kevin returned, simply.

Barbara moved closer, dragging the armchair to the side of the bed.

'Is it yours?' she asked, in an undertone.

'Course not!' Kevin cried, his eyebrows shooting up.

'I didn't mean anything… it's just… you're a man, after all.'

'We were just kids,' Kevin explained, 'and nothing actually happened… though I wish it had.'

That brought a smile.

'Then, why did she come here,' Barbara continued, 'and, with her boyfriend, too?'

She had poured them both another drink and joined him on the bed.

'I hadn't seen her in years – thought it was about time,' he paused, 'but I guess everything's changed… I hardly even know her anymore.'

'You mean, she's pregnant,' Barbara said.

'It's not just that – it's *everything*…' Kevin sniffed, as Barbara leaned across to take his head into her hands.

'It'll be okay,' she said, and for some reason he believed her. 'You've got your whole life ahead of you,' she added, running her fingers through his hair.

It was a relief to have someone to talk to – someone who would listen.

'You look like you need some more,' Barbara said, passing the bottle to Kevin, who tipped it back onto his chest to take a swig, coughing as he pulled it away. 'When was the last time you saw her?' Barbara resumed.

'About five years ago,' Kevin said, feeling something release.

'Five years!' Barbara spluttered. 'Well, of course she's bloody well changed – what did you expect?'

'I'm not sure – it's just…'

Barbara was lying next to him now and seemed in no hurry to leave, though he knew she still had her shift to complete.

'Can I ask something personal?' she resumed, drawing his cautious consent. 'I'm guessing you're not a virgin, but… when was the last time you had sex?'

The reply was automatic.

'August twelfth 1982.'

'Well, no wonder you're so bloody upset!' Barbara cackled, pushing further up the bed, drawing a smile. 'And, the sex must have been really good, if you still know the exact date!'

'I've only ever had sex once,' Kevin returned, seeing no reason not to tell her.

'Oh, you poor thing,' Barbara almost whispered, 'I really wouldn't have guessed… you've always seemed so mature, if you don't mind me saying…' Kevin shifted, as Barbara pulled him onto her chest. 'It's okay,' she said, rubbing a hand over his back, before brushing out her skirt and shifting back to the edge of the bed. Lying prone, Kevin felt exposed. 'We all have our problems,' Barbara resumed. 'Take the people in this place, for a start…' she chuckled, as another door slammed shut, 'and my life's hardly a bed of roses.'

'But, you seem so... *together*,' Kevin stuttered, sitting up.

'Things aren't always the way they appear,' Barbara replied, 'and, after twenty years of married life, it's hard to keep that spark.' She gave Kevin a look then, and he blushed. 'I don't really feel like much of a woman anymore,' she continued. 'I mean, we haven't had sex for over a year.'

'You're a very attractive woman,' Kevin told her, recognising the presumption before the words were out (recalling that her husband was a lawyer from Leeds).

'People move on... and they grow apart – sometimes, we're like strangers.'

'I'm sure you'll work it out,' Kevin said.

'No, not this time,' Barbara mumbled back, before breaking into tears.

She had dropped onto the bed again, and – when Kevin tried to comfort her – she moved closer, lifting her head onto his lap. Her breathing had grown deeper and he thought she was asleep. Then, she shifted, turning her head as she spoke.

'You're lovely... you really are – and that girl's making a mistake in letting you go.' Kevin swallowed hard, trying not to breathe, as Barbara sat up, brushing her hand down his chest, her fingers over his face. 'I don't know how anyone could refuse you,' she whispered.

When she pushed her lips onto his, and kissed him, he didn't move, accepting that when she pulled away again, it was nothing but a gesture of sympathy. When she resumed, he opened his mouth wide, to let her tongue in – clicking teeth – and then he was kissing her back.

'Well, that was a nice surprise,' Barbara declared, standing up to fix her clothes.

'Yes,' Kevin replied, savouring the taste of her – the mix of wine and tobacco – desperate to feel that soft mouth again.

'I'll call in at the end of my shift,' Barbara said, without turning, and Kevin, who gave no concern to their relative ages – they were twenty-one and forty-two – wondered if this was an affair. 'Shall I help you into bed?' Barbara resumed, with a smirk, Kevin dropping back to the mattress as she drew off his clothes (sharing a smile at the sight of his stiff penis).

His eyes wide and expectant, Kevin shuffled under the covers as Barbara put out the light.

It's like The Graduate, he thought, sitting up, too excited to sleep. He still had an erection and could hardly deny the fact that Barbara turned him on: that he wanted her.

The wait was interminable, though – announcing herself with a muffled rap – Barbara had returned within the hour.

'Kevin, are you still awake?' she called, in a contained cry.

Shaking with excitement at her soft tread as she entered his room, Kevin – listening to her clothes falling to the floor – didn't answer, or give any acknowledgement.

'Told you I'd be back,' she whispered, shuffling into the bed, her hands running over his chest and down to his groin, circling before taking hold. 'And, what have we got here?' she giggled. 'Looks like someone's pleased to see me.'

Kevin lay still – silent – as Barbara pressed her mouth onto his and kissed him. When she dropped lower – taking up his penis and rolling back the foreskin – he let out an involuntary whimper.

Shifting position, so that she was crouching over him, with her knees pressed into the mattress on either side, his partner guided him in, Kevin groaning in shock as much as pleasure. When he felt her breasts tapping at his chin, Kevin drew out his tongue, slobbering, as his mate rocked them back and forth.

She was wet, with everything so smooth inside, and – thrusting up from the hips – Kevin was already on the brink. If he had ever worried that Jane's heart wasn't in it, Barbara clearly wanted him just as much as he wanted her. This was lovemaking between equals, but Barbara was the one setting the rhythm, while Kevin simply bounced along – free and uninhibited.

'Easy, tiger,' Barbara hissed suddenly, bringing her hips to a halt.

'What? Are you okay?' Kevin asked in fright, blinking through the half-light.

'Yes, yes... just, *slower* – so you don't come,' Barbara said, before mounting once more.

The rhythm lost, Kevin almost immediately came loose, and – when Barbara rolled off to the side (fixing him a quizzical smile) – he thought the chance had gone.

'How do you like to do it?' Barbara asked.

'The bed's too bouncy,' Kevin answered, without thinking. 'I find it easier on the floor.'

Leaning across to kiss him, Barbara pulled the bedspread onto the carpet and helped him down.

Sex, it transpired, was just another practice that Kevin could perform in much the same manner as anybody else, given minimal adjustments (he was glad to report).

Barbara never got round to telling him that it was okay to come inside her because, with a shudder – his breath lost for the moment – he already had, his sticky semen drooling onto her fleshy thighs.

Giving a kiss to his perspiring brow, Barbara moved away.

'That was lovely – thanks,' she said, 'but, I'm on shift again at six, so...'

She had turned on the lamp and Kevin hardly knew where to look when she pulled on her tights before fixing her bra. *She's a woman – and married; and, old enough to be my mother.* Sworn to secrecy, Kevin was already wondering what his friends would think.

He was smiling when he rolled into the foyer the next day and he didn't care what anyone said. Barbara was sitting behind the desk, the whole room transformed.

'Morning, Mrs Atkins,' he called across.

'Morning,' she replied, before turning back to a colleague.

She had her hair up; was wearing a silk blouse.

Whistling a joyful tune, Kevin was hoping for curiosity when he wheeled across to his desk, at the office, but he was ignored, and eventually forced into giving his own account, describing – in detail – the evening he had just spent in Barbara's company (Shirley already forgotten).

Andrew was quick to disillusion him.

'She'll lose her job, if Social Services find out,' he said.

Nicky looked ecstatic.

'It's abuse – plain and simple,' she said, adding wistfully, 'but I wish someone would come and abuse me!'

'Abuse...' Kevin expostulated. 'How can it be abuse, if we're consulting adults?'

'Yes, but Mrs Atkins has a duty of care,' Andrew explained.

'She can't go around fucking every patient she takes a fancy to,' Nicky cried, 'when she's supposed to be looking after the poor buggers!'

Kevin turned his chair, indignantly.

'I'm not a patient,' he spat. 'Barbara's a friend... and, I live in the staff quarters.'

The distinction was lost on them, and – suddenly full of doubts – Kevin circled round to his desk, only speaking to Andrew again when he had him alone.

'I don't see what the problem is,' he began.

'I know, and you're right, but if anyone found out, Barbara would have to account for her actions.' Kevin was still shaking his head, as Andrew's tone softened. 'We should really give her an alias – to protect her identity,' he said. 'How about Doris? She looks like a Doris...'

Though Kevin refused the comparison, the office had soon made the decision for him, and the name stuck.

Returning to Briar Moss that night, Kevin was disappointed to learn that Doris had already left and wouldn't be back for three days. On the third night, he was waiting for her when she pushed in (he had left the door on the latch).

'You decent?' she said.

Offering her wine, from an expensive bottle – bought on Mr Black's recommendation – Kevin was grinning when he filled the glasses he had set on the table.

'Expecting someone?' Doris teased.

'I was hoping you'd come...' Kevin said.

'Well, here I am – cheers!' Doris replied, clinking glasses.

They fell to small talk, with Kevin already starting to doubt his memory of that night. Yet, starting up on a second glass, his eye was drawn to the flesh of Doris' legs, showing from beneath her short skirt.

'I'm up here,' she advised, 'and, I'm not just a pair of legs.' Kevin was blushing, as he offered his apologies. 'And, I'm surprised – I always thought you had more about you... what did you think – that I'd come over here, you'd pour me a glass of wine, and then we'd jump into bed again?'

'No, no – I'm sorry...'

'Well, that isn't how it works, Kevin – and, I'm disappointed, I really am.'

'I didn't mean anything... it was just nice to see you again.'

'Well, thanks for the drink,' Doris said, 'but I need to go,' slamming the door as she went, while Kevin stared insensibly after her.

He was glad of a second opinion the next day, but disheartened when his colleagues all sided against him.

'She's got a point,' Andrew said.

'What point?' Kevin cried, his arms flapping in exasperation.

'Well, she's married, for a start...' Andrew resumed.

'With two little kiddies,' Nicky added, for good measure.

'You can't just expect her to drop everything.'

He hadn't expected anything, but had thought that she liked him, at least.

When she called on him again – two days later – Kevin didn't hesitate, but bolted across the room to open up. He was encouraged by the familiar perfume, her steady-treading heels. He already had an erection.

'I'm sorry about the other night,' Doris said, before she had even taken a seat. 'I over-reacted… I'm all over the place at the moment.'

'No, no, I shouldn't have presumed…' Kevin replied.

'It's not your fault, Kevin. I genuinely am fond of you… and, the other night was lovely – just what I needed… but, I'm married, and the children are my primary concern.'

Kevin nodded, dropping his eyes.

When Doris leaned across to take his head into her hands, before pulling him down to her chest, there could be no more confusion. She was whispering, brushing her mouth over his ears – he couldn't make out the words – and then she was up on her feet again, securing the door.

She stopped, halfway back, dropping her skirt where she stood, and then the rest of her clothes, while telling Kevin to do the same. Within minutes, they were having sex (for the second time) on the living room floor.

Even in the throes of passion – and as wholehearted as ever – Kevin never imagined that he was in love. He didn't even fancy Doris that much, he admits, but he was not going to look a gift horse in the mouth.

An experienced hand was a help, too, with Kevin feeling able to experiment in ways he had not been able to before, exploring both his desires and his physical capacities.

'Can we try it from behind?' he was already asking, on their third turn, knowing that – given his particularities – he needed to be bold.

Doris was a willing accomplice, and – their passionate coupling effecting a subtle transformation – she was the woman who made a man of him, before all others.

Adultery is a habit, of course, and once started, the adulterers inevitably continued: up the stairs and down the stairs; up on the bed and down on the floor – sex, by all manner of manifestation. They were soon forgetting themselves, and – just two weeks in – were very nearly discovered *in flagrante.*

For greater privacy, they had taken their latest session up to Doris' room, and they were already halfway up the stairs when they heard footsteps on the corridor below. They stopped, and were waiting in place, when Mary – a care assistant – started to rap at his door.

'Kevin, are you in there?' she called, continuing into the silence. 'I'm just checking that everything's okay?'

The stranded lovers were only metres away, up a half dozen steps (to Mary's left), and – having thrilled to the sense of risk – they were naked, with Kevin's fleshy bulk now starting to slip, as Doris clung on.

Mary, who had taken a shine to Kevin from the start, knocked again, with more force this time, waiting – for what seemed an eternity – before turning around and padding away. Listening to her footsteps recede, the lovers could finally complete their ascent, Doris releasing Kevin to the floor just as soon as she had him inside.

'Another ten seconds and I would have dropped you,' she cautioned, her circulation returning.

'If Mary had looked up, she would have seen us,' Kevin muttered, the full ramifications not yet hitting home.

They were laughing again, when they mounted the bed – their pleasure tinged with relief – though it was only when they were parted, that they considered how close they had been to discovery (the blinkers of lust and desire lifting).

'If David were ever to find out…' Doris started.

Baring his teeth, in a mournful smile, Kevin wondered whether they would get a place together, then – if the children would come…

Rising and falling with eager squeals, while the bedsprings rang out, they were making feverish love again the following night, but that near miss had done its work. Though the association would continue for some months, the lovers would never venture up the stairs again, and they were already looking over their shoulders.

Chapter 18

Wheedling into his mother's numbed affections with what seemed like indecent haste, Mr Kirkwood had arrived a month or so after Kevin turned sixteen; an unwanted gift, he would still be there when Kevin turned twenty-one and – discerning the nature of that gilded cage – made the decision to leave.

'He'd be perfect,' the hairdresser had explained, 'especially now you're all alone in the world.'

Agnes blushed.

'And, with two hungry mouths to feed…'

'And Kevin, of course.'

'Yes, and Kevin…'

Her face exposed to the mirror, Agnes worried at the laughter lines and the crow's feet (the idea of a man having got her thinking).

'There's no reason for either of you to give up on your lives just yet,' the stylist resumed, 'and Jim – well, he's divorced… but, he's only just turned fifty and he really is quite charming.'

It was an optimistic note to end on, Agnes giving a final look to the finished cut before being helped to her feet.

With Agnes still considered vulnerable, Joan provided a chaperone, with the set intention of running a rule over the new man. Wanting no part, Kevin was surprised to find his mother applying lipstick and mascara with such care, filling the air with her perfume when she rushed out at the cry of a cab.

Stopping to look in through the window of the restaurant, Agnes was satisfied to find her date already there ahead of her, in a jacket, shirt and tie, his thinning hair slicked back. He smelled of Aqua Velva, she noted, when she was closer, wondering that he would go to such trouble. If she had been alone, she might well have left him there, but Joan had already placed a guiding hand around her waist.

Reconstructing the known biographical facts – that Jim was a divorcee, with an estranged son, who lived alone and played golf – Agnes was suddenly queasy. She reddened when he stepped up to greet her, pulling out her chair with a ceremonial bow.

'It's a pleasure to meet you, Agnes… I've heard such good things.'

This was clearly a serious proposal, with Jim explaining how he wanted to 'start again', within minutes (despite his date's reticence).

'That's nice,' Agnes replied politely, sipping at the wine she had uncharacteristically accepted.

He's presentable enough – dapper, she adjudged – taking another glass, already imagining how he might be accommodated. By her third measure, the evening sailing by, she had lost all sense of where she was and, when Jim helped her gallantly into the waiting cab, she blew a kiss and waved a hand.

'He's a real gentleman,' she declared, falling into her daughter's lap.

Back home, her head spinning, Joan had almost to carry her up to bed.

'She likes him and she's going to see him again,' Joan declared smugly, over breakfast.

Kevin shrugged, hardly able to credit that his mother could harbour such desires. Informed by little more than prejudice, he would declare Jim a 'creep', on first inspection and once they had seen their way past first impressions – weak wrist, feeble chin (nothing like their father) – Joan was inclined to agree.

'I don't know what Mum sees in him,' she said. 'But, she needs some company.'

'But she's got us…' Kevin returned, facetiously.

Jim moved in two weeks later and was giving advice as soon as he was through the door, suggesting to Kevin that he shouldn't be staying out so late (especially on school nights).

'Your mother doesn't like to say anything, but she's had such a hard time…' he would note, as though Kevin hadn't been there the whole time.

His eyes glazed, Kevin didn't argue. Sneaking home again, in the early hours, he also didn't comply, though – preferring disguise and misdirection – he knew better than to flaunt his intransigence (and suffer Jim's whining disappointment).

Regular meal times had soon been reinstalled, with the four current housemates bowing their heads, with smirks from the youngsters, when Jim first proceeded to offer grace. The unholy racket that Kevin continued to make up in his room, on his state-of-the-art stereo, was considered unchristian, with Jim suggesting that he take up classical music instead. Welcoming an ally, Agnes nodded eagerly, though neither of them had ever worried the gramophone (or, likely knew how to work it).

Kevin could only put up with such controls and limits for so long, especially once he had started work and felt, in all respects, an adult, who should be treated as one.

'I won't take the car,' he told them, on the evening he finally made his unwitting escape, 'and, don't wait up.'

'Do you want a lift?' Jim broke in.

'No, I'll take a taxi,' Kevin replied.

'Why throw your money away?' Jim weaselled, as Kevin dropped – silently – to the floor. 'If you tell me when you're finished, I'll come and pick you up… your mum will feel better, knowing you're safe.'

'I'm alright,' Kevin repeated, the sight of his mother's familiar tweed skirt and her thick, greying hair, giving pause: it was inconceivable that she could still think of him as a child; that she hadn't noticed how he had grown.

Jim followed him through to the hall.

'Shall we say half nine out front?' he tried, gamely.

'The party won't have even started by then,' Kevin replied, without turning, the thought of Jim beeping on his horn outside

Ellesmere House bringing an involuntary shudder.

'How about ten o'clock, then?' Jim resumed.

'I can get home fine by myself,' Kevin said, before darting up the stairs.

'Well, okay – but, any problems, just call. Do you hear?' Jim added, after getting no response.

'I don't want a lift,' Kevin called down from the top step, 'and I won't be ringing.'

He had no idea, then, that he would be leaving that house for the final time in less than an hour.

When a horn sounded out on the street – a people carrier, with wheelchair access – Kevin thumped down the stairs to meet it, brushing past Jim at the door. He hopped onto the back seat, leaving Jim to show the driver how to fold the chair.

It was a typical Donnellon exit – a circus – but Kevin held his tongue, smirking as he gave the address, having neglected to mention that he would be going to Mark's for a drink on the way.

Agnes and Jim were standing on the path to watch him go; Kevin would never appreciate just how much he meant to the thinning lives he was leaving behind.

'I'm not going back,' he hissed.

'And, a good evening to you, too,' Mark replied, with a bow.

Handed a can of beer, Kevin swigged it down without even saying thanks; Mark immediately handed him another.

By the time they reached Ellesmere House, they were already drunk and – after making a brief round of the room – Kevin already wanted to go.

'Shall we do one?' Mark said, sensing his discomfort, and Kevin nodded, trying not to catch Nicky's eye (though her inebriated shrieks were carrying from across the room).

Kevin was still complaining when they got back to Mark's flat (it had been agreed that he would stay the night).

'Go and see Geoff in the morning,' Mark suggested. 'I'm sure he'll be able to find you something.'

'If he can't, then I'm camping out in his bloody office,' Kevin snorted, Mark glad to see his humour return.

Waking – surprisingly clear-headed – to the smell of ground coffee, Kevin mounted his chair and headed towards the kitchen, where he found the breakfast laid out and Mark in his dressing gown. He was reading *The Guardian*.

'Morning,' Mark said, putting the paper aside. 'How you feeling?'

'Great,' Kevin declared, pulling into a bay, before buttering the toast that Mark dropped to his plate.

There was classical music playing on the radio; Kevin smiled at the wilful sophistication.

Mark dropped Kevin home, but didn't stay to watch as his friend darted furtively across to his car, which was parked on the front path of the family home. Turning the engine, Kevin backed out onto the street, his mother and Jim emerging too late.

'I'm not leaving until you find me a flat,' Kevin declared, bullishly.

'Well, okay then,' Geoff began – knowing the conversation of old – 'I guess we're just going to have to find you a flat…'

He smiled and Kevin smiled back (appreciating the wry humour of a man he considered a friend).

Kevin was still turning his head about the room, to settle his nerves after his recent flight, as Geoff reached up to a shelf for a thick file, which he flipped purposely through. Dialling, he motioned for silence.

'We don't seem to be having much luck,' he admitted, after the first couple of calls.

'Well, I'm not going anywhere,' Kevin maintained.

Geoff lit a cigarette, which he smoked through in silence.

'Briar Moss!' he cried, then. 'I don't know why I didn't think of it.'

'Where's that?' Kevin asked, quickly.

'In Litherland, near The Cabbage,' Geoff replied, having already opened up the Yellow Pages.

'And, what is it?' Kevin asked next.

'It's a home for the mentally disabled,' Geoff told him, pushing on despite Kevin's frown, 'but there's a separate wing for the staff – and that's where you'd be... in a self-contained flat... all fully accessible, of course.' He had found the number and was dialling. 'It's a temporary measure, remember.'

Kevin moved in that same day, with Joan bringing some of his clothes from home, though it would be two months before Geoff had found him somewhere more permanent (a room at Leonard Cheshire).

Already settled at Briar Moss by then, Kevin didn't share his enthusiasm – he didn't even want to move anymore, having clearly forgotten the temporary nature of his current accommodation.

He was given no choice but to drive over with Geoff, to '*see* the place, at least'.

'What do you think?' Geoff asked, with a nod towards the large, grand-looking property that sat behind a crisp lawn.

'It's alright,' Kevin mumbled, noting – with a sniff – the mock Tudor design, as he pulled into one of the disabled bays (there were any number).

It's a hospital, he thought, noting the barred windows and heavy, leaded fire doors. With his mind on the free run he enjoyed at Briar Moss, Kevin was paying close attention. Chasing up the path after Geoff, who had gone on ahead, he already considered Leonard Cheshire a demotion.

'You're Kevin, I take it?' the manager said, by way of greeting.

Kevin caught a look then, and – heading back to the car after the demoralising tour that followed – he wouldn't forget it.

'I like Briar Moss, now,' he started, directly. 'I feel at home.'

'But you can't stay,' Geoff explained. 'The authorities are on my back and they need you out. So – please – just sleep on it, at least.'

Kevin didn't need to sleep on anything – could already feel a knot in his stomach at the thought of being moved against his will. He was tired – soft, stuck in his ways.

'You sound like one of the residents,' Doris had recently teased, when Kevin had complained about the late arrival of his lunch.

'Well, I like things to be on time,' Kevin muttered irritably, pushing up out of bed.

Doris tutted.

'And to think, at your age I was out every night snogging boys – not sitting around, waiting to be fed. You'll be institutionalised, if you're not careful – like in *One Flew Over the Cuckoo's Nest*!'

They had been through this discussion before and he couldn't really argue, with those same words ringing through his head when he took the tour of Leonard Cheshire (which was a step too far).

They had been shown into the communal living area first, where a TV was blazing from a stand against the far wall, with a handful of residents lounged before it. An elderly man was drooling in his sleep, with a book on his lap, while another had a drip hanging from his nose. Kevin had seen enough, but on they trudged.

The dining room was bare and basic, with the places set in strict rows, while the bathroom had a rota pinned to the wall – Kevin recalling the baths he and Doris enjoyed.

The bedrooms looked like cells, with Kevin struggling to get his chair in, or out, before the heavy metal door whipped shut at his back. Having already made up his mind – Leonard Cheshire was a non-starter – Kevin left the formalities to Geoff and, walking back to the car ahead of him, was glad to be free of the place.

'It was horrible,' he declared, on his return to Briar Moss, drawing an audience of the staff. 'I can't believe Geoff thinks I could actually move into a place like that,' he added, indignantly.

'Geoff's got no right,' Doris declared. 'You can stay here for good, as far as I'm concerned.'

The room fell silent. Kevin blushed – knowing what he knew – but was relieved all the same.

'Geoff said I've got no choice…'

'Well, Geoff's going to have to deal with me, if he wants you out,' Doris assured him, stepping across to plant a kiss full on his lips before clicking away.

Kevin turned his wheels in embarrassment.

Having refused to even consider Geoff's offer, Kevin was soon just as entrenched at Briar Moss, as ever. He had only won the battle, however, and would return from work the following week to find that steps had been taken in his absence.

'What's going on?' he asked, his head turning left and right at the sight of two trainee students sprawled out on the sofa.

'Oh, hi – didn't they tell you?'

'Tell me what?'

'That you've got new flatmates!' one of them announced, with a cheerful smile.

Giving up his spacious double, Kevin was to be moved into the smaller single, with the council authorities seeking to force his hand. The strategy proved ill-judged, with Kevin finding new friends in those same students, who were of a similar age and temperament.

'Black in the middle,' he announced, before lining up the cue and potting the winner, in his own inimitable fashion.

They were playing on the table that one of the students had brought from home and Ahmad, one of the care workers, was already racking the balls for another round.

'Can't – stuff to do,' Kevin said, hurrying him out, having decided – in the weekend absence of his flatmates – to invite Doris over instead; they'd had hardly had a minute together since the change of living arrangements.

It would be one of the last nights they ever shared.

Doris was right about Kevin and the fact that he was now a part of the furniture at Briar Moss, and Geoff was no doubt doing him an inadvertent favour in seeking to move him on. Kevin's intransigence would, however, lead to an improved offer, with Hornby Housing Association eventually ringing through to explain that one of their wheelchair-using residents had recently passed, leaving behind a vacant and – crucially – an *adapted* flat.

Keening for the security and freedom that Briar Moss refused, Kevin accepted without hesitation and he was bouncing about in his chair as he let the phone go, only then acknowledging the stress of their ongoing dispute.

The timing felt right, too – Doris' point about his institutionalisation was valid enough – while the sex they practised had ultimately run its course (being a thing of habit now, and little more).

He was pleased that Doris sought him out, on his final day, to suggest that they do something.

'For old times' sake... Can you get rid of the boys?'

'They're working tonight, anyway,' he told her, his pulse quickening at the thought of having her one last time.

Doris kissed gently down on the top of his head before wheeling him out to his car, and he could still smell her perfume when he turned onto the dual carriageway, considering – with a degree of pride – just how much he had grown these past few weeks. He was a man, now – that could no longer be denied.

He returned to candlelight, soft music and a chilled bottle of wine – and he was surprisingly sentimental.

'I see you've made yourself at home...' he teased.

'Someone had to give you a proper send-off,' Doris returned with a smile, and, as Kevin took a turn about the room, they were both, suddenly, shy.

'We must keep in touch,' he said, accepting a glass of wine.

'Oh, we will,' Doris assured him. 'You don't get rid of me that easy!'

There was sadness, in that – it was Doris, after all, who had given him the strength to walk away. He was grateful – had no regrets.

They were laid out on the single bed together when Doris broke into tears.

'It's okay,' Kevin said, resting his fingers on her shoulder as he turned, while Doris dropped her face to his chest.

Damp with tears, she lay motionless, and – feeling the moment – Kevin thought to tell her what he imagined she wanted to hear.

'I love you,' he said, and Doris was almost immediately up on her feet again, bestowing a final kiss with a crooked smile.

He was relieved to find that she wasn't on shift the next day, when he packed his bags into the cab and made what felt like an escape. She was already visiting him a week later, however.

'Thought I should come over and see how you're getting on,' she said.

Pushing through each of the rooms in turn, Kevin welcomed the chance to show her round, while Doris – who had placed dozens of clients into accommodation, in her time – brought her professional eye to proceedings (checking the fittings, the ramps and the revamped shower).

'This is marvellous,' she declared, when they had completed the tour. 'It's clean, comfortable… and the modifications seem up to scratch. You must be pleased?' Kevin could hardly keep from smiling, as he nodded back (considering, again, that his own mother had refused to come). 'I take it you still know how to make a cup of tea?' Doris added brusquely, sending Kevin hopping off to the kitchen.

Kevin liked Doris, though within an hour he was driving her back to the salubrious semi that she shared with her husband (and two children) in West Derby and returning to Nunsford Close without a second thought.

Two years later, he would call her up again, in desperation.

'Everything's fucked,' he bellowed. 'I don't know who else to talk to.'

'Well, I'm glad you thought of me...' Doris began.

He didn't let her finish.

'It's Klara, the bitch...'

'Okay, but you need to calm down,' Doris broke in, and the tone was enough. 'We're just having dinner, so why don't you drive over in an hour or so, and then you can tell me all about it?'

Kevin raced across the hall to answer the phone, when it started to ring again – thinking it must be Klara (calling to apologise).

'Yes? Hello?' he cried, high-pitched.

'How you doing, mate?' a familiar-sounding voice asked, though it was only after another line or two that Kevin remembered Ahmad: a stranger these past two years.

'What do you want?' he asked, impatiently.

'Doris asked me to phone – to check you're okay,' he explained. 'Said you could do with some support?'

'What?' Kevin puzzled, as the arrangements were made for them to go over together.

He hadn't once considered the husband, but it was his music that could be heard coming from the house as they walked up the path (the keys tapping at his conscience).

'Don't mind David,' Doris said, as she led them in past the piano.

Kevin blushed, the very idea of Klara – and their tempestuous, off-and-on relationship – seeming absurd in such a peaceful domestic setting.

Mechanically turning his chair, Kevin forced a smile as he rolled past the two, tousled children, who were standing to attention at either end of the piano, before parking up in silence.

'Are you still working?' he heard Ahmad ask, as his attention drifted towards the music – Beethoven's *Appassionata* (though he didn't know it) – his mind running through the particulars of his latest fight with Klara.

By the time Doris had made them drinks and directed them to the sofa, the musicians had already plunged into the second movement (a beautiful, lilting passage).

'So, how's Briar Moss?' Doris pressed Ahmad, while glancing across at Kevin. 'Has it changed much since I left?'

Kevin didn't interrupt, but when Doris asked if he would like to see the garden, there was a sudden shift in tone.

'I need five minutes with Kevin, if you don't mind,' she told Ahmad, who nodded back in confusion.

With the thick curtains drawn against the encroaching dusk, they were soon sat outside, with their backs to the patio doors. Recalling the reason for his visit, Kevin was initially hesitant.

'It's a long story,' he sighed.

Doris took his hand into hers – told him to take his time.

'We've got all night…' she chuckled, releasing him.

Kevin finished off in silence, his eyes in his lap. Doris moved closer.

'You're worth a dozen of that woman,' she said.

'But, I love her…' Kevin moaned, lifting his eyes again.

There was silence then, as Doris placed a finger on his lips and a hand on his thigh before leaning across to kiss him.

'God, I've missed you,' she said.

Shifting position to make room as Doris climbed on top, Kevin noticed the curtains flapping in the window behind her (as small hands prised them apart).

'Watch out!' he hissed, pushing her off as Christopher's soft-featured face loomed through the steam of the glass, his hand giving a wave before he was whisked away. They only noticed then that the music had stopped and the night was drawing in.

'We'd better go back in,' Doris said.

Watching as David took their children up to bed, wishing them goodnight over the banister, Kevin felt his exclusion more than ever.

'I'll call you a cab,' Doris told Ahmad.

Kevin wondered if he should go, too, but a bed had been made up for him on the floor before the taxi had even arrived. Doris joined him there, once Ahmad had taken his leave – the house silent but for the rumble of pipes.

'I missed you so much,' Doris said, brushing up close.

When she kissed him, the excitement of Briar Moss came flooding back, but Kevin somehow pulled away.

'I'm tired,' he said, softly. 'I think I'm just going to sleep, if that's okay?'

'Of course,' Doris said, her voice traced with sadness. 'You've clearly moved on… and I can understand that you'd prefer to be with someone your own age.'

'But you're married,' Kevin reminded her, 'and you've got children.'

Without another word, Doris kissed down on the top of his head, before heading quietly up the stairs.

Waking to the shrill shriek of children and thumping, hurried feet – and remembering where he was – Kevin knew that there was no point staying in bed.

'We're leaving in about ten minutes,' Doris called from the kitchen.

Wriggling free of the covers, Kevin buttoned his shirt and hitched up his pants, before climbing into his chair and wheeling through.

Doris dropped a piece of toast onto a plate and brought it across, placing it next to a scalding cup of coffee; the children, gratifyingly, were too busy with their cereal to even care.

'Bags… packed lunches,' Doris directed, as they dropped to the floor. 'Ready?' she said then, to Kevin, who immediately backed out.

Doris saw Kevin out to his car, to make sure that the lift

mechanism didn't stick, before waving him away through a fine film of rain. It was the last time he ever saw her.

Chapter 19

Born of Irish immigrants (the youngest of five), John Richard Donnellon would be shovelling coal into the industrial boilers at Gladstone dock by the age of fifteen.

Pushing against narrow expectations, he attended evening class at the same time, with the two-year Engineering course he completed securing him the position of chief engineer (for Ray's Tugboat Company) and the responsibility for the twenty-two diesel engine tugs that operated out of those moorings. His promotion brought a domestic upgrade, with the family moving to Litherland Park (and a different sort of life).

Built in the inter-war period, the bungalow they purchased there was a picture-book property that cost around £12,000 (in 1968), with modern estimates putting the value at somewhere nearer £300,000. A steep, privet hedge marked the boundaries of their sizeable grounds, with the striped lawn at its south-facing rear leading down to an orchard of annually fruiting trees (pears and plums). A gnarled old Grenadier stood in the corner and, in the summer months, the air would swirl with its airy pink blossoms (amid the strains of cider).

Describing a horseshoe, with the arched toe breaking into the two branches that lead to the heels, Litherland Park connects to Sefton Road at two different points. Sandstone pillars mark the entrance to the original keeper's lodge, though the Second World War's desperate call to arms had required the removal of wrought-iron gates that proved too heavy to take flight.

There was history and security – and peace – in those Elysian suburbs and, in an apprenticeship that raised the hackles of unrealistic expectation, Kevin was spoilt rotten.

A powerful, dominating presence – and the still heart of the marital home – John Donnellon had long since conceded the talking ground to his wife (ground where he felt neither the need, nor the desire, to assert himself).

Thus, when the 4-tube, colour EMI 2001 cameras first came to call (for documentary purposes), in the autumn of 1972, and panned slowly over the living room, Mr Donnellon could be seen leafing, unperturbed, through the previous day's red top. His high-boned face was unyielding.

With his children, he was firm but fair, with the merest indication (of the threat) of a belt, sufficient to the belt itself – which he never had reason to use – just as the mere suggestion of a raised voice was enough to bring order.

Kevin's arrival would provide further strains to a marriage which was already in its tenth year. The financial ramifications of providing for a fifth child, whose disability necessitated a host of additional costs and considerations, was difficult enough, without accounting for the emotional burden of such a child. There were three reported suicides (and more, unreported) of mothers who had given birth to thalidomide children, while over half of those marriages would eventually end in divorce.

Agnes never really forgave herself, yet Kevin, who would enjoy a happy and innocent childhood, rarely suffered the presumed hardships. Plied with sandwiches and fizzy pop whenever they came to call, his friends would look on Kevin's living quarters with envy, with his train set a particular cause for admiration. He had been treated to an upgrade, after the move from Coronation Road, with the complex trail of rails running the full length of a specially mandated room.

'Come and see,' his father, the chief architect, had said – his eyes giving way to pleasure – as Kevin, who thought the trains were still in the boxes he had packed them in, shuffled excitedly after him.

'Wow,' was all he could think to say, when he was lifted up to see.

Taking his place on an elevated platform, behind the litter of controls – with everything within reach – Kevin had quickly made the place his own, spinning the trains with a concentrated eye.

The sloping, dormer roof at his back was sky-blue, with alto-cumulus clouds dotting the jagged alpine peaks of some generic mountain range and plastic Swiss chalets lining the track.

There were no qualms over topography: in Kevin's world, regular station platforms, with ordinary passengers waiting for ordinary trains, would find helicopters and planes, zebras and hippos (escaped from some imagined zoo), all competing for space and attention. Best of all, like a God from above – his imagination running wild – were the dramatic pile-ups that would result, when he set the trains racing head first, scattering the miniature human figures to left and right, as a variety of paint-chipped vehicles were sent to the rescue. There was something appealing in such wilful destruction, Kevin setting up a racket that would more often than not bring his parents charging up the stairs.

Having already taken two trips up to Edinburgh by rail (to be fitted for his prosthetics) and several more down south (to the chambers of London lawyers, in their continuing fight for justice) – journeys he would pass gazing, rhapsodically, from the window – Kevin knew about trains.

Naturally observant, he took in what he could, seeking out first-hand knowledge from passing inspectors, who – seeing Kevin, and noting his interest – would generally stop to introduce themselves.

'And how fast can the train actually go?' Kevin would quiz and, 'What's the quickest train in the world?'

The top speed was always the most pressing concern, Kevin receiving a pat on the head and a ruffle of the hair, but persisting.

'Would you like to keep it?' one of those guards asked, holding out an official British Rail whistle as they pulled out of Crewe, and Kevin could hardly speak for excitement, nodding instead, as the prize was tied about his neck.

Commandeered with ever-increasing authority, the toot of that whistle carrying down to the lounge, Kevin would spend a great part of his childhood turning trains about this track (to which new pieces would be added every few weeks).

If he ever tired of his locomotives, Kevin had only to cross the landing and make for the second of his playrooms. Here, there were Action Men, or he could massacre an army of tin soldiers, but – more often than not – he would read, lifting up books that were bigger than he was (in the company of the family's West Highland terrier). Kevin was self-sufficient – had a nature that could occupy itself, just as much as it could draw every eye in the room.

In the holidays, his mother would be forced to seek him out.

'I've done you a boiled egg and toasty fingers…'

Dropping his toys to floor, Kevin glanced across.

'Is the egg runny?'

'Just the way you like it,' Agnes returned, as she crept back down the stairs.

Whatever the financial limitations, with the family mortgaged to the hilt of their income, Agnes was determined that Kevin, who was kept in all the material comfort their budget allowed, would never know it. If they scrimped and they saved, Kevin – who seemed to get everything he asked for – could never tell.

Agnes wanted little on her own account, but – suffering the guilt of grief – she increasingly turned to sleeping pills and tranquilisers. When the parents argued, there was relief in releasing their recriminations.

'You didn't carry him for nine months,' Kevin would hear (carrying up the stairs), 'you didn't give birth to him…'

His father's familiar voice would follow, advising Agnes to calm down, though John was gladdened to see the fiery woman he had married, in a flash, fifteen years before, briefly returned. There were words said, on either side, that they would both come to regret and wish to retract, though every parsed phrase would ultimately bring them closer. Bound hand to foot to a grief that no one else could possibly know, they couldn't have gone on alone.

'On 7 November 1976… just before my fifteenth birthday,' Kevin replies, writing the obituary. 'I think the last thing he ever said to me was 'behave yourself, son,'' he added, recalling the fact that he had been sent, once more, to Aunt Lucy's.

He wasn't to know and, having spent the summer circling ever closer to Shirley (his first love) – with eyes only for her – the impact was softer, when it came. The slow and unexpected withdrawal of his father would almost pass the teenager by.

Sent home sick from work for the first time in his adult life (in October), John was as implacable as ever. There was no suggestion of the pain and the sorrow below the surface in the gruff, cloaking cough that indicated that he should be left well alone.

'What's wrong with Dad?' Kevin had finally deigned to ask.

'Your father's poorly,' he was told, 'but don't worry, he'll be back on his feet again soon.'

Agnes was keeping to the story. Lacking any sense of time or mortality, as yet, Kevin took the words at face value, with the consequences only properly felt in the years to come.

It was Joan who eventually sat him down to explain that his father had fallen at work and cracked his head on the concrete floor. Taken to the canteen to recover, he had refused to see a doctor and was back in work the next day (at dead on seven).

Complaining of headaches and dizziness, John had known there was something wrong, even as he denied it.

'You have cancer,' the doctor told him, the following week, 'most likely brought on by your fall.'

'Is there anything I can do?' he asked.

'At this point, the best we can offer is palliative care,' the doctor said, giving his prognosis. 'You'll need to inform your family.'

They shook hands at the door, John's grip still firm.

Fighting back tears on the return drive, he wondered how he could possibly tell his wife, or his children – and, what would become of them. The conversation proved simple, in the end, with practical matters taking precedence.

'We need to prepare,' he advised, 'but I don't want Liz and Kevin to know anything, just yet… we shouldn't worry them, until it's absolutely necessary.'

Shocked into silence, Agnes embraced her husband. Pulling away, John suggested she make a start on the dinner.

Kevin remembers very little of those final weeks and, to this day, he wishes he had known. He was told, simply, to leave his father in peace, which he did, hunkering over his revision books during the week and meeting up with Shirley at the weekend.

When he would, on occasion, look in on his father, he would find him curled up on the bed, or coughing into his hands. Sometimes his mother would suggest that Kevin keep him company, and he was happy to. With the curtains drawn, even in the day, it was like entering a crypt.

'Dad?' called into silence, before clambering onto the bed.

'Son?' his dad, shifting in answer, his eyes suddenly youthful.

They would sit and watch TV together then – *Opportunity Knocks* or *George and Mildred* – on the small, portable set that had been moved in. He couldn't have said why that time was so precious, but he knew it, somehow.

In the breaks and the lulls, Kevin would tell his father about his friends at school and the books he was reading.

'And, you're happy?' his dad asked, in one of their last conversations – turning – and there were tears in his eyes. 'In life, I mean…'

'Yeah, fine,' Kevin returned, blasé, 'but I can't wait for the holidays.'

'You're a good lad,' his father croaked, drawing Kevin onto his broad chest, before they were separated by a coughing fit.

His father had undoubtedly changed, but such were the distractions at that time, that Kevin could hardly see it, and – as the weekend trips to Aunt Lucy were gradually stepped up – he was allowed to forget.

'Best behaviour, now,' his mother would advise, kissing at his head, mussing up his hair.

Kevin would groan, failing to see what all the fuss was about – he had been enough times, by now – never imagining that his mother wanted him out of the house because of his father.

Aunt Lucy, who was no relation, had accepted that she would most likely be the one to break the news. In what proved a sombre game of musical chairs, the music would finally draw to a close on the following weekend, with John's condition having deteriorated substantially over the preceding twenty-four hours.

Kevin was surprised to find Aunt Lucy waiting on the yard when he wheeled out of class.

'What are you doing here?' he asked.

'Your mum's got a lot on,' Lucy said, 'so you're staying with us.'

'I haven't packed...' Kevin started, thinking of being stuck in his school clothes all weekend.

Lucy explained that she had already been to his house, to pick up what was needed, and they were soon chasing down the road again, scooting past the head teacher's car (in the outside lane).

Given the news in the early hours of Monday morning, Lucy had decided to wait until Kevin was up and dressed, and he was already in his uniform when he joined her (his blazer hanging over the back of his chair, his school tie drawn in a fat knot). She let him finish his breakfast, before directing him into the living room.

'Have a seat,' she said, as Kevin reversed into place and she considered how little trouble he was. 'Something awful has happened,' she began, 'and, your mum will need you to be strong.' Kevin nodded, and – in two or three stuttering sentences – she told him. He nodded again – blinked; seemed to be taking it in. 'There was nothing anyone could have done,' she said finally. 'Your father was at peace in the end.'

It wasn't true – John had suffered immeasurably over those last few hours: grinding his teeth beneath his heavy jaw; forcing his bulk up, as his family looked on; a man who had always taken everything in his stride, now barely able to move.

The truth lost to the sheer rush of emotion, Agnes would offer similar assurances, telling Kevin that his father had looked 'peaceful, when he went'.

It seemed that his father had merely gone away, and might be back.

Kevin heard the words, but could think of no response. Aunt Lucy's eyes were swimming with tears and he felt like he should offer some consolation.

'Am I going to school?' he asked instead.

'No, Kevin – not today.'

He understood that, at least.

Father's dead, he thought, trying it out, before turning back to Aunt Lucy, gratified to find tears of his own. He considered his uniform, laid out beside his bed that morning; the essay that was due. He was in his final year of secondary school.

'Let it out,' Lucy whispered, as Kevin sobbed freely now, his mind drifting momentarily to Shirley.

As the man of the house, Kevin had presumed that he would be expected to step up, but instead he was shut off from everything that followed. Kept home (with Aunt Lucy), he attended neither the funeral – at English Martyrs – nor the wake, with his return to school delayed by several weeks.

His sister Liz, who had remained at the family residence throughout (with the curtains drawn against curiosity) had no more involvement than he did, though she would find herself inadvertently attending the very funeral she had been kept from, when her class – quite miraculously – made an impromptu visit.

'Come along now, girls, and silence, please,' the teacher instructed, leading them into the chapel, a chill striking at their collars as they respectfully removed their hats.

A run of giggles passed through the ranks – at hymn books, casually upended – Liz in the thick of it, and they were warned to behave (a stern eye passing over the pews).

They were sat towards the rear, at an oblique angle to the main group of mourners, who now lifted their veils before rising to their feet for the hymn: *The Lord's My Shepherd.*

That was when – standing, too – Liz saw them.

It seemed they were speaking in tongues, but there was her mother, and her brother, and her sister; her uncle; her grandfather (who had recently been unwell).

'He lays me down to lie,' she mouthed the words like a mute, taking no further part.

Ushered out at the end of the service – with time losing all meaning – they were marched back to school in orderly double-file, the prim pleats of their skirts billowing in the breeze.

Lara was trying to tell her something, she realised, but she couldn't make it out. The boater's blue ribbon beat at the wind; her gaping mouth catching at the salt on the sea air.

'Mum…' Liz whispered, the fingers of one hand reaching for her friend, while the other moved, instinctively, to her hat (to set it straight).

They couldn't stop, weren't even permitted to turn, and there was no one to ask as they took their places at their desks for the next class: matriculation.

She had seen them, of course – known their faces even through the crisp veils – but it didn't seem like they had seen her and it was already too late, with Liz wondering (in later years) whether she hadn't imagined the whole event.

With Agnes struggling, the children were left to their own devices.

'Go and play,' aunts or uncles (they couldn't place) would direct, with no account given to the fact that they were teenagers now and not so easy to distract.

With the extended family long-since dispersed, Agnes had no one to help and, as executor, she was expected to put aside her grief and carry right on. Thus, Agnes would organise the wake and the service that followed – with sandwiches for the mourners – while also taking up the invitation to pick out a headstone for the family plot. The house was full of flowers she couldn't smell.

They say it's good to keep busy.

Laid to rest on the drizzly morning of November 14, John Donnellon joined his parents, Lillian and John, and his sister, Ellen – who had preceded him by three years – in Ford Cemetery, on Sterrix Lane.

Ten years later, Kevin would be moved into a flat that backed onto that same graveyard and he would often take a stroll through the grounds, though he would never seek out his father's resting place. His mother's ashes would be interred there, too (in April 2017).

'There's nothing to worry about,' Agnes assured him, numb to the truth of it. 'We'll be okay if we stick together.'

She had no idea, and – on the advice of the family doctor – she was soon taking Valium to calm her anxiety.

'I don't think she ever recovered,' Kevin now contends, his mother no longer here to offer a defence. 'She was never really the same.'

Following Agnes's subsequent breakdown, it was decided that Kevin would remain with Aunt Lucy for an extended period.

'Your mother needs some time,' he was told, recalling that the same had been said of his father.

His departure offered little comfort to his mother. Needing anchors of a greater weight, now that her world had fallen apart, Agnes kept stridently to her routines: the dishes in the sink following a dinner (that she could barely taste); the steaming iron and the rumbling wash cycle.

Worst of all was the mid-afternoon lull when, picking up the phone in the anticipation of hearing another voice, she would lose all hope, and – crawling up onto Kevin's bed – she would try to sleep it off.

Sometimes, surprised by the silence, she would call out his name – thinking *oh, he's at school,* before remembering that he was gone. She thought back to the hospital, when Kevin had been taken away (confusing past and present), while poring through the clothes in his wardrobe and seeking him out in the records still stacked on the sideboard. When, increasingly helpless, she sought relief in medication, it was Joan – who had recently moved home – who found her, tapping colour into her drawn cheeks.

Kevin wasn't told. His mother had already remarried by the time he learned of the attempt, his hindsight bringing a more generous understanding of what he had taken, at the time, as a rejection.

'We tried to keep you out of it,' Joan explained, 'because Mum couldn't cope.'

Kevin had always liked Aunt Lucy, so moving into her sizeable semi in Maghull, even for an extended period, was no great hardship. He liked the family too: talking war and trains with Uncle Barry (an engineer at Ford's), while Clive, their son, was the big brother he never had.

With his mother still struggling, the stay was extended indefinitely, and – revelling in his new-found freedom – Kevin no longer asked when he was going home. It was 1976, and he had priorities of his own, with Shirley, and their trips into town (which his new carers actively encouraged), uppermost, while the end of the year would bring public examinations.

Events unseen would soon outstrip him, however, with all interested parties coming to the settled belief that Kevin would be better off living with Mr and Mrs (Lucy) Jones full time.

'Adoption?' he asked, in surprise.

'Yes, we think it's the best option, in the circumstances,' his aunt replied, sharing a look with her husband, who was standing to the side, 'and, it would certainly give your mum peace of mind, to know that you're being properly cared for.'

The turntable was turning, but the record had finished.

'Will I have to change my name?' Kevin asked, at last, his eyes wandering.

'Yes… I suppose… if you like,' Lucy returned, with a smile. 'You'd be Kevin Jones – doesn't sound too bad, does it?'

Kevin gazed back at her – he had never much liked 'Donnellon'

– thinking that this could be the reinvention he had always wanted.

The papers were drawn up within weeks and there was nothing left to do but sign.

'You do like living here, don't you?' Lucy asked, sensing hesitation.

'Oh, yes,' Kevin replied, sheepishly.

He liked the idea, even if adoption seemed a step too far.

Jarred by the conversations he had walked in on that had been shut down, quick – with looks passing between the adults – he wondered at their enthusiasm.

When he returned from school to find a skip straddling the front drive, he sensed another agenda.

'Come and see!' Lucy cried, meeting him out front. 'We've started on an extension,' waving an arm towards the kitchen – now minus a wall – 'to make more room for your chair…'

He hadn't thought there was a problem, but listened patiently as Lucy elaborated on the plans. It wasn't until the work was complete that he could see it for what it was: a brand new, high-end kitchen (with built-in appliances and glistening worktops).

He wondered, idly, at the expense.

'It'll be so much easier for you, like this,' his aunt insisted.

Kevin thanked her, as he backed out, considering whether they would now expect him to cook, too.

There were more renovations to come, with a new set of builders arriving every other week. Kevin never once speculated on where the money was coming from and it was only when he was older, and wiser – and knew the system inside out – that he finally understood.

'They had been applying to the Thalidomide Trust, on my behalf,' he explains, 'arguing that the house required structural changes to support my condition.'

There was no malice in the words, just a rueful grasp of human nature.

At the time, Kevin hadn't seen that – or cared – and was more concerned with the way Aunt Lucy had turned on his mother. The change was subtle, but no less critical.

She had come on him alone, in the living room.

'I don't like to say anything,' she said, 'but your mum really is a mess, at the moment… doesn't know if she's coming or going.' He nodded, not knowing what to say. Lucy had her hand on his chair – he couldn't have moved if he had wanted to. 'I called her last night and she was incoherent.' The air was still – *close*; Kevin turned the lever, forcing Lucy up to her feet. 'I know you worry,' she continued, 'and, I do as well… but, you need to understand that your mother's always had problems… and that me and Barry are here for you, and more than happy to take you in.'

Kevin held her gaze, feeling that something was off.

'Thanks,' he said, his nod suggesting gratitude.

'Your father, God rest his soul, really did have the patience of a saint,' Lucy concluded, with something like a bow as she backed away (and that settled it).

The following week, when his Aunt Lucy and his Uncle Barry set off on an unexpected cruise (on the Mediterranean), Kevin was sent home, again.

'We'd have taken you along, if we'd known,' his new parents explained, 'but we had no idea you'd be moving in like this…'

Kevin didn't care – a cruise sounded boring – and he would have missed his friends.

Though apprehensive about the state he would find his mother in, Kevin was glad of the opportunity to look in on his old home. Joan had come back to take charge, and Liz was there too, so he didn't imagine it could be so bad. He would have, simply, to be delicate – to keep his own counsel and not expect too much.

He was pleased to find, when he arrived, that very little had changed in his absence, remembering in an instant all he had forgotten.

'Your mum's missed you,' Joan said, as she picked up his bag and helped him in.

She wasn't out of bed yet, so Kevin went straight up to his room, to reacquaint. It wasn't until he heard his mother's voice straining up the stairs, after him, that he stepped out again.

'How are you?' Agnes asked, summoning a strength she no longer had, brushing aimlessly through his hair. 'Have you got everything you need?'

They were only words and didn't mean much, but Kevin, who had had time to think over his aunt's warnings, was quick to take the chance to air his misgivings.

'Your mother's not well,' Lucy had reiterated, when she had bundled him into the cab, 'so, it's important not to upset her, or say anything that could be misinterpreted… We've always been frank with you, Kevin, because we care,' – she was on her knees now – 'for both of you, but your mum's vulnerable at the moment.' Kevin nodded, thinking her done, but after closing over the door, she was suddenly at the window again and leaning in. 'You do understand?' she asked, holding his eye. 'You mustn't say anything.'

The confused biology of a fifteen-year-old boy coming to the fore – his loyalties no longer divided – Kevin was blabbing just as soon as he was through the door.

Given her supposedly stricken state, Agnes took it surprisingly well.

'Yes, I'll be here,' she told Lucy, arranging the pickup.

She was standing at the window, watching, when their car pulled up outside.

'How was your holiday?' she asked, at the door.

'Oh, it was lovely, Agnes… thanks for asking,' Lucy replied, glancing across at her husband.

'Well, that's good, I am pleased,' Agnes continued, 'but – while you've been away – I've been making some decisions of my own, and the first thing you should know is that Kevin's not going back with you… and there won't be any adoption, either.' She paused, standing tall. 'A child should always live with his mother, where possible, don't you think?'

Lucy was shaking slightly, her skin – with its golden tan – pale now: *Kevin must have told her,* she thought, finding peace, oddly.

Still holding tight to the small bottle of sangria she had brought back as a gift – her bright holiday clothes looking ridiculous, now – she was swaying on her feet. Agnes left them standing on the front step, waiting, with a certain degree of impatience, for their departure.

Kevin, who had some sympathy for his Aunt Lucy now – and wasn't really sure what had happened – couldn't look at her. He turned to Barry instead, expecting an understanding smile, but found that he was glaring across with something like contempt. Kevin stared right back, the thirty years between them a mere detail.

With no one else prepared to speak, it was left to Agnes to set the record straight – running, forensically, through everything Kevin had told her – and this marked the point when her life started over.

'He's my son, after all,' she concluded. 'What did you think – that you could use him against me?'

Barry didn't move a muscle – simply took the blows – while Lucy accepted everything that was said with an unexpected grace.

'I'm sorry,' she said, at last.

'Now, can you leave us, please?' Agnes concluded, having exhausted every grievance.

She was shaking – didn't see them to their car, nor stand to watch them drive away.

Kevin has mixed emotions, now, and cannot be sure what he thinks he knows. He remembers the watch that Aunt Lucy gifted him on his seventh birthday, and how – explaining the hands and the digits – she had set about teaching him to tell the time.

'Every young boy should have a timepiece of their own,' she had declared, when she pinned it on.

His mother's eyes bearing down on him, Kevin had unaccountably blushed.

'Thanks,' he mumbled, and – looking, rather proudly, on her tottering nephew – Aunt Lucy leaned in for a kiss (the air awash with perfume).

She had always treated him well, as far back as he could recall, and he had loved that watch, a silver nurse's fob (of comforting heft). Following the second hand's skipping progress, counting down to the end of class – in school – he would time his circuits of the garden too (chasing a personal best).

Kevin took such pleasure in that contraption that he insisted on wearing it at all times, and one day, as he dismounted the toilet, it came loose – the glass cracking against the side of the bowl, with water bleeding into the delicate mechanisms.

Kevin – who would have been Kevin Jones – looked on, aghast.

Chapter 20

They were full of *When Harry Met Sally* that summer and it felt appropriate at the time, with Kevin pushing at the limits of a relationship that grew deeper by the day. The distinctions were eroding and I can see how he could struggle to understand that the intimacies Karen allowed him were firmly fixed within the natural restraints of friendship (and could go no further).

'I feel like I can tell you anything,' she conceded, after one particularly fraught session.

'You can,' Kevin answered quickly.

'I've never felt this comfortable with anyone else in my whole life,' Karen added, linking fingers, as dusk fell.

This felt like a moment, and Kevin nearly made his move.

Once admitted to, such feelings were hard to ignore.

Leave the fucker, he would sneer, in silence, if Karen ever asked his advice, gleefully noting every slam of the door when she left the house or climbed into his van, her face bleached with tears.

'He's a cretin,' Karen grumbled, as she wound down the window.

Kevin pulled away from the kerb, believing that – given the force and frequency of her complaints – it was just a matter of time. He didn't say a word, but let her speak. Despite his impatience, he wanted Karen to come freely (when she came) and on her own terms.

It can't happen, I thought, as he ran on excitedly. *Whatever he says, or thinks, it can't happen.* For, Karen could have her pick: love, respect and affection were no match for those missing arms and legs.

I was thinking of you, too: once established, such shortfalls can never be met.

They were discussing Karen's desire to have a family of her own, one day, coupled with Dan's steadfast refusal to have so much as a conversation.

'I'm sure he'll come round,' Kevin suggested flippantly, though he knew there could be no compromise on such a matter.

'No, he won't,' Karen returned, with certainty, adding – with a rueful smile – 'he said I was fat enough already.'

'What? You've got an amazing figure,' Kevin blurted out, considering how he liked her just as well in her jim-jams, with odd socks, as he did in her swimsuit (the image of which still hadn't lost its power).

'Flattery will get you everywhere,' Karen cooed.

That almost seemed a promise.

A riffle shuffle to the already dishevelled pack, Nicky's return would bring an unexpected release. She was Mrs Tandy now, and Kevin had kept in touch through all the long years of their acquaintance. Despite an intimacy born of shared experience, since he had met Karen – eighteen months before – Kevin had been playing his new life close to his chest.

He had mentioned Karen (how could he not?) with an unconscious skip in his voice – his pupils dilating – and Nicky knew Dan, from the afternoons he would come over to work the garden, but somehow Kevin had managed to keep those two worlds apart.

They had taken a tour of the garden earlier in the day, with Dan pointing out the bluebells and the azaleas – planted in the autumn and now in bloom – while Karen nodded her appreciation at the delightful flood of colour.

'What the hell's that?' Dan called out, as he stumbled over the metre-long, stone crocodile that Kevin had recently added.

'Thought I'd liven the place up a bit,' Kevin replied, with a smirk, before directing Karen to the oversized butterflies he had had Joan pin to the surrounding walls.

'And what's with all the cats?' Dan mused, counting them up.

'And, what the hell's *this*?' he cried, raising a hollow metal tabby over his head.

'Mad Maureen,' (his sister) Kevin replied simply, with a nod to Karen, who knew the whole story. She gave a grin, and it seemed then that Dan – who had set the coiled head of another feline rattling back and forth – was no longer there. 'And there's Fanny,' Kevin added, as his faithful old retainer, returned to him after his sister Liz had left for Canada (following her divorce), ambled into view.

The granddaughter of Trotsky, her white belly turned to the sun, Phantom was a cat with a heritage.

Leaving Dan to the flower beds, Kevin and Karen took the chance to speak more freely inside. It was the usual story: how great everything had been at the start – all the plans they had once made.

'I thought you two were the perfect match,' Kevin admitted.

'So did I,' Karen returned, 'and, I still love him,' – Kevin's eyes dropped at that – 'but sometimes I don't even think he cares anymore.'

'Oh, I'm sure he does,' Kevin replied, holding her gaze.

He didn't push further, knowing – from embittered experience – that just when it seemed they were through, they would suddenly start up again (and everything would be hopeless).

Joining Dan on the patio, for a smoke, Kevin took a brief drag, before passing it on to Karen, who flapped her hands in refusal. She rarely participated anymore – didn't like the effect – yet that had been one of the things that had brought her and Dan together on the night they met. That seemed another lifetime: they rarely laughed like that anymore, nor fucked with the same passion.

The doorbell sounded and Karen jumped in answer, drawn to the sound of banging and the shriek of a voice, as she stepped into the hall.

'Kevin! Kevin! Open up!'

Pulling the door with curiosity, she found a woman of a similar height, and a strict bob of mousey hair, standing before her: it was Nicky, who hissed, 'Where the fuck is he?' before pushing past.

'In the back,' Karen told her, but Nicky had already gone.

'Kevin? *Kevin*?' she yodelled, in a squall of varying register.

Vulgar in her youth, it was fair to say that Nicky had only coarsened in the interim.

'Oh, I thought I'd find you lot in here,' she hissed, casting a sharp eye over the room, 'sat on your arses, as usual... and, the wolfman himself,' she added, spotting Dan.

'Afternoon,' Kevin returned.

'Well, are you going to introduce us, or do we have to wait 'til hell freezes over?' Nicky continued, with her eyes on Karen. 'Who – pray tell – is this lovely young thing?'

'Karen – this is Nicky; Nicky – Karen,' Kevin said.

'Pleased to meet you, love,' Nicky replied.

'Likewise,' Karen returned, with a smile.

'Likewise – oh, that's lovely!' Nicky cooed, showing the gap between her top teeth (her distended cheeks spotted with freckles). 'Finally, someone with bloody manners,' she continued, 'not like wolfman, here – oh, she's lovely... I like her. I like you, Karen, I do. I like her, Kevin,' she repeated – evidently pleased with the phrase – her eyes flitting about, before settling, once more, on Karen. 'So, what do you do, love,' she begged, with careful enunciation, 'and, how do you come to be friends with the lovely Mr Donnellon?'

'She works for me,' Kevin put in, quickly. 'So, why don't you stop asking all these bloody questions and go and put the kettle on? Then you can tell me what you want.'

'Oh, you've done well there, haven't you?' Nicky resumed, undeterred. 'She's lovely, this one – a little bit of class... oh, you're a picture aren't you?' she added, giving what she considered a winsome smile. 'Yes, a lovely little flower,' she continued, as she backed into the kitchen.

Taking a seat, while the kettle boiled, Nicky left Dan – who was pleased to make his escape – to finish off.

'So, what *do* you want?' Kevin asked.

'Why does everyone always assume…?' Nicky started. 'Can't a lady make a social call?'

'Yes, yes,' Kevin chuckled, 'but what is it you want?'

'Well, as a matter of fact, I was going to ask if you wouldn't mind casting a quick eye over this essay,' she said then, pulling out some papers.

'You mean, you'd like me to write the bloody thing,' Kevin snorted.

'No, no, not at all,' Nicky shrieked. 'Oh, my God! I just want you to check it's okay, that's all – can't you say anything, without all these smart-arsed answers?'

Nicky now explained to Karen, with what amounted to a bow, that she was studying for a diploma in cognitive behavioural therapy: the essay in question concerned 'empathy' and 'listening skills'.

'You know what they want better than me, that's all,' she elaborated, turning to Kevin. 'I mean – you're the professor…'

He let the flattery pass.

'It looks fine,' Kevin judged, after leafing, briefly, through the papers.

'Yes… but I can see you're busy now, so I'll leave it,' Nicky returned, 'and you can have a proper look when you've got the time, if you don't mind, thank you, please…'

Her eyes pinned to this peculiar new creature, Karen was trying not to laugh, while Nicky – sensing she had an ally – played increasingly to the crowd.

'Still fucking about in the garden?' she asked Dan, who had brought the drinks through. 'And still taking drugs, no doubt?' she added, with a shake of the head. Mumbling as he lifted his drink, Dan shuffled uncomfortably in his seat. Nicky was smirking, her dimples showing. 'But what I really want to know,' she continued, 'is how on earth you managed to snare such a beautiful girl (no offence)?'

She threw her head back at that, cackling as she gathered up her bag and her coat, taking her leave.

On her next visit, given the time to think it over, Nicky was no less indignant.

'But seriously,' she sneered, 'how on earth did those two possibly end up together?'

'They're in love,' Kevin replied.

Nicky gave a shriek of disbelief.

'And you say that Karen works, with you, at the university?' she continued. 'And she's got a degree and everything, like you?' Kevin nodded, interested to hear her opinion, given the obvious bias. 'Then what – pray tell,' she said, pausing for effect before spitting out her conclusion, 'is the poor girl doing with Danny boy?'

Grinning across in colluding silence, Kevin welcomed this unlikely alliance – the girls were genuinely fond of one another – just as he did Nicky's increasingly frequent visits.

'I mean, you're a proper brainbox,' she would begin again, leaning in to her new friend, 'while Dan… well, I'm sure he has his uses,' giving that toothy grin, 'but you're worth ten of him, you really are.'

Flattered and amused in equal measure, Karen could hardly deny the thrust of arguments that fed into her own pre-existing doubts, and – if Kevin felt guilty for bringing them together – he could hardly be blamed for those wild declarations, while Karen, who was increasingly seeking her out for advice, was old enough to know her own mind.

'Have you got your eye on anyone else?' Nicky would probe, with a sly nod.

'Course not,' Karen blushed, shy in comparison.

'Well, you're too young to be tied down just yet,' Nicky resumed, Kevin hardly knowing where to look.

On another occasion, after a glass of wine, Nicky climbed to her feet to announce that Karen would be 'better off going out with Kevin, than that moron Dan – and, that's saying something…'

This time it was Kevin who blushed.

'You don't know what you're talking about, you daft bat,' he charged, as he shuffled his papers, in an attempt to look busy, before bolting out from behind his desk and skipping across to his room.

Standing before the floor-length mirror, his chest heaving, he tried to think up an excuse for such an abrupt departure, eventually returning – all smiles – in a top hat and monocle (which served as a distraction).

He felt transparent, even in such a disguise – foolish and false – hardly able to believe that Nicky had gone ahead and said what he had been agonising over for months.

Persistent, if nothing else, Nicky would be back, of course – and circling the same topic – but she would never mention Kevin again in such a way, suggesting instead that Karen should find herself a 'nice doctor, or perhaps a lawyer'.

'Don't settle down, until you've had some fun,' she advised. 'It's no use getting bogged down with kiddies just yet.'

Karen raised an eyebrow, in wry amusement.

'I would like to have children one day, though,' she admitted.

'And you'll make a great mum when you do, but just not yet!'

'Dan won't even talk about it,' she continued, sadly.

'Even more reason to dump him,' Nicky hissed, 'and find a man who'll do the decent thing...'

Excusing herself, Karen gave no answer to that, but when she returned she looked like she had been crying. Kevin wanted to hold her then – and give her what she wanted – but he was glad to find the subject closed, for now, with Nicky finally leaving them in peace.

Her influence over those first few weeks was unquestionable; Karen was never the same carefree girl again. Kevin regretted that – even as it served his purpose – noting how the influence went both ways, with Nicky now talking with more freedom about her own children (Karen's generous nature drawing out a softer side).

Watching as Kevin drew closer, I wanted to pull him away – to save him from what I thought would follow. Perhaps I should have taken instruction instead. For, if he was misguided and foolish at times, he was no coward and would say what he needed to say (when the time came) – that was a satisfaction I never knew.

When he did finally tell her (and told me, in turn), I felt my breath go, at the thought of such a drastic decision – as though I had made that declaration, too.

He didn't seem to care (as I did).

'At least, now, she knows how I feel,' he declared bullishly.

I hadn't heard from you in a month, by then, but had sent out a letter to explain, only suggesting that we meet up when it was already too late. *If you love someone, set them free*, I had thought, while Kevin – pursuing the long game (with small bets and wide odds) – wasn't going anywhere and refused to throw in his hand.

It was only when you stepped – carelessly – into the taxi that you had unconsciously hailed, that I understood that you had left me weeks ago.

You didn't want to hurt me, you said; I had never known such pain.

Off, and on – how does it ever begin?

Chapter 21

Kevin made his first appearance on the small screen at the age of ten, in October 1972. In a spectral nod to the Russian dissident, Alexander Solzhenitsyn, that few outside of the BBC's Oxbridge intelligentsia were likely to note – while also making reference to a famous track by a regional band (that local residents were all too quick to recognise) – the documentary was broadcast under the title *A Day in the Life of Kevin Donnellon.*

The *World in Action* van that turned onto the small schoolyard, on that drab and drizzly Tuesday morning, was navy blue, with aerials jutting from a corrugated roof and the Tyne Tees logo emblazoned down one side. With his hair freshly trimmed for the occasion, Kevin was the only one in his class who had any idea; his uncharacteristic discretion – given the circumstances – brought its own reward.

'Where are my shoes?' he had bellowed impatiently, at his mother, that same morning, despite the fact that he had no need of the shoes that he stuck so stubbornly to the base of his prosthetics.

His mother had, it transpired, only taken them off for a spit and a polish.

The school knew they were coming, of course, and had given clues in the previous morning's assembly.

'We have a surprise for you tomorrow, children,' Miss Skelly had said, leaving the pupils to imagine just whatever they wanted.

They had forgotten the promise by the end of play.

The Bedford KML that pulled up on those rain-spattered grounds the next morning wasn't particularly exciting, though the children (a dozen or more smudged faces lining the windows) cheered its arrival when the vehicle grumbled to an unceremonious halt.

'We'll be famous,' one of the more savvy Junior 4 wags crowed, having noted the sign, while Kevin beamed back with pride at the thought of the crew being there just for him.

A rap of chalk on board wrested their wandering attention.

Under the tutelage of his favourite teacher, Mr Ray, Kevin was, by then, a confident and forthcoming member of the class. The attention was nothing new. Thus, even though he was the putative centre of the day's unexpected events, Kevin – acting with a carefree nonchalance that not even the teachers were able to affect – was unfazed; acquiescing to the gathering hubbub with a commendably sure step, he refused to fuss.

His mother was to make the point in the documentary that aired the following week, wringing a welter of responses from the sentimental viewing public (all taking sides, in their particular ways).

'I would say sixty per cent [of people] look at Kevin as if... They stop, stare, don't believe... *shudder*.'

Kevin didn't mind – rather revelled in topping the bill.

'Oh, yes,' he would reply, while displaying his above-average facilities (his small fingers a rush of dexterity), 'I can do most things just like you.'

When the producer came to fetch him from class, Kevin had simply tidied his desk away in his customary manner, before following him out. All eyes were turned his way, as usual: the camera and the viewers at home just another audience to take in his stride.

Shuffling, with studied insouciance, down the ramp to the foot of his desk, Kevin scuttled across the polished floor to the ramp outside, mounting his waiting chair with a practised drawl.

'Thanks, Laura,' he said, as his classmate, despite the reduced range of her arms – she was thalidomide, too – grasped the reins and led him away.

The resulting film would illustrate all that Kevin *could* and *couldn't* do at school, with each clip edited to best suggest that small boy's inspirational fortitude, in the face of such struggles, while the dulcet voiceover kept to a sombre tone.

'Kevin, of course, takes no part in PE,' the patriarchal presence soberly informs. 'While his friends play games together outside, Kevin remains inside, alone, following a course of physiotherapy under the direction of the school nurse.'

The camera cuts to Kevin, now flat on his back – and trussed up to a metal spring-like contraption – his face a study of concentration, as he rocks back and forth.

In the next shot, Kevin is shown in his prosthetic legs, beaming a distracted smile down to the camera as, with forceful shimmies of his oversized hips, he thumps his way across the woodblock; then, a jump-cut, to show him mounting the steps to his desk, via several jolts of his straining glutes.

The montage, backed by the high-pitched squeals of children at play, ran for around two minutes, before concluding with a mid-shot of Kevin (seen through the glass windows that lined the walls) being wheeled back to class through dappled sunlight.

The message was clear, if somewhat subverted: Kevin's brave and indomitable spirit was something that we – by shaming analogy – might learn from. There was no mention made of the falls he had suffered, as a result of those constitutionally dangerous legs – those monstrous, meandering mimics. Nor was any explanation given of the process by which Kevin was first tethered tight to their seat, as numerous hands drew him cautiously up to his feet – off camera – before being obliged to pace over that same stretch of floor, until they had the footage required.

The viewers saw the miracle, not the trick; Kevin's feet were groaning with blisters by the evening.

'Cut!' the director called, as Kevin tottered towards the safety of a supporting wall. 'In your positions, please!' he was barracking, again, after a quick glance at the rushes.

Kevin barely had time to catch his breath. It was only after five separate takes that he was released, to generous applause, and could drop wearily down to the floor again.

The school segment concluded with a tracking shot of Kevin heading along an empty corridor, to his next lesson. The light had faded and there was an elegiac tone, with Kevin seeming to have the place to himself; he did – the rest of the school had been sent home hours ago.

Only Laura, who had been picked out for the role of Kevin's companion earlier in the day, remained. She had neat russet pigtails, a fine scatter of freckles and she was wearing the pretty summer dress that her parents had brought in, at the film crew's request – her hands, sprouting from reduced arms, just about showing from the bunched sleeves. Fearing that a greater part in the piece would confuse the narrative, Laura had trotted away as soon as she had parked the chair, leaving Kevin – who had immediately dropped to the floor – to shuffle inside, alone.

Here, he was shown rounding the front row of desks, before hopping adroitly up the ramp to his seat (unassisted), just as the bell sounded and the other children (kept back for the purpose) rushed in around him. Already well acquainted with the armless little boy toiling gamely in their midst, the children did their best to ignore the camera, while dodging under the boom.

Following an advertisement break – the documentary had been produced by Tyne Tees TV – *A Day in the Life…* resumed with an account of Kevin's home life and routines on Litherland Park.

A slow pan played across the living room, where Mr Donnellon was sat upright in a high-backed chair, with a newspaper folded over his lap. As directed, he made no concession to the camera. Cindy, the family's West Highland terrier, was perched beside him and, having already ruined two earlier takes, John was now holding her in place.

The room was laid bare and looked smaller than they had expected when they saw it back on the screen. The side cabinet, from which Agnes had earlier removed all the knick-knacks and family portraits, in order to dust, looked decidedly drab (despite those efforts); the wallpaper, garish and outdated; the room as average as the family itself.

'It was a right state,' Agnes would complain, and there was soon talk of getting the decorators in.

The camera moved on to the kitchen next, where Agnes was leaning back against the chrome-yellow cabinets, her small feet tapping nervously at the chequered floor.

'Of course, we've had to make adjustments throughout the house,' she told the camera – in close-up – before giving a scrupulous breakdown of the completed amendments, with a jump-cut to the eerily deserted bathroom showing the recently adapted Clos-o-mat. 'As soon as we understood the practicalities of having a thalidomide child,' she continued – well-worn words, by now (and hard won) – 'we looked into what we could do practically, fitting out the bathroom with an adapted toilet, which Kevin could use as he got older.'

Through careful edits, the film was able to contrast the privations faced by Kevin, in even the most basic of actions, and the life of his sister, who – agile and light on her toes – skipped around his immobile form, to scrub at her teeth, gargling and spitting, while Kevin awkwardly attempted the same (with a pre-loaded brush).

Liz (Elizabeth) gave a girlish smile, as she tidied away, and then she was up on a chair in front of the mirror beside her brother, brushing fussily – and with unconcealed pride – through her long, straight hair. This vignette was followed by one showing Kevin's mother grooming his rather foppish locks *for* him – his small hands twirling, redundant, in the vicinity of his shoulders (while he chatted on).

Both children set square upon their distinct ablutions, Mrs Donnellon now put a more pertinent question to her son, who had so far been presented in such a resourceful light, speaking rather brusquely (into the mirror).

'What sort of things can't you do at school… that the other children can?'

It seemed cruel to ask, though Kevin had heard all such questions before.

'I don't do Games,' he said, clarifying. 'If the school attendant's in, I do exercises on my limbs, instead.'

It was a nonchalantly delivered line, Kevin's eyes wide below raised brows, with the way he was shown getting about with such ease seeming to prove his case. No suggestion, or indication, was ever given of the difficulties Agnes would face at home over the long-drawn summers, however: how she would be left to cope, single-handed, while her husband went out to work; how, with her children running her ragged, she would need a tranquiliser just to get her through the day.

After pausing for an establishing shot back in the living room, the camera panned left towards Kevin, who was now down on the floor beside his younger sister, Liz. As though to emphasise exactly what Agnes had meant, when she spoke of the restrictions a 'special school' would necessarily place on her son – and why she had fought the Education Department, so assiduously, to have him removed – they were playing chess.

Kevin's expression was studied and serious (with no quarter given).

'My little boy,' Agnes had bristled, when the contrary view was put, 'though he was only four and a half, *did* have a brain… that had to be used.'

Mrs Donnellon – in an extended close-up – brought *A Day in the Life* to a close with an almost clinical breakdown of the many difficulties that still lay ahead. Over a series of solemn minor chords, plucked on a reverberating cello – chiming their way through to the closing credits – she pointed out the extent to which Kevin would struggle to do what everyone else took for granted.

'I just hope Kevin's happy,' she considered. 'I mean, he'll never be able to get a job, or get married or have children but, as long as he's *happy*, then it's all worth it.' Staring the camera down in unflinching conclusion, her grey eyes barely blinked. 'I'll do whatever I can to make his life more comfortable and more pleasant.'

He was a beautiful boy, Kevin, in that film, with his soft feathery lashes drooping slantwise over wide, wondering eyes: optimistic in the face of his suffering. He was self-aware, self-reflexive and knowingly precocious (and refused to accept any of the judgements that sought to define him). He was a survivor, and more – the film made that clear.

Kevin was ten years old, and he was beautiful – how could I have known?

'I still cringe when I watch it back,' he admits – though he had already sat me through several showings.

'You were beautiful,' I noted, with a degree of surprise.

'Still am,' Kevin shot back, sensing a caveat in the compliment – the damning of faint praise.

We were back to the old games.

Yet, my mind was drifting, as – grasping at an unmapped recognition – I struggled to register where I had seen such a face before (because I *had* seen it). It wasn't the face, as such, but something in the attitude and the expression – in the precocious hauteur of a preternatural child.

Back home, I remembered, and sought out the book, with the boy (on the cover) sitting in an embroidered display, his flounced hair coiled over either ear: Jean–Paul Sartre. I considered, again, Kevin's suspiciously ready reply, to the question of what he wanted to be when he grew up.

'Historian,' he had replied, rather pompously elaborating his preference for the 'industrial age'.

His was the separating instinct, of playing to an ever-present audience, in the knowledge that every eye is trained his way; watching; *assuming*… the wearying panoptic of one who has greatness thrust upon him.

Sartre's recollection, of his gilded childhood, was similar in tone, if not in circumstance; flicking through that half-forgotten autobiography, *Words*, I had soon found what I was looking for.

'I enjoyed the princely freedom of an actor,' Sartre writes, 'who holds the audience in suspense and improves on his own performance.'

Performance. Resemblance. *Semblance*. A miniature, pocketbook child – with pursed cherry lips and an unseasonably furrowed brow – giving off the intellectual airs of a sophisticate: the unexpected and the incongruent, startlingly dissonant bedfellows.

'I'm particularly interested in the industrial age,' Kevin had said, without pause.

He was used to such questions – and the avid interest that people took in his life; practised in the praise he would draw at every step, every success – how he brought wonder; he was used to turning heads (and would have been lost without it).

It wasn't by chance that the film had showed Kevin playing chess – the sport of gnarled intellect – his prosthetics placed with care (and the director's stipulation) at the back of the combatants.

Escaping the viewing public's sentimental gaze was the fact that when Kevin asked his sister to move a knight for him (to take her queen), she had started to lift one of his pawns, instead – to capture her bishop – while leaving the more powerful matriarch (his intended victim) untouched.

Alert, wary – and *competitive* – Kevin had made his intentions clear (even as the film ran on).

'No, the *queen*,' he stressed, facing down his sister's attempt at a cheat.

It took Kevin little, in truth, to enthral his perpetual audience, who – staggered by his very existence – were astounded to find him capable of doing so much more. Surprisingly malleable, the world was offered up with ease, Kevin playing willingly on such preconceptions.

While busy providing for such illusions, Kevin failed to see the constant – if benevolent – deceptions that were being simultaneously played on him (and had been, since the day he was born). For, notwithstanding his admitted capacities, Kevin would always perform with a net – even if he didn't know it – his life and times only ever *resembling* the realities of his peers.

Recorded preparing for school – being dressed and breakfasted – before making the final adjustments to his tie, as he waits for his lift, nothing seems amiss. Kevin discards the crusts of his toast, shrugging off his mother as she wipes the jam from his face – his, the morning ritual of a thousand homes.

Then, he is out again, a tracking shot showing him borne aloft in the arms of Mrs Lofthouse, who would accompany him on his journey to school, and out onto the street, where Old Bill can be seen folding his chair carefully into the boot. His mother waves from the door, as they set off for another day – Kevin is going to learn, like any other child: what could be more natural?

It is already half past four, however, and the school day has already finished, and it is all a mirage… For, Kevin isn't going to school at this time – he is simply going down to the end of the garden path and back again, and everyone around him is playing a part, even if the sun has missed its spot and would give him away if we looked.

The game of chess that they had set up and documented so elaborately, would – likewise – never be completed (and was never truly played), Kevin and Liz leaving the board to its glacial statues the moment the camera stopped.

Liz was never called out on her attempt to take deceitful advantage.

Chapter 22

If it was a shock to learn that his mother still entertained such desires, to take up with a man as far removed from her recently departed husband seemed indecent – an erasure of the preceding years.

Thin and reedy, in body and manner, Jim's knotted brown eyes were a blur behind the opaque panes of his thick-framed glasses. It was 1978 – Kevin would have been sixteen – and the hand he took into his own, in introduction, suggested a weakness he could never forgive.

Seeing desperation in the patent need to be liked, pedantry in the desire to give help where none was required, Kevin wouldn't advance beyond those first impressions. Having so often been the subject of preconceptions on his own account, Kevin wasn't judgemental, but – dragging frayed suitcases that any other man would have carried straight – Jim had moved in before the end of the month and there was no denying him.

'All my worldly goods,' he declared amiably.

'How long's he staying?' Kevin asked in return, directing the question to his mother, still imagining that – whatever this was – it couldn't last.

If Agnes had been justifiably excited at the prospect of having a new man in her life, grasping in despair at the possibility of losing herself – without further recourse to medication – she was just as quickly disabused.

Even allowing for the mitigation of wine – 'he's lovely', she had gushed to Joan, after their first date – Agnes had harboured doubts from the start. Meeting up for a second time – sober, and in the cold light of day – would only confirm her suspicions. *There's not much to him,* she thought, as Jim padded back and forth on the mat for a full minute before finally stepping inside.

'What a lovely house you have,' he declared, having ventured no further than the hall.

'We moved in when Kevin was nine,' Agnes replied stiffly, in something like embarrassment, taking her usual frame of reference.

Jim nodded considerately.

He's a man, at least, she thought, her eyes settling on a stray grey hair growing out of his brow.

'But where are my manners,' Agnes resumed, leading Jim into the lounge.

He seemed pleased with that, bowing again as he followed her through.

That submissive nature represented a reversal of the roles that had held in marriage (and took some getting used to).

'Must be a godsend, to have a man around the house again,' one of her friends would suggest.

Agnes merely shrugged, recognising that – aside from the jobs Jim would willingly perform, at her bidding – the changes were negligible.

Still suffering from the depression of bereavement, Agnes would still spend whole afternoons strung out on her bed, with Kevin's return the only reason to rouse herself. Jim was kind and considerate – seemed to understand and accept the mood swings that inevitably followed – but, by this point, Agnes would have preferred leadership and strength to the docile servility he provided.

It was Jim who would eventually prevail on them to move, however, arguing that the change would do them good. Kevin shrugged, as he dropped from the table, though he was pleased to find, when they decamped, that the new property was a substantial upgrade; he wondered, with a smirk, how his mother would accommodate the unsightly chintz she insisted on bringing.

'Well – what do you think?' Jim asked.

'It's alright,' Kevin allowed, as he rolled into the lounge.

I could get used to this, he considered, as he took inventory of the six bedrooms, ranging over two floors, of which he was given first pick... delighting, now, in the sizeable reception room that opened dramatically out from that cavernous hall (providing space enough to spin a chair).

Agnes Road was a palace and Kevin took the largest room on offer (first floor, front), which afforded an unobstructed view over the tree-lined rail track that ran below. While Jim was fitting a rail to the stairs and his mother clattering helplessly through the kitchen cabinets, Kevin glared with disdain at the pandas and bamboo shoots lining the walls – imprints of the former occupant (a child).

'Mother!' he cried, recalling the room he had once decorated with Shirley, his voice dying away at the realisation that he no longer cared and was more interested in the equipment he might be able to cram in.

The TV came first, fitted into the alcove facing the bed, so that – propped up on pillows (the fat remote to hand) – Kevin could flick through the channels at will.

'And I'd like a socket here, as well,' he advised the obliging telephone engineer, indicating a space to the right of the bed, already imagining how – given a long enough cord – he could lie back on his bed and talk to his heart's content.

Within the hour, testing the length of the cable, while cradling the pale blue touch-tone model (he had specified) – with a modern metallic tone – to his pimply chin, Kevin had made his first call.

'Good afternoon,' he declared breezily, 'may I speak to Aileen, please,' the two friends setting off on their usual round of gossip.

There was more to come, with Jim honouring the promise he had given, during protracted negotiations, for a new and bigger train set.

'We could use the room at the top of the house: the old servants' quarters,' he had suggested, with undue enthusiasm.

Though Kevin had lost much of his interest, he couldn't deny the sentimental draw of continuity, with those rails leading right back to his father, who would stand and watch at his shoulder as he set the carriages in circles.

Kevin missed him, and didn't refuse this third and final train set, though he would ultimately make little use of it.

Retracing his own lost childhood, Jim would take up the reins instead. Thus, when *World in Action* made their second visit (in the spring of 1981), it was Jim – well and truly established by now – who insisted on filming in the train room, with Kevin propped up on a stool beside him.

The renovations would descend all the way down to the basement, in time.

'We could do something with this,' Jim noted, as he nosed through the dust of the occluded rooms at the foot of the narrow stairwell.

'It's gloomy,' Agnes returned brusquely, struggling to make anything out by the single bulb hanging overhead (with the recessed windows at either end painted resolutely shut).

Holding her chest against the damp air, she wondered how they could ever want for space in such a voluminous property.

They had already turned around and were heading back up when they flipped on the light in the second of the two rooms and found a sinister bank of eyes staring back at them.

Agnes gave a muted shriek and stumbled, stepping forward again when she saw that they were only photographs (of one and the same face).

'It's that woman,' she puzzled, 'the MP…' – Shirley Williams, who had recently helped establish the SDP.

Her agent, Agnes now remembered being told, was the person selling the house.

'We'll need to get it cleared,' Jim muttered to himself, seeing the potential.

He couldn't have guessed at the eventual transformation, even if it was his idea to build a bar as a means of keeping Kevin home (and maintaining control over his intake of alcohol).

Agnes had agreed at once, with Kevin returning from college one afternoon to find the house full of builders (weaving a dusty path down to the basement).

'Hi, son,' Jim smirked.

'Afternoon,' Kevin replied, as he edged away.

With no desire to enter into a conversation, or to touch on a subject that Jim was clearly keen to broach, Kevin dropped to the floor, before scrambling hand over hoof up the stairs.

The hammers and the drills – and the drawl of saws drawing through timber – continued and, in the end, he couldn't resist. His mother, who had been waiting, followed him down.

'We were thinking how expensive it is for you to go out drinking, even before you consider the toilets… and, we've got the space here, so why not build a bar of our own?'

Kevin looked on in confusion, given the warnings his mother had always made against drinking. *A home bar,* he mused, needing no reminder of the problems he faced when venturing out. *And, I'll be able to invite anyone I want,* he considered suddenly, thinking – now – of the girls he had taken a fancy to in college, imagining Debbie or Denise and what they might get up to (left to their own devices).

They were talking at crossed purposes, of course, though there were boisterous cheers at the unofficial opening, when Kevin cut the ribbon tied to the door frame and rushed right in.

'Pint, please,' he gasped, tapping his fingers on the polished countertop that constituted the bar and watching – in disbelief – as, standing before a row of glistening optics, Jim drew a drink from the pump.

'What you having?' Kevin asked, turning to his friends.

His mother pulled him away.

'What do you think?' she said, pointing out the electric heater fixed into the renovated fireplace, the benches fitted into the alcoves. 'And, I got some of the art you like, too,' she continued – nodding a head towards the Impressionist reproductions tacked to the wall – before directing his attention to the ceiling beams (touched up to emphasise the mock Tudor stripes now lining the freshly plastered walls).

Kevin turned, forlornly, towards the bar, as Agnes took his arm and led him across to the studded leather bench now running the length of the sunken bay. Taking a seat, Kevin waved his friends – the brothers Bernard and Boris (*née* Edmund) and Dick (*née* Richard) – across, before calling, with a raucous cry, for more beer. Returning with a tray, Agnes set the four dimpled jug-glasses – standard twenty imperial ounces – onto the beer mats that Jim had requisitioned from a local hostelry.

The freedom and excess proved short-lived, with Agnes already advising, by the following day, that Kevin should consume no more than two half pints at any one sitting – that a free bar and free drinks came with strings.

'What are you having, boys?' Agnes crooned, the next time his friends were over. 'On the house, of course!'

She looked like Annie Walker, in her outdated checked dress. The resemblance didn't end there. Nestled deep in their leather seats – their jubilant faces pink with pleasure – his friends loved it.

Needling away with a right she believed she had earned, his mother would object if Kevin ever suggested that they go out instead.

'Where are you going now?' she would clip, with incomprehension.

'Meeting up with some friends,' the gruff reply.

'Why don't you invite them over instead? The pub's expensive… and it's not fair to ask your friends to help with the toilet.'

Long since inured to such embarrassments – as his friends were (to a degree) – that comment had nevertheless strayed below the belt.

'Need a change of scene,' Kevin countered smoothly, Agnes dragging her feet as she followed him out to the cab.

Struggling to fit his keys on his return – his friends long gone – Agnes would usually be waiting up for him. Balking at the very idea, Kevin would push past, keeping to a sober-looking line as he traversed the hall, before hopping tentatively up the stairs (knowing one slip would have her running).

When, with some reluctance, he *would* invite his friends, their very presence would be used against him, and – though they took it all for a joke – that lack of loyalty chafed. After everything they had shared, Kevin had expected them to take his side, at least.

'What do you think about Kevin wanting to move out?' Agnes asked, as she brought the drinks across.

'It's none of their bloody business,' Kevin hissed irritably.

'He won't find anywhere more suited to his needs, I know that much…'

'Will you stop going on about it…' Kevin spat, resenting the encouragement his friends gave those pointed queries (and their complicit smiles).

By their sixth visit to the Donnellon snug, Kevin had already decided that it would be their last; the break was final. He was done with the bar, too, with Jim left to change the barrels and check the pressure (just as he alone would set the trains spinning round a track for which Kevin had no further use).

Beating his way down the stairs with a broad smile, the *official* unveiling (six months after the first) was the last time Kevin took any pleasure from that quickly redundant bar. Weaving through the assembled guests, turning confident loops of the room – happy to oblige their assumptions – Kevin welcomed the attention.

'Mum Builds Bar for Brave Son!' read the headline in the local paper, with Kevin – a frothy pint clasped to his chest – pictured in his wheelchair beside Jim.

Taking in the room, in appreciation of the changing cast, Kevin had moved on since dropping his old friends (who he hadn't invited), with Ellesmere House now the place where he felt most at home.

No longer a child, or a student, Kevin was now rubbing

shoulders with adults in positions of influence instead, like the senior social worker for the deaf, Geoff Grimes, who was leading Bob Formby down by the elbow.

'Where's the bloody party?' Nicky Mathers bawled from the rear, her heels catching on the final step. Spotting Kevin, she rushed across to plant a smudged kiss on his left cheek. 'Tonight's the night,' she whispered gleefully – with a nod to her companions – and he shuddered at the memory of what she had said about Bob (and getting into his pants).

There had been a month of innuendoes, before she finally asked him out, declaring that 'he must be gay' when he subsequently refused. Scowling at the laughter directed her way, Nicky seemed to be the only person in the office with no knowledge of the open-secret affair Geoff and Bobby were conducting.

'Careful, watch out,' Kevin heard from the stairs, in a familiar tone, as Andrew Kavanagh led his family haltingly down.

His sister and his brother, who both now worked at Ellesmere House too, came next, then the doddering parents. Kevin merely greeted them in passing, preferring to float between the different groups than be drawn into extended conversation. He was enjoying the night on such terms, when Jim broke in, rattling at his glass for attention.

'Just a few words, if I may,' he said, 'to thank you all for coming… to help us celebrate Kevin's special night,' raising a glass. 'He's a special boy – deserves everything we can do for him.' Kevin blushed, his mind something of a blank when Jim went on to announce their 'special guest for the evening – Mickey Flynn!'

The choice of such an outdated comedian was a travesty for Kevin, but – well on their way to inebriation – the guests applauded generously, with the party quickly descending into joyful chaos as the funny man launched into his scurrilous routine.

Now stationed behind the bar, Nicky was in her element.

'I'll work the bar for you Agnes, love,' she shrieked, rubbing her chest against the beer pump, before breaking into her trademark cackle.

She hadn't given up on Bobby yet and continued to shout salacious innuendoes over the heads of the assembled crowd. Bob Formby would give only the briefest acknowledgement each time, before ducking away again. Nicky looked crestfallen when Kevin revealed that Bobby and Geoff had already gone.

'Why didn't you say something?' she snapped. 'Poor fella couldn't keep his eyes off me...'

The *World in Action* documentary that was put out two years before the grand opening of the bar was titled, aptly enough, 'Kevin at the Crossroads': the implication being that, with Kevin now nineteen years old – and an adult – everything was set to change. His parents were the only people who couldn't see it.

'And, how long do you intend to be Kevin's arms and legs for?' the journalist asked as the camera rolled, the light catching at his glasses.

'For as long as God gives me the strength,' Jim answered sanctimoniously, lifting a hand to shield his eyes, as he pointed a finger up to the sky.

Kevin, who was watching with the rest of his family, could see the job they had done on him.

'The garden looks nice,' his mother noted.

Sitting through to the end – he could hardly walk out – Kevin considered the Marxist critique of the 'means of production' that he had been studying on his Politics course and wondered why he had ever agreed to appear in such a film. *I didn't agree,* he revised... *just didn't refuse.*

'I suppose I let him do too much,' he concedes now (of Jim) – accepting the fault of his own compliance – 'and, then, he sort of became indispensable.'

For the two years that Kevin spent in college, it was Jim who generally drove him, sometimes helping him into the building itself. While Kevin had hoped to make a new start, Jim gave all the appearance of being a carer.

Sitting before that documentary, Kevin was set to thinking about crossroads, too – of where he might be headed, sensing that he couldn't go on as before.

It would be six months before he made the definitive break.

No longer a child, but not yet quite a man – and struggling to straddle the divide – Kevin's final years at home would have been difficult under any circumstances. Jim's presence only added to the pressure.

The caravan was a case in point.

'Why don't we get ourselves out to Gronant?' Jim would suggest, when the weather permitted.

'We could, I suppose,' Agnes allowed, grudgingly.

Unless he had a good excuse, it was presumed that Kevin would join them.

'It's settled, then,' Jim declared, his face betraying a rare hope.

Up ahead of them the next day, Jim would back his grey Vauxhall Magnum Estate – which, crucially, had room for a wheelchair – onto the path, from where he would check the water and the oil, before ensuring that the four tyres were sufficiently inflated. Sometimes, he would even clean the thing.

'There's perfectly good cafés along the route...' Agnes complained, at the insistence of a king-sized flask.

'Saves us making any unnecessary stops,' Jim replied, while packing provisions that would generally make the trip home with them, too (disdainful looks passing between mother and son).

Jim, who kept religiously to the legal speed restrictions (or below) – with no account given to the motorists piling up at their bumper – had his own idea of fun. Once they had hit the road proper, for instance, he would suggest that they sing something to pass the time (and meet with silence).

In preference to the recently inaugurated A55 – which Jim said 'lacked character' – they would take the coast road instead, pushing against the grey westerly winds, as they snaked through Flint, towards their creaking caravan. This was pitched on an exposed hill overlooking Prestatyn, where shivering children loitered on the promenade, arms about their thin chests, in swimming trunks and buoyancy bands.

'Are we there, yet?' Kevin would periodically call – making his mother smile – when, in truth, he knew every station by heart.

The caravan was massive, with its steep sides pitted against the overgrown grass. Despite boasting wheels and a galvanised hook, it had not taken a single step away from its gloomy home pitch in seven years.

'Faces due north,' Jim informed them proudly, imagining he saw the flicker of interest.

Pushing his chair up to the edge, Kevin took a breath of the salty sea air: grey and gloomy, with a ferocious high tide.

'Well, it's too cold to be stood out here, chatting,' Agnes declared, as she opened up the caravan and had Jim fix the ramp to the front step.

Squeezing through to the main living quarters, Kevin hopped across to one of the soft benches that ran along the three walls (beneath a window that looked out on the slanting rain).

There were two bedrooms – a double for the parents and a low-stacked single for Kevin – while the bathroom, which featured a steaming hot shower, was nestled behind a plywood concertina door, Kevin catching greedily at the bacon frying on the griddle that would herald the start of each day.

There was a radio and a TV, too – that could pick up BBC Wales (when the reception allowed) – though the idea of trapping three such misaligned individuals in one small box was hopeful, at best.

It usually rained – their mooring providing a microclimate all its own – and then they would be forced to make their own entertainment. They would play cards – whist, pontoon (betting with matches) – and Agnes would knit, while Jim tuned the radio to distraction in the hope of finding something of which Kevin approved. If the clouds even briefly parted, they would immediately step out to take the air.

The local walks were uninspiring and none too accessible: a narrow path took them down to the beach and all the way back up again, while the waterfall, at Dyserth, could only be reached by car (with Kevin left to wait at the base with an Orange Maid).

When the weather allowed, they would set their deckchairs out at the side of the caravan, while the evening would find them tramping down to the on-site social club.

Jim led the way, on their first night, when – after seven hours cooped up in the confines of the caravan (it had been raining straight through) – they were inclined to desperation.

'It'll make a change,' Agnes noted stoically, as Jim took her hand (in a rare show of affection) and they marched down in tandem, with Kevin taking up the rear.

At the door, Agnes combed through her matted hair, before baring her teeth in a public smile and taking Jim's arm.

'Shall we?' she said, pushing Kevin in ahead and scurrying to a table as the caller gave the next number and a distant jukebox droned.

Signing them up for the next round, Jim was in his element and competed with glee, though the Donnellons were not amused and – henceforth – Jim would venture forth alone, the beer on tap his sole consolation.

'I suppose you've been drinking again?' Agnes would chide, on his return.

'Just a couple,' Jim would answer carefully, before slipping into the bathroom. 'You should have come down – they had a band on...'

Through the steady, drizzling gloom of Gronant – with few enough breaks for light (as Kevin recalls) – Jim had more need of Dutch courage than ever. Sometimes he would slink off before they were even unpacked, helping them in with the heavy cases – and a quick look up to the darkening sky – before stepping quietly out again.

'I'll go down and see what they've got on…'

He wasn't missed and there was an almost palpable lifting of tension, but – seeing him trudging, alone, down the hill once more – Kevin suddenly felt something stir and chased out after him.

Kevin hadn't attended the wedding, performed in haste at a pale registry office, but had to acknowledge that Jim was hardly to blame if something had died in his wife along with her late husband (or, for lacking the imagination to help).

Kevin and Jim had little in common, but – as the drink flowed – they made subtle accommodations. Kevin even had Jim laughing, at one point, and it seemed that they might make a fresh start; his mother was a difficult woman, he would never deny it, while Jim clearly did what he could.

'Agnes finds it hard, sometimes,' Jim conceded, as he set the drinks down. 'I genuinely think that having you around is the only thing that keeps her going.'

'You help, too,' Kevin admitted; it was the first time he had allowed such a fact.

There was no going back, of course, but this new understanding would help set subsequent (and past) events into relief.

On another trip to the caravan (in early June), Agnes would terminate what was not even the beginning of an argument with the decision that Jim should immediately drive their two guests – Maureen and Dom – all the way home again.

'Can't we at least wait until the morning?' Jim suggested, as a compromise. 'It's getting late…'

Agnes, who was already helping her friends out with their bags, ignored him and was in no mood for reconciliation on Jim's return to camp three hours later.

'We're all packed,' she said – without further explanation – 'and we're leaving right now.'

Jim wasn't even allowed a cup of tea, with the kitchen cleared in his absence, and they drove the homeward trail in silence, Jim's bleary eyes holding to the stuttering parallel lines – below the rain-dusted clouds – as night descended.

Stoically acceding to demands that went beyond what could be considered acceptable – and taking their criticism without complaint – Jim had much to recommend him.

'I like helping Kevin,' he had told Agnes, early on – when she had worried at the additional burden – and he had been true to his word, seeming pleased to have a purpose.

Too compliant – taken for granted and rarely thanked – his luxurious caravan, on top of that glowering hill, was just another white elephant: a symbol of how out of step he was.

'It must be so hard,' he had said, broaching the subject to Agnes, in the lamp-light of the bedroom, shortly after moving in, as they followed Kevin's thumping progress up the stairs, to bed.

He had known the challenges Kevin faced, but had never quite appreciated the practicalities.

Balking at the sentimentality, and the overreach, Agnes was sharp with him for the first time – 'Kevin's fine,' she snapped – and the truth was that Kevin would always come between them.

He was her son, and John's – nobody else had a right.

Thus, when Kevin finally took his leave, devastated – and in mourning – Agnes almost immediately kicked Jim out, too.

'I only married him because of you,' she explained, as Kevin stumbled out with the last of his clothes.

'What's Jim got to do with me?' Kevin asked, in genuine confusion.

'This is it, I suppose,' his mother said then, stepping out in front of him. 'I'll probably never see you again…'

'Don't be daft,' Kevin scoffed. 'I'll be popping round all the time.'

'This will always be your home – just remember that,' Agnes insisted.

Kevin offered no contradiction, but he never returned.

His departure brought a relapse for Agnes, whose grief – it seemed – had only been postponed. Sick and sleepless, she was taking ever-stronger medication just to get through the day.

Her practicality was a muscle, with a memory all its own, however, and would see to the divorce and to the reversion to her maiden name, while – desperately severing ties with all that was lost – she would also move house again. Hatherley Avenue – a four-bed semi (off King's Way) – was the first home Kevin wouldn't share.

At first, Kevin had called her every day, but – meeting with reluctance and hostility – this correspondence was soon down to once a week, his mother claiming not to recognise his voice for several minutes, before maintaining that she was busy and couldn't talk. Sometimes she would hang up before he had even said goodbye; duty done, Kevin rarely rang back.

'She's not well,' Joan explained, in her defence. 'Thinks you've deserted her.'

'I was always going to leave one day,' Kevin returned, in an emollient tone.

'She says she would have helped you move, if you'd asked – that she could have found you a flat…'

'Then, I saved her a job.'

'And, with Jim gone, too…' Joan resumed.

While accepting no responsibility for his mother's private life – and believing that he had stayed home for as long as he could – Kevin didn't argue, though he wondered at his mother's complaints, given that she refused to visit him (and had not once invited him to her new home).

And, she's still got Lizzie, he considered, not yet willing to admit that his situation would always be judged on different terms.

By the following spring, Lizzie would be gone too, and – rattling alone around a house made for six – Agnes had even less resistance. She blamed Jim for making them move, 'when we were quite happy where we were', with the saleable value of the property on Litherland Park having tripled in the two years since their departure.

She was thinking of John too, knowing now that she should never have tried to live with another man.

It was a year before Kevin saw her again and, by then, Agnes had – despite such reservations – already married for a third time and was moving house once more.

'Widow, aged 60, seeks companionship,' Joan said, reading from the classified ad she had encouraged her mother to fill out.

'Sounds like a real catch,' Kevin sneered.

'Well, she can't stay cooped up in that house for the rest of her life,' Joan returned irritably.

Excepting for a three-month period at Woolston Mead nursing home, at the back end of 2017, Agnes would see out her remaining years in the pebble-dashed semi on Brookfield Avenue, where she eventually set up home with her third husband.

Despite such changes, Agnes was reluctant to accept that Kevin was no longer the child she had thought he would remain. Kevin was seven years on Nunsford Close – his first home – but his mother only visited once.

She arrived in the company of an old friend, death and divorce having drawn them together, the two senior citizens thrown by the sight of a door giving way unassisted (Kevin had applied the release without a word of warning).

'In here, Mother,' he called, having teased enough.

'Oh Kevin, I am glad… I thought I had the wrong… this is Aunt Nelly – you remember Aunt Nelly?' she gabbled, and he could see, now, that there was nothing to fear.

They took tea in the living room, with Kevin providing a selection of sandwiches and a plate of biscuits, to help fill the gaps when the conversation flagged.

'You live here… all by yourself?' Aunt Nelly asked, with a quiver in her voice, Kevin confirming the fact with a cheery nod of the head.

'Just me and the cat,' he added.

That was Trotsky, who – drawn to the unfamiliar chatter – was following their reunion from behind a pot plant.

'I'm sure it's very nice,' Agnes allowed doubtfully, with her nose in the air, her straight back barely brushing the cushions.

There the conversation stalled, with Agnes at a loss for anything positive to say about such a basic – barely furnished – flat, in a neighbourhood that had her fearing for her son's safety. Despite misgivings, she kept her counsel, with Joan warning that she would lose Kevin if she didn't respect his decisions.

'It's good to see that you're well… and happy, I hope?' Agnes broke in, looking dubiously across (through the thick lenses of her new spectacles). 'But, we really do need to go,' she added, setting down her cup.

She would never come again, but a truce had been called and Kevin was now invited home on a regular basis, his car creeping to a still on the street outside, while he considered – once again – whether to go through with the visit.

'Hello, Mother,' he would assay cautiously, no longer sure of the terms.

'Kevin,' the terse reply, as he turned about the hall, noting ornaments he had grown up with, wondering at all we drag along with us.

A handsome property, set back from the road, with purple rhododendrons bowing under their own weight over the stooped front wall, a peaked roof and a two-storey projecting bay, Brookfield Avenue was a stone's throw from her previous residence, so Agnes hadn't fallen far.

Yet, there was a new dynamic at play and it would take several tourneys to establish their new roles, with neither side quite prepared to be the person they had once been.

Kevin would arrive by noon, with lunch set for one o'clock, taking a ramp up the two front steps into the hall, before wheeling through to the living room, where the Sunday papers would be laid out for him (while his mother skipped off to the kitchen).

'I'll bring you a cup of tea now,' she would call through. 'Dinner's in half an hour…'

'Ta,' Kevin would call back, noting the pleasure in her voice (and indulging it).

The conversation would only be properly joined when they were sat down to lunch, Agnes asking – with a keen desire – after his sisters; of those friends she knew by name; of his days in the office. Now that she had no real hold on him, Kevin no longer resented such intrusions, and – with his mother hanging on every word – he would regale her with carefully excised comedic accounts of Ellesmere House.

He rarely mentioned his domestic – or social – life.

'Have you got enough of everything?' Agnes would ask, dropping another potato to his plate.

'Oh, yes – a veritable feast!' Kevin pronounced, glad to be able to offer satisfaction.

'You've always had a good appetite,' she reminded him, with affection – looking ten years younger – and, listening to her padding about in the kitchen, Kevin could see that even briefly providing for his care brought her the balance she lacked.

This balance would shift, again, with the arrival of Arthur Turner-Bone.

'And, you must be Kevin?' he said, offering his hand – with a stoop – at the door.

'And, you're Arthur, I guess?' Kevin returned with a smile, waiting to be let inside (wondering where his mother was).

He felt distinctly underdressed, wearing yesterday's lightly soiled threads, while Arthur sported a crisp shirt and a strict tie beneath a corduroy suit (his Sunday best). They had been to church, he was grudgingly informed, already feeling the gulf – knowing that the shutters were down and he wasn't welcome.

Given such an arid nature, Kevin was surprised to learn that Arthur had three children of his own, though they were adults by now and he would only meet one of them in person.

Their engagement had been announced within weeks, with their pet names – 'Charlie' for Arthur and 'Sam' for Agnes – suggesting something false from the start, while Mrs Turner, as she was now known, would only take on half of Arthur's double-barrel, as though she was only ever half involved.

'He's a real gentleman,' Agnes noted, 'and always immaculately turned out.'

The tensions, which were implicit all along, would only surface when Arthur discovered that the house he now called his own was anything but.

'John left it to Kevin, when he died,' Agnes sought to explain.

'Yes, but, Kevin doesn't live here anymore…'

'I know, I know,' Agnes concurred, sadly.

With the equity accrued from the bungalow (on Litherland Park), which his father had bought outright, having passed between the various properties in the interim – with bridging loans from the Thalidomide Trust to make up the shortfall – the house had value, too.

Kevin had never made any particular claim, accepting the fact that he had moved on: that the property – which Agnes had bought and sold, in the past, without ever asking his permission – was hers to do with as she pleased.

'It's your home, as much as mine,' Agnes assured her husband.

'But I'm not blood,' Arthur returned, his eye passing idly over the mantelpiece (with its litter of portraits). 'And, if anything were to happen…'

Agnes, who had suffered loss enough of her own, was sympathetic and could understand how Arthur – who had recently had to pay off the remaining instalments on their TV, after the thalidomide payments had fallen through – would want some security. She had wondered, briefly, whether Kevin would one day expect her to pay rent, too.

'If the house was put into your name,' Arthur pursued, 'then, we'd both have peace of mind…'

Agnes agreed to speak to Kevin, when he came over for his usual Sunday visit and she was true to her word.

'I think you were right to move out,' she conceded, as Kevin put aside what he was reading. 'Everyone has a right to a place of their own – to feel safe and secure…'

'Is everything okay?' Kevin asked, his eyes turning towards Arthur.

'It's the house,' Agnes said, at last, 'and the fact that, with the deeds still in your name, you could evict us at any time.'

'Why would I do that?' Kevin scoffed, while recalling that the Thalidomide Trust had recently suggested as much (as a means of releasing the equity).

He had told them that the house was his mother's, as far as he was concerned.

'We don't feel safe…' Agnes resumed.

'Well, you should – this is your house and I would never interfere.'

'That's very kind, but… in legal terms, I don't have any rights. And, what would happen to Arthur, for instance, if I was to pass on?'

'Oh, there's still a few years left in you,' Kevin chuckled, 'and, I'm sure Arthur can look after himself,' he added, with a nod of acknowledgement.

'We've talked it through,' Agnes continued – Arthur had now taken her hand – 'and, we think, if you really have no further claims, then it would best if you turned the property over to us. There'd always be a home for you here, of course, but we'd be able to rest easy, too.'

Her hands were shaking – her face drawn; her lips dry – and, though he understood that she was pleading her husband's case rather than her own, Kevin knew he couldn't refuse.

'If it really means that much to you,' he said, leaning closer, 'then, of course…'

After giving a reassuring smile to her husband, Agnes broke into tears and Kevin could suddenly see just how old she was.

The documents were already set out on the dining room table when Kevin arrived the following weekend. After working a Parker ballpoint between his fingers, Arthur directed Kevin on where to sign.

'That should do it,' he said, collecting up the papers with a lightness of step. 'It'll be a weight off your mother.'

He hadn't seen his mother yet, and – musing on the power of the pen (how a handful of squiggles had released the equity that had resided for so long in his name) – he wondered where she was hiding.

Kevin had thought that they would grow old together, at least – that Arthur was his mother's last hurrah – yet, two years into their union, Agnes had broken with Arthur too.

She kept the name – Agnes Turner – and, such was the affection she still maintained, when she heard from one of his daughters that Arthur had taken ill, she immediately stepped in to help.

If Arthur returned but a shadow of the man he had once been, he was possibly a better man for it.

'I want you to come home,' Agnes insisted.

There were tears on both sides, with Agnes never wavering in her desire to help Arthur see out his last days in love and companionship.

Chapter 23

53 Nunsford Close,
Litherland,
Liverpool,
L21 0JW

Given Kevin's particular lexicon, the postcode would always bring the Jehovah's Witnesses to mind, but – as the place where he finally came of age – Nunsford Close was memorable in its own right.

'I've found you a flat!' Geoff gushed into the headset.

'Where?' Kevin chipped back, sceptically.

'Netherton… it's perfect,' Geoff replied.

As they turned onto the winding cul-de-sac of two-storey maisonettes, where Kevin was to reside for the next seven years, there was much to recommend it. Although no longer the properties they had once been, with their flat roofs naturally susceptible to rain and the untreated paintwork peeling from the windows, the communal garden – that backed onto Ford Cemetery – offered a generous lawn, while a line of laburnums provided for privacy.

Nunsford Close was an estate that predominated in 'problem' families, with truanting children roaming the streets by day and the night providing cover for vandals and petty criminals. Untaxed cars – with flat tyres and mismatched doors – were sat up on the grass verges, while whorls of razor wire decorated the defensive walls between the properties.

Oddly enough, Kevin sensed an immediate kinship.

'I won't carry you over the threshold,' Geoff quipped, before leading him in, Kevin sniffing at the fresh emulsion.

Ten minutes later, Kevin – the master of all he surveyed – was beaming when he waved down to Geoff from the top of the ramp.

'This will always be your real home,' his mother would remind him, on his next visit, but he hadn't seen her in weeks (by this point) and she wouldn't come to call on him for another three months.

Already adapted for the previous (deceased) tenant, the front door was operated by an electric fob, with the floors stripped back for use of a chair. The living room led through to a narrow kitchenette – with a patio door opening out on the garden – while the bedroom had built-in wardrobes, with Kevin already imagining the use he would make of the double bed wedged into its restrictive confines. The installation of a Clos-o-mat brought a welcome familiarity to his ablutions.

Engaging the services of Andrew Kavanagh's brother, Liam, Kevin had soon made the place his own, with shelves and pictures fixed to the newly decorated walls and an additional set of taps fitted to the junction beneath the sink to give Kevin independent access (and the chance to fill a kettle).

A temporary solution to a bewildering oversight, that makeshift plumbing would still be in place two years later, when a film crew called on Kevin once more – for Anglia Television's *Tin Lids* – with the hero happy to show off such ingenuity as a further mark of resilience.

Despite having to sit in the dark, because the switches were all – as yet – too high to reach, Kevin could only see the positives on his first night. It was quiet, for a start, a welcome change from the rattling corridors of Briar Moss, and he was well and truly alone.

As the wind picked up outside – and the rain beat at the windows – Kevin was stretched out contentedly on the floor, when a roll of thunder followed a volley of hail and – finally – lightning struck: a line of electricity that illuminated the room. Kevin cheered it on.

'Oh, what sound and fury!' he boomed, mangling the Shakespeare he had learned in school, those slithers of verse peppering an idle imagination (thinking, erroneously, of Lear).

A series of thumps on the window nearly lifted him up off the floor, and – fearing a cracked pane – Kevin galloped across to check, pulling in a panic at the blinds.

He was met by a set of wild eyes staring out from a dark mop of matted hair and he backed away, only edging closer when he saw that the man was trying to get his attention.

'Next door,' the grinning stranger mimed, as Kevin chased round to the front to open up. 'I'm Dave Burns,' the man panted. 'Thought I'd come and check you were okay.'

'Pleased to meet you,' Kevin returned, flipping his stub digits up to the hand he was offered, his guest entering with a pronounced limp.

'What you doing sat in the dark, anyway?' he asked, as he drew to a halt.

'Can't reach the switches,' Kevin conceded sheepishly.

Flipping on the overhead lights, before fixing the blinds into place, Kevin's new friend took that as his cue.

'Wanted to make sure you were alright, like – saw you rocking up in your chair this afternoon…' seeming, only now, to consider that his companion didn't have legs.

'Sorry about the mess,' Kevin returned, nodding towards the boxes piled up against the far wall.

Dave was rather more concerned with finding somewhere to sit.

'Don't mind me,' he said, joining Kevin on the floor. 'Just need to take the weight off me legs.'

'I'd offer you a cup of tea,' Kevin said, 'but I haven't got any milk.'

'Well, you should have said,' Dave cried, scrambling up to his feet.

He was back within minutes, and bearing gifts – a thick-cut loaf, a carton of milk and a packet of custard creams – and quickly banging his way through the kitchen in search of the kettle (which he set to boil).

He would stay for the next two hours and, given the need to explain – and to set out the preliminaries he so often struggled to get beyond – Kevin welcomed the chance for a lengthy introduction.

When Dave asked if he could smoke, Kevin waved him nonchalantly on.

'Weed, like...,' Dave clarified, a shy smile showing through his missing teeth – he was already fitting the roach. 'It's medicinal... for me MS.'

Only after lighting up and taking a couple of slow draughts, did he hesitantly offer it across to Kevin, who wedged the stump into the crook of his three fingers – releasing a spark of hash – before taking a quick, self-conscious breath and passing it back.

'You should have said you smoked,' Dave – a regular visitor over the next seven years – offered in apology. 'I would have made you one.'

A pounding on the door was followed by a cry through the letter box.

'Hey, kid – open up!'

It was Big Eric, and – already knowing his reputation – Kevin had no choice but to answer, releasing the catch with unease, before turning to face this latest inquisitor.

'Peace offering,' Eric said from the door, raising a six-pack of beer, before stepping across to offer his hand.

It was early for Kevin, but he took the proffered can. With Eric generous and respectful, but rarely standing on ceremony, that first introduction settled the relationship.

By his third visit, knowing now that Kevin rarely secured the front door, Eric would generally push in unannounced – they were friends, after all – and they would sit and put the world to rights, with Eric just as interested in Kevin's description of Ellesmere House as he was in outlining the range of his criminal activities

(Kevin agog with curiosity). Eric was witty and – refreshingly – lacked any hint of condescension.

Eric was, inevitably, the first to see the potential when Kevin turned onto the estate in his sparkling new van.

'Great Rev Head!' he would christen the proud owner, after spotting the licence plate, his steel-bright eyes flashing at the possibilities. 'Right – everyone in!' he snorted and it seemed like half the street had squeezed aboard when they finally set off for the first jaunt of many.

Having genuinely taken to the youthful welfare advisory officer, Eric took these liberties as his right, with his new friend's better nature giving him what he considered free rein. For his part, Kevin was – under Eric's tutelage – now practically untouchable.

Turning a forlorn circle, as he stumbled from the cab to the kerb, Kevin would return from a Bahá'í conference (in New York) to find that same van gone.

'What the fuck… it was right there,' he cried, before racing into the house and tapping 999.

He never suspected Eric, who – grinning triumphantly from behind the wheel – was rumbling back onto the estate within the hour. Kevin ran out to meet him.

'What the fuck do you think you're doing?' he bawled.

'Bit of business, lad,' Eric called down nonchalantly, before cutting the engine, Kevin only now wondering how he had managed to work the pedals.

Eric led the way back to the house, with Kevin's anger sliding imperceptibly into bewilderment.

'What business?' he snapped, once he had him inside, leaving Eric to explain how he had come into possession of some 'knock-off' beer, with the van the perfect way to offload it.

'Here's your cut,' he added, dropping a thick wrap of notes to his lap.

Kevin glared across, without even looking at the money.

'You've no right taking my van,' he hissed. 'I thought it had been stolen – I rang the police!'

'The police; what the fuck… when?' Eric spluttered in panic.

'I called them back when I saw you, but…' Kevin clarified.

'I thought you were going to say you'd shopped me, then – shit!' Eric chuckled. 'How was New York, anyway? Fancy a brew?'

They took tea together and Eric elaborated with an unusual note of contrition.

'I would have asked, but you weren't here,' he said, 'and… it was too good an opportunity to pass up.' He paused, the big man suddenly small. 'I didn't break in, or anything,' he added. 'I remembered where you kept the spares… I honestly didn't think you'd mind.'

He was grinning again, and he was hard to resist, though Kevin wondered what would have happened if Eric had been discovered… how he would have explained the circumstances to the Thalidomide Trust.

Curiosity would bring all of Kevin's neighbours around, in due course, their scepticism turning to grudging respect when they saw how – screeching to a halt at a thirty-degree angle to the lines of his reserved space – the 'thalidomide kid' went about parking. He didn't even lock the doors, they discovered – after trying them, naturally – though the adapted controls were enough to stop them rooting further.

When, pumping his fist into the air and bumping at his horn, they first saw Kevin chasing off to Goodison Park with a blue-striped scarf throttled about his throat, the estate was naturally split.

Taking his first independent steps in the world, Kevin was open to suggestion and keen to show his allegiance.

'What have you done?' his mother asked, of the prodigal, when they finally met up again, though the thick ash-brown perm and the well-developed moustache were mere physical manifestations.

These were superficial – strategic – changes, with Kevin making no play of his intelligence or ambitions in a setting that didn't require them.

Though he had been quickly taken into the fold and had an admitted affinity, Kevin never once imagined that he would be living on Nunsford Close forever. Thus, when Tom Black, the colourful new boss at Ellesmere House, turned a missionary eye onto his domestic life, Kevin welcomed the chance to stretch his legs.

Exiting the cab on the street, sniffing at an ill wind – plastic melted on a bonfire; dog dirt smeared along the kerb – Tom was more than conspicuous. *How can Kevin live in such a hovel?* he mused, with a shudder.

Kevin hurried him inside, Tom stepping over the stripped boards with a look of genuine concern.

'Where's your furniture?' he cried, pinpointing his unease.

'Not got round to buying any, yet,' Kevin conceded casually, while – measuring bare walls with wide strides and drawing the curtains back to see how the light fell – Tom strode through the other rooms.

Kevin's living quarters would be dealt with in time, with interior design proving yet another field of expertise. Within six months, there wasn't much Tom hadn't turned his hand to, and – after the limitations he had experienced at home – Kevin welcomed the freedom to indulge (finding, in Tom, a man after his own heart).

If there were tensions, Kevin didn't see them.

'He told you about Mr Black?' Gary asked (when the name emerged).

'Yeah, and he's a great character,' I replied, having almost forgotten that Gary had known him, too.

'It wasn't right – Mr Black was very manipulative,' Gary said, bringing silence. 'He took Kevin's credit cards,' he resumed, 'and would use them for himself.'

There was disdain in the tone – the sense of a battle gone through.

'Kevin told me he was controlling, but he doesn't think he ever stole anything…'

'He did,' Gary insisted. 'He was a right creep.'

'He's a great character, though,' I resumed. 'Some of the stories are crazy.'

'They were strange times,' Gary allowed, drifting into silence. 'But, I suppose you'll have to change the names…'

'Why?' I asked, with the thought having never occurred (and the veracity of the text so important).

'It could be seen as defamation, though,' Gary rejoined. 'Perhaps you could call him Mr Blake, instead?' he added, with a chuckle. 'Yes – that would work…'

I forced the phone down, feeling an erasure in that winnowing of truth; in the dilution of the stories I could hear in my head.

It was Saturday night and the cab had deposited them in a part of town they didn't know, the two friends following their guide – in confusion – as he set off at pace down first a side street and then a narrow ginnel.

They turned the next corner to find him rapping energetically at an unlikely looking door.

'What the hell's he doing now?' Kevin hissed, wondering at another wild goose chase.

'It's a bit tricky to find, that's all,' Tom called back, 'but, bear with…'

Kevin had turned his chair and was ready to roll away, when – at the sound of footsteps somewhere inside – the door came open and Tom waved them in.

While the lock was being bolted behind them and Tom was shaking hands with one of the attendants, Kevin and Mark were gently frisked. There was music coming from several directions and – stumbling into a dimly lit club of some kind – it was a struggle to get their bearings.

'What the fuck's this?' Kevin shouted to Mark, with Tom having already left them.

'I'll get some drinks,' Mark called back, leaving Kevin to make his self-conscious way across to an unoccupied table.

'I think it's a gay bar,' he told Mark on his return, giving a nod to the dance floor.

'Yeah,' Mark agreed, 'some old geezer just propositioned me!'

It was Jody's and, perched high in his unwieldy chair, Kevin felt more conspicuous than ever.

'He's got some nerve bringing us here,' he hissed; having shared a bottle of wine before coming out, he was already feeling at his bladder. 'It's the last bloody time,' he added, after a tentative sip.

'Where the fuck's he gone, anyway?' Mark asked.

'There,' Kevin cried suddenly, spotting him – up against the wall, in the arms of a man.

Mark gave a smirk.

'Do you want another one?' he asked, tipping his glass.

'No, but ask Tom where the toilets are,' Kevin replied, watching Mark work his way across the crowded room towards Tom, who he took by the arm, before circling back to the bar (suddenly feeling unaccountably sad).

'He said we're not staying long,' Mark announced, after dropping their drinks to the table.

'Where are the bogs?' Kevin broke in.

'Down the side, behind the bar – Tom reckons the bouncers will give you a hand, if you ask.'

Having been forced out against his will and now needing to take a piss without recourse to an accessible toilet, this latest indignity broke him.

'Fuck Tom,' Kevin thundered, ramming his chair at the table and forcing his way through the straggling dancers, as he barged in a straight, uncompromising line towards the exit.

He offered no apologies, knowing only that he needed to leave and wouldn't be back.

Looking on his friend's single-handed retreat with admiration,

Mark downed the rest of his pint before setting off in pursuit (on a more circuitous route). He appreciated the help he was given at the door, just as Kevin rudely refused it. Stepping outside, he could already hear his friend roaring out expletives.

He had to jog to catch up, calling across to Kevin as he ran on ahead, ramming his chair up against the kerb.

'I'll ring a cab,' he said, placing a hand on his friend's shoulder (wondering whether his drink had been spiked).

'I don't want a fucking cab,' Kevin moaned, nearly tipping his chair as he turned. 'I just want Tom out of my fucking life!'

'I'm sure that can be arranged,' Mark returned with a smile, stepping back to the wall as Kevin came careening past. 'Whoa – watch out!'

'Fuck off,' Kevin shrieked, crunching his wheels over some broken glass. 'Tom's a twat and I hate the fucker,' he bawled, bringing cheers and catcalls from those within earshot.

'I can see that,' Mark said, 'but you need to calm down, or you'll have the bizzies on us.'

'Ring a fucking cab, then,' Kevin hissed disdainfully, before setting off up the road again, leaving Mark – who was now laughing openly – to dig through his pockets for change.

'Taxi, please,' he slurred into the mouthpiece, surprised to find that the phone – that was sat in a shattered booth – was still functional, remembering (at the last moment) to order an accessible vehicle.

It was a relief to be going home and, slumped back against the wall, he watched Kevin chasing about like some kind of wind-up toy, bashing into doors, scraping at the shop fronts.

'Taxi'll be here any minute,' he advised, with a yawn, when Kevin was in range.

'And, you can fuck off, too,' Kevin retorted, spinning away again.

Drawing up to the bus shelter, Kevin stopped to make a brief study of his reflection in the glass: his tousled hair standing on end, his best shirt soiled and torn. There was comedy in such a riposte, and Kevin – who was now ready for home – was almost tranquil when he wheeled back towards Mark (who was slouched against a wall).

Then, the evening he had just spent rushing back to him, Kevin turned full circle and raced his chair, full speed, into the side of the shelter, shattering the glass, before punching his fingers through the criss-crossed pattern that clung to the frame.

'What the fuck have you done?' Mark cried, hurrying across.

Kevin, who had blood on his shirt, looked ecstatic when he was bundled aboard the taxi that pulled up a minute later, his eye drawn back to the metal seats and the glass that littered the street.

He woke up on his bed and still in his clothes, with a bandage wrapped about his hand, struggling to reconstruct how Mark had managed to get him inside. He groaned when Rhona arrived and pulled the curtains, in an attempt to rouse him, his head banging as the light poured in. He let the phone ring.

In work, on Monday, with scratches on his face and a freshly laundered bandage, Kevin kept his head down and kept busy, steadfastly avoiding the boss. He was relieved to find that Tom, who didn't seek him out, seemed also to understand.

In the evening, back home – with the phone unplugged – he felt like he had his life back; it was only then that he acknowledged just what a hold Tom had managed to secure.

When the weekend came and went, without further contact – he had taken what precautions he could – he knew it was over and returned to the office on Monday with an overriding sense of relief. The air had cleared, and he could now see what he couldn't see before.

Andrew was almost immediately taking him aside to explain that a meeting had been called to discuss Mr Black's inappropriate behaviour around the office, with a number of their colleagues set to lodge a complaint.

'Do *you* have any grievances?' he asked.

Kevin's eyes smarted, when he set about explaining what he

thought everyone already knew, surprised to find that – though he had suffered more than most – nearly every other member of staff had something to complain of (be it a single incident or a sequence of events).

Kevin's were the only accusations that extended beyond the workplace, however, and he could admit to a glimmer of guilt when he slipped past Tom's office, recognising the extent to which he had initially invited those advances.

If Kevin's fingers were all over the completed list of grievances – with Andrew having each witness sign a duplicate copy – he accepted his responsibilities, too.

'It was all too much in the end,' he admitted, those twenty-four years finally catching up with him.

For, when he considered the way he had let Tom make such use of him – how keen he had been to please – Kevin was taking account of himself, too. *I could have said no,* he thought. *No one made me do anything.*

The details that emerged were a surprise to his workmates, who hadn't appreciated just how close they had become.

'There's enough here to get him the sack,' Andrew judged, and Kevin felt a loss then, that he couldn't quite explain.

When Tom was called into a meeting with his superiors the following week, Kevin finally understood that freedom should only be given with caveats. His eyes pinned to the door of the conference room, there was no more guilt – he was only glad to have Tom out of his life.

The afternoon passed in rumour and supposition, with Tom remaining in his office until the time came to leave it, which he did without a single word of correspondence. They would hear, later, that Tom had been too appalled to even deny the charges, and – in the circumstances – he had been given two options: move to another office, or resign.

'Where's Tom?' Kevin asked, the following day.

'Not here,' someone answered blandly, yet he had known it the moment he walked into that open-plan office, his nose reaching unconsciously for the three pyramid notes that usually held sway: the upper register – of bergamot, coriander and lime; the tender 'heart' notes – of nutmeg, jasmine and sage; the discordant base – of amber and vanilla.

Calvin Klein Obsession (1986), the 'perfume in the air' – the sharp, herbaceous scent of Tom Black – was gone and, in diminishing returns, forgotten.

It was 1985. Kevin was now twenty-four years of age.

Chapter 24

If leaving home had drawn an irrevocable line and Kevin was now free to do as he pleased, the first relationship he embarked on – with Doris – had necessitated the sort of secrecy he had hoped to leave behind.

Fixing pictures – of Kevin's choosing – to the living room walls, while carefully arranging the furniture and the rickety shelves (which were crammed with 'enriching' literature), Liam Kavanagh had helped him decorate.

'I suppose this is what you'd call a bachelor pad,' Andrew opined, on his first visit, stroking blindly down the book spines and pinching at the potted plants (to check they were real).

'It's just a flat!' Kevin barked, before dismissing his friend in his usual manner. 'Now, bugger off!'

He was still to unpack and it would be some time before he felt properly settled; longer still before he could find a woman interested in sharing his life.

Bachelorhood was a lonely state for Kevin, whose family had always been close by; operating an open-door policy from the start, he increasingly craved company.

By 1984 his working life had changed too, and – no longer based at Ellesmere House – Kevin was surprised at the extent to which he missed his former colleagues. Bored and underemployed, initially, in his new post, Kevin would call through to Klara Haywood on the switchboard, or to old friends (in the hope of catching them).

Talkabout was a BT telephone service that allowed as many as nine people to speak together on a single line, at the same time, with monitors listening in to prevent the exchange of numbers or addresses.

'I probably only went on half a dozen times,' Kevin said, confessing in his way, and I remembered friends who had dropped their coins in just for the chance to profane down the line, until the censors caught up and cut them off (taking what remained of their credit).

Kevin, who at twenty-two years old was already wearying of the sorts of conversations he would have to wade through, dialled reluctantly, and was following the distended banter with dispassion, when he picked out a voice he hadn't heard before. It was a girl, with a lilting tone.

'Hello?' she tried hesitantly – that doubt, a draw in itself. 'I know it's a bit boring, but is there anyone sensible on the line?'

'I'm sensible,' Kevin submitted quickly.

'Good, because I need some distraction…'

'Me too,' Kevin agreed. 'Right now, I'm sat in the office, bored rigid!'

It seemed – miraculously – that they had the line to themselves (with ears only for each other) and they took advantage.

'I'm meant to be revising,' the girl admitted, 'but nothing's going in, so I thought I'd take a break… clear my head.' She sighed. 'It's such a beautiful day, while I'm stuck inside…'

She sounded lovely: calm and level-headed.

'What do you study?' Kevin asked, seeking to establish a rapport.

'O-levels,' she replied, 'and tomorrow – for my sins – I've got French oral.'

'Well, I don't remember much of my French from school,' Kevin conceded, 'but perhaps I can help you revise?' He paused, working the words in his head (mangling the accent). '*Quel est votre el telephone numero?*'

The girl gave it back to him in turn – '*Neuf deux quatre neuf zero sept huit*' – within the earshot, but beyond the wit, of their warders.

'Well, nice talking to you…' Kevin said quickly, fearing some reprisal. 'Perhaps we can speak again, later?'

The girl was Tracey and he phoned her back after work.

'I'm sixteen years old,' she explained, the six years between them not the chasm he might have expected. 'I live with my parents, in Fazakerley,' she continued brightly.

'I've got my own flat,' Kevin returned, 'and I drive an Escort XR3,' he added, telling what – given the recent amendments – he considered only a white lie.

'Is that good?' Tracey asked cautiously. 'I'm going to take lessons, but I don't know the first thing about cars.'

'Perhaps I could take you out for a drive, sometime,' Kevin said, fixing a date – without considering the implications – 'help you practise?'

They prattled on in such a manner for over an hour, and the time simply flew, their conversation taking in their respective schools and the dreaded public examination system.

Kevin brought laughter when he described his job (and his work-mates), before moving on to music and films, and (never flagging) the general stupidity of the majority of the callers on Talkabout.

'There should be some sort of procedure to weed them out,' he suggested, drawing an excited squeal. 'Maybe an IQ test…'

'Don't be mean,' Tracey exclaimed, with a giggle.

'No exceptions!' Kevin declared, to a bleat of suppressed laughter. 'Though I suppose they wouldn't make any money then, would they?'

More laughter, and – a mix of naivety and intelligence – he already felt like he knew her.

They got to talking further over the next few days and suddenly his time in the office had a purpose and a routine, with Kevin generally ringing Tracey straight after lunch.

'I read up on photosynthesis this morning,' she declared breezily – Kevin hanging on every word – 'and, after this call, I'm studying enzymes and digestion.'

Kevin gave encouragement and offered praise, while exaggerating the importance of his own position (promoting himself several times in the process).

Anonymity was liberating, but – five calls in – Tracey was already seeking more.

'Can you tell me what you look like?' she asked. 'Hair colour… eyes. I'd like to try to picture you, when we talk.'

Kevin felt himself colour, but – keeping as close to the facts as he felt able to – he told her, deciding not to ask about her appearance, in turn (he didn't much care).

'You sound nice!' Tracey said, the silence that followed feeling decisive. 'And, how tall are you?' she broke in, before he could turn the conversation.

'Five foot ten,' Kevin guessed quickly, adding on instinct (more wish-fulfilment than outright lie), 'and I live in Crosby.'

He left it there, telling her that he had a lot of work on – that he'd try her again tomorrow.

He did but, circling the same narrow subjects each time – with the fact of their physical selves hanging over every word – they were soon pretty much all talked out. Without any new incident, or *shared* experience, there was little left to say.

Tracey had the least to lose (she imagined) and, on their seventh assignation, decided – independently – to move the relationship on.

'You sound really interesting,' she began, edging to an intimacy that Kevin had sought to avoid, 'and I think it would be great to meet up for real, one day.'

Staring blandly into space, Kevin struggled to ground himself.

'Yes, it would,' he batted back, before bringing their talk to a premature close – someone was at the door, he said – looking around his flat, with fresh eyes, as he imagined what it would be like to have her there with him, in the flesh.

It was all he had ever wanted, but fearing to disabuse her he tried to remember what he had said, exactly: wishing – now – that he had been honest from the start.

They didn't speak for the next five days and Kevin hoped she would forget.

'I was thinking we could meet up sometime this week,' Tracey began, almost immediately, 'now I've finished my exams.'

Kevin flinched, with a shiver of apprehension.

'There's no hurry,' he said. 'I'm happy as we are… and, it's really busy in work, right now,' he added, with a sigh.

'Surely we can arrange *something*?' Tracey tried again. 'I don't mind coming to you, if it's easier, or you could come here…'

'Yes, I'd like that,' Kevin replied, 'but I'm having some work done on the house at the moment, so perhaps we'd better leave it for a couple of weeks?'

Tracey reluctantly agreed, but she didn't forget, so after three more weeks of ever less frequent calls, she decided to force his hand.

'Good evening, Mr Kevin Donnellon, of… 53 Nunsford Close, Litherland, Liverpool, L21 0JW,' she read, haltingly. In the silence that followed, Kevin even considered pretending that he wasn't there. 'I'm coming over in a taxi, right now,' Tracey resumed.

'But I'm going out,' Kevin prevaricated.

'What about tomorrow?' Tracey persisted.

'I'll call you… it's just…'

Tracey stopped him.

'Don't you like me?' she said.

'Course I like you, it's just…'

'Just, *what*?' she asked, her voice dropping as she considered the possibilities. 'Are you married, or something?'

'Course not,' Kevin snorted.

'Well, then – are you seeing someone else?'

'No,' he told her, switching the phone, illogically, to his weaker left ear, when Tracey fell silent.

'Are you gay?' she asked, after a pause.

'No!' Kevin shot back, indignantly.

'Well, what then,' Tracey cried, 'because, we've been chatting on the phone every night for more than a month and we get on really well, but you don't seem to want to meet up.'

'I do, it's just…' Kevin began, knowing now that he had to come clean, 'well, remember when I told you I was five foot ten?'

'Yes,' Tracey returned, quietly.

'Well, I'm not really that tall. In fact, I'm much smaller.'

'*Much* smaller?' Tracey began hesitantly. 'Do you mean, like a midget, or something?'

'Not a midget, no,' Kevin replied.

'Well, how tall are you?'

'Under three feet.'

'Three feet?' Tracey calibrated, measuring up mentally, before concluding (with a smile in her voice he hadn't expected), 'then you *are* a midget…'

'No, I'm not,' Kevin restated, while – weighing up the confounding questions and answers – Tracey quietly took stock. 'Have you heard of thalidomide?' he asked. Then, in gradual stages, he set about explaining.

Listening to Tracey's close, steady breaths, he expected her to hang up.

'Why didn't you say something?' she asked instead. 'Five foot ten – you cheeky sod!' she chuckled. 'But it doesn't change a thing… I like you and you like me – so, can we meet up now, please?'

Promising not to keep anything from her again, Kevin agreed.

'You know everything, anyway,' he said.

'In that case, I'm coming over right now!' Tracey shrieked. 'See you in ten!'

She had dropped the phone before he could object, with Kevin darting about the flat in a panic, to tidy what he could, while changing his shirt and fixing his hair.

He needn't have worried, because Tracey was every bit as amenable in person as she had been on the phone. A big girl, with pale blue eyes, her mousey-blonde hair cut in the style of Diana Spencer, Tracey had wide hips, a broad chest and the innate confidence of self-possession.

After examining Kevin, with a quick, inquisitive peer – while he stood, examining her in turn – Tracey leaned down to peck his cheek, before nosing shyly about the house, as he gave the tour.

She was pleasant, naturally curious and didn't seem bothered, in the slightest, by his 'condition'.

'And how are the neighbours?' she asked, twitching at the curtains.

'Oh, they're alright,' he told her, his smile hiding a multitude of sins; within minutes they were talking as freely as they did on the phone, with the relaxed irreverence of old friends.

'Would you like some wine?' he asked, when he could drag his eyes away from her statuesque frame, recollecting his manners and the bottle left to chill in the fridge.

'Don't mind if I do,' Tracey returned coquettishly and Kevin sent her off to get it.

Open and sympathetic, the conversation didn't flag, though Kevin kept it cautiously in mind not to try *too* hard, or to force anything (or to want a thing too much)... For here he was, in his own home, at last – at the age of twenty-two – sharing a bottle of wine with a beautiful sixteen-year-old girl.

When, rolling with laughter at another unlikely anecdote, Tracey spilt wine down the front of her blouse, Kevin directed her to the kitchen for a cloth.

'Put some salt on it,' he advised, turning to see that she had released all the buttons and was taking off her top to get at the stain.

'Where do you keep it?' she asked.

She was standing before him in a translucent, white bra, and it was all he could do to tell her. Blushing, Kevin skipped across the floor to flip the record.

'Do you like Steve Harley?' he asked. Tracey shook her head. 'Well, you've got a lot to learn.'

'It's so good to get school over with,' Tracey enthused, as she dropped down to the couch, 'and to make a new friend.'

'You must come again,' Kevin said, wondering if he was asking too much.

Half an hour later, he was standing at the door as Tracey took her departure, and – emboldened by the wine (and the evening's success) – he decided that he couldn't wait and had to know.

'Am I going to see you again?' he asked, with a force that surprised him.

'I bloody well hope so,' Tracey replied. 'I think you're brilliant!'

She was crouched down at the side of his chair and now leaned across his chest, pressing her mouth to his. Kevin opened his lips and welcomed her tongue, licking at her firm teeth, sucking at the wine that clung to her palate.

When Tracey pulled up at the beep of her cab, he was shaking uncontrollably – could only sit and watch as she skipped away.

As the summer stretched on, they would meet up with increasing regularity and there was a freedom to everything.

'What day is it?' he would ask Rhona, when she came to rouse him, hardly caring (knowing only that, before the day was out, he would be seeing Tracey again).

'Thursday… and you're late, so you need to get up.'

He didn't care. Idling – happily – in the shower, he was still trying to figure out what had happened.

After her initial invitation, Tracey didn't ask Kevin back to hers again, recognising the fact that having her parents sitting in the room below was hardly conducive to the copulation they had almost immediately embarked on. Experiencing a genuine sense of equality for the first time in his life, Kevin could hardly believe how good the sex was.

Shy, at first, Tracey had proved a revelation, with Kevin feeling confident enough to set her straight on both preferences and positions.

'Can we do it on the floor?' he had asked, the first time they tried.

'Kinky,' Tracey giggled, as she dropped off the bed and pulled down the duvet.

'And, it's best if I'm on top,' he added, with an authority that inspired trust.

Tracey was smiling, content to finally be going out with a man – Kevin clearly knew what he was doing – instead of the boys of the past.

Returning from work, Kevin would often find Tracey waiting for him on the front step in a thin summer frock, with a cigarette hanging from her painted lips – the whole day put into sudden perspective. He would toot the horn gently, as she leaned in through the window to proffer a kiss.

Barely over the threshold, they would already be stripping off their clothes, to *fuck*, usually in the bedroom, but sometimes there and then on the living room floor. It was all so easy.

After making use of the facilities, Tracey would return, bright as a button – with water dripping off her hair – and give a gentle bite to his bared chest. Looking over her soft skin, her smooth legs curled about his torso, Kevin had never felt so secure.

They would sometimes go at it again, then, but otherwise they might head off to the pub first – Kevin driving – to meet up with some of Tracey's friends, before returning home, to fuck some more.

Kevin can still recall the pride of being seen with a girl like that, in public. He also remembers how, on one of their first nights out – in the Bootle Arms (where Andrew Kavanagh's dad worked) – he had overheard a conversation between Tracey and one of her friends. He was standing at the bar, supposedly out of earshot.

'The sex is amazing,' she was telling her friend, with a coy, backwards glance. 'I can't believe it!'

Kevin took his time with the drinks, composing himself.

There were four of them that night; staggering giddily up the ramp, they all came back.

'I've got a bottle of wine, somewhere,' Kevin told them, as he rattled through the fridge.

Bringing the bottle through, Kevin took up his place on the floor, with Tracey and Jackie – her friend – joining him. With a nod across to her boyfriend, Mick, Jackie shuffled closer.

'We were wondering if you wouldn't mind us using the bedroom,' she said. 'Tracey says you're pretty open-minded.'

'Go ahead,' Kevin answered, without breaking step.

'Thanks so much,' Jackie said, with a bright smile.

Settling back onto Tracey's lap, he watched them go. Within minutes – as they sat on in silence in the living room – there were squeals of laughter coming through the thin partition wall; then, the springs of the bed and the headpost thumping.

Kevin, who couldn't get the idea of Jackie out of his head, already had an erection; taking note, Tracey wrapped her hands about him from behind. Kevin turned with a groan – lifting her skirt – and they were soon going at it, too.

'Maybe we should do a swap?' Kevin suggested suddenly, as the volume in the other room reached a crescendo.

Tracey pulled him close.

'Oh no – you're mine!' she hissed.

Kevin lifted his face to hers.

'I love you,' he said, and – in that moment – he meant it.

'I love you, too,' Tracey told him, building up a rhythm from below.

It was just sex – he knew that – but he would never feel quite so free again.

The rest of the summer continued in much the same manner: they would meet up after work, talk for half an hour (over a glass of wine) and then fuck.

When anything else was required, Kevin would suddenly feel the distance between them and start to question what they actually had in common. He often felt old in her company and was embarrassed by the public shows of affection.

'What do you think?' she asked, as she emerged from the changing room.

'Fine, fine,' Kevin returned, his voice betraying impatience.
'She looks lovely, doesn't she?' the shop girl cooed, from behind.
'Yes, yes, the blue one,' Kevin answered.

Yet, with the generosity of low expectations and a natural affinity (on both sides), what they had generally flowed along quite nicely, until it was brought to an abrupt end when Tracey turned up at his door, with hooded red eyes, to announce that she was pregnant.

'Fucking bitch – how could you?' Kevin spat, without thinking, as Tracey backed away.

'I'm sorry, I didn't mean to,' she sniffed, slipping to the floor.

'Didn't mean to – I suppose it was just a fucking accident?' Kevin roared, turning in circles.

'No, but I didn't mean it to happen, honestly – I love you...'

'Then, what are you doing fucking somebody else?'

Tracey looked up then, with burning cheeks, and tears in her eyes.

'I don't understand,' she said. 'I love you, Kevin... and, I've never slept with anyone else in my whole life. How could you think I could go behind your back?'

The question pulled him up short, because he had never had reason to doubt Tracey's sincerity. Looking down on her crumpled frame, bundled up against the wall – her face in her hands (her frame shaking) – he knew, suddenly, that she was telling the truth. Yet here was no other explanation...

'I'm sorry, it's just...' and – despite the openness of his nature – he still couldn't say it, but his mind was running back over the tape (and all the scenes he knew by heart).

'He'll never be the father of children... he's sterile: damaged down below,' his mother had said, addressing the camera, which immediately cut back to Kevin, alone in his room.

He had thought it strange how – first with Jane, and then with Doris – everything had worked just fine, though he had never thought to take precautions (and those two women had taken their own).

He did his best to explain.

'Poor love,' Tracey said, shuffling across to take him into her arms.

'I'm sorry,' he sniffed.

'It's not your fault,' – Tracey had sat up (her tears gone) – 'but, what are we going to do?'

His head clear, Kevin took up one of her hands.

'We're in this together,' he said, meeting her eye. 'And, I'll stand by you, whatever you decide.'

He felt warm, suddenly, and knew he could make it work – he loved her.

The matter would be quickly taken out of his hands, when Tracey's father rang to inform Kevin that he was a 'fucking rapist' and that the police had been called.

'You won't be seeing Tracey again, so you can put that out of your head, soft lad, and – spaz or no spaz,' he sneered, 'if I ever set eyes on you again, I'll knock your fucking teeth in.'

Kevin was shaking, and had no idea how to defend himself – on what grounds. He felt sick – beaten, broken – and it was even worse to have to listen to Tracey, and her desperate sobs, as she pleaded his case in the background.

'Dad, Dad,' she bawled, in despair, 'leave him alone. It's not his fault.'

'What sort of a man are you, anyway?' the father continued contemptuously, before dropping the phone that still rang in Kevin's one good ear, as he staggered away (the whole world changed, once more).

Reflecting on the shocking events of the day as he climbed into bed, Kevin had to own that, despite his sadness at the way things had turned out, he was too young to be a father and it was probably for the best.

With no way of making contact – and knowing that her father would be vetting her calls – Kevin had no word of Tracey, until six months later, when she wrote to him.

She had had an abortion, she explained, and she was sorry, but she didn't blame him for anything.

'I just hope that one day we'll be able to look back and be happy about the lovely times we shared. I'll always love you,' she concluded, with her customary grace.

There were more letters, with less regularity, over the forthcoming months, but Kevin didn't speak to Tracey, directly, for another ten years.

By then, he had just split up with Paula, and was staying with his sister, while he waited for the move into his new flat. Still vulnerable, and in recuperation, his thoughts had drifted back to Tracey, and – wondering what had become of her – he had looked up her number, bolstered by the fact that it had been the phone that had first brought them together.

He had the confidence, by now, to come right out with it.

'How's your love life?' he asked.

'Brilliant,' Tracey volunteered gleefully.

Kevin's heart sank.

'Really?' he asked, not doubting it.

'Aren't you going to ask me why?' Tracey goaded.

Kevin played along, running through every reason he could think of, wondering at the possibilities.

It was only in desperate jest that he stumbled, haphazardly, on the truth.

'You're not a lezzer are you?'

Tracey was already chuckling before the question was out, and – as she explained her new-found proclivities – it suddenly seemed obvious.

Tracey was, it seems, still the same big girl, and she was still the same *kind* girl, too… but now, apparently, she had a shaved head (instead of the Diana bob) and no desire to fuck any man at all – legs or no legs!

Kevin dropped the phone with a lingering sense of regret.

◊

I didn't even have a suit. That had seemed important at the time.

Having taken the train from Liverpool, one of your brothers had picked me up from Stafford, though I wasn't sure why I had come.

When you had called, unexpectedly, to tell me what had happened – and asked to see me – it had already been several months since we had last met up; such communication had felt redemptive.

I found you there ahead of me, waiting at the station with a friend and, while you stood, in silence, beside her – your dull eyes wandering – I was told that you hadn't wanted to take the train alone. I nodded, to show I understood, as she turned to ask you whether you were happy to be left on your own.

Lifting your eyes to hers, you mumbled that you were fine.

It was only when your friend had turned and left us that you gave your first smile. It was instinctive – nothing more needed to be said: it was love, or some degree.

You shuffled across, I took you into my arms, and that was enough: the warmth of your body against mine; nervous fingers clenched and unclenched; that small, button nose, sniffling into my shoulder... When you stepped back, your cheeks blotched with tears (as so often before), you gave another smile, with a mumbled apology.

Having no idea where to go, as we headed back from the station, I decided – given the fine weather – on the park. We walked in tentative silence, with nothing, yet, to say, though I was soon bridging that silence in my familiar way, by telling you about the book I was reading: *Ada*.

I showed you the cover, relieved to see your eyes brighten with the interest and attention that you couldn't help but give to others. It seemed, then, that whatever else had come between us – while we were apart – the essentials remained.

Nothing had changed: it was still you and me against the world.

When we eventually spread ourselves out on the grass, under a sonorous blue sky, and you began – with dry, rasping sorrow – to tell me about your brother, I could hardly believe your vulnerability (and how unfit for the task)...

Sat in silence, I let you talk.

Stuttering, you told me that there was no one else you could go to – that none of your friends knew anything about your life – and I pulled you close, telling you that I was glad you had called and would be happy to attend the funeral: that you had only to ask.

The look you gave me then – a trust I hadn't sufficiently cherished – stole my heart all over again.

Back at the house, sat on the edge of the bed – your eyes filled with tears – you asked if you could hold me, *please,* and we slowly dropped down. We had held each other like this a hundred times and it seemed unthinkable, now, that we had ever stopped. Everything was easy and natural, and – within minutes – we were making love, in concentrated silence. We finished in silence, too, under the covers now, holding tighter still.

Following a sombre service, in a cold, reverberating hall, and then out – scattering soil on the grey rise of land beyond the church – we returned to the house by car and immediately took ourselves outside.

The wind was brushing at our faces, as the light dropped away, but we hardly noticed. You took a pouch of tobacco from your cropped, weather-beaten leather jacket and rolled us both a cigarette, the sour flavour filling our mouths as a host of memories stole through. Passing the lighter back and forth, struggling with the wind – the cigarettes wouldn't always take – we had found something to occupy us, at least (neither of us having anything more to say).

You were exhausted, dead on your feet: the emotions of the last few hours – the hands shaken; the conversations you had forced your way through – having finally worn you down. When you placed your head onto my lap, I nestled closer, breathing in the long-forgotten scent of your hair.

We had sat against this same wall on my first visit – with no idea of what was to come (the world so open) – with Tim Buckley and Nick Drake pouring forth from a portable cassette player. Caught up in the blossom of the country air, your hair a spider's web, I had never lost that memory, or the hope it promised.

Your warm, quick breaths were a pleasure I had hardly expected, our hearts beating a feverish rhythm each time we dipped in for a kiss; then, turning sober – time stopped quite still – I would stroke, gently, down the line of your neck, each brief touch a new discovery. There had seemed to be no end at the time.

In your room, later – leaving the guests conversing below – you proceeded to undress me with a directness you had rarely shown before, working small fingers into the buttons of my shirt (that you dropped to the floor). I pulled off my shoes and trousers and climbed under the covers to join you, on the low, single bed (in the room where you had spent your childhood).

I would be here again – one last time – in less than a year, hunched against that same stone wall, as the light drained imperceptibly from a clear sky, a chill setting in, but you were no longer there.

I tried to explain, to one of your friends who had come out to sit with me – I was not, after all, alone – what that particular spot meant: what we had once shared... There was sympathy – understanding, even – but she couldn't know. Another of your friends, and they had all come to *this* funeral, had delivered a beautiful elegy earlier in the day, that had missed something essential; leaving some things forever unsaid.

The weight of time grown obdurate, I would never finish *Magic Mountain*.

Chapter 25

We trust in the adults, as children – in truths that sometimes have no privilege.

As a child, Kevin had believed what he was told – that the exercises prescribed by the physiotherapist and administered by the nurse, which he would repeat through pain – his fingers clenched (with stern concentration) – would eventually prove their utility (like algebra or trigonometry).

'You're doing really well,' he would be told, their encouragement pushing him on.

He wasn't told that these exercises were primarily designed to accommodate the vertiginous legs he was now forced to parade around in (and not to help him get more from what he had).

'Do I have to wear my legs today?' he would ask, a question usually ignored.

It had already been suggested by different doctors, at different times, that the perfectly formed feet that Kevin was, naturally, so proud of – five toes each – should be amputated, to better fit those prosthetics (so that he could 'walk').

With a parent's charity, his mother had refused to countenance such a removal... *what with all the other missing parts.*

'He's got such lovely feet, doctor,' she pointed out, stroking her fingers over the arch, sole and instep – all present and correct – before counting through the halluces and phalanges (as though to check).

There wasn't a single blemish: those two feet being the most complete part of Kevin's otherwise distorted anatomy.

Agnes refused, and – in hindsight – it was the right decision, with the young boy's faltering spine ultimately too weak to bear such a weight, while Kevin would continue to enjoy unaided mobility throughout his life, by methods of his own.

'Like a fucking crab,' as Paula put it.

Seeking to extrapolate from what wasn't there (and what they couldn't know), the medical professionals had all concurred and converged on an attempt at normalisation.

Fortunately, other people had other truths (and Kevin was saved the knife).

The ultimate prima donnas, Kevin's 'perfect' feet had known their worth from the start. Shirking physical contact, they had also refused display, the workings and mechanics of those feet going, for the most part, unobserved. Considering the butchers waiting at their pleasure, they had good reason to hide.

'They're my feet,' Kevin explained, as though the question was in doubt.

When he first started school, and his feet first went public, Kevin had his mother cut his trousers to a length that covered the toes, before stitching them shut (to conceal the subterranean manoeuvres that went on below). That is how he continues to wear them, though – despite the restrictive nature of such swaddling – his feet remain powerful and skilled operatives.

The accelerator that Kevin accosts, with such violence, when he drives, is worked by his shrouded right foot, for instance, while his left peg – reacting in opposition, to that great play of speed – controls the similarly mounted brake (with the ball and arch).

Viewed by the doctors as an intrinsic part of their young patient's identity and existence, those prosthetic legs were a form of magical thinking: neither necessary, nor sufficient.

Introduced to Kevin when he was barely out of the crib – the basic design little changed since their development in World War I – his first legs had consisted of a plain plank of wood, set on a stout iron frame, to which the feet would be stapled flat. Awkwardly cajoled, the hips were secured to a stiff leather bucket that held the torso in place. Peeping unrepentant from the bottom of their rigid frame, Kevin's precious feet refused to collaborate – hence the possibility of, and the argument for, those feet being chopped away completely.

A fat leather belt was fixed around the waist, with an adjustable buckle allowing for better access. Kevin could, theoretically, come and go as he pleased, but once in place – tottering high above legs that refused to bend – he would need help to free himself.

'They would lay me out on the floor, as soon as I arrived,' he tells me, recalling the indignity of being treated in such a manner (having already made his independent way across the yard).

Flailing, as the heavy contraption was attached, the tree would then be pulled vertical. *Timber!*

Kevin had been given blockers – two shoeless chunks of wood (set within a wooden frame) – at eighteen months, once his spine had been deemed strong enough to support his weight. Kevin would sit quite happily on those blockers, just eight safe inches off the carpeted floor, though he quickly learned that by rocking them back and forth – like some cocksure toddler – he could wander freely from room to room.

As he matured and the legs grew more sophisticated Kevin would need to be fitted for prosthetics every two years, in a process requiring a plaster cast from the waist down to shape his new legs to his hips and his feet. The emergence of pubic hair only added to the trial when the plaster was peeled back again, with each cast taking a matted mound along with it. Kevin, who was known for his stoicism – like father, like son – rarely cried out, but he couldn't deny his disillusionment at a process that grew ever more tortuous.

Clothes were a problem, too, with Kevin – whose load was fixed primarily on the seat and the seams – wearing his way through a fresh pair of britches every other week, no matter the patches his mother applied.

'I can't imagine what you get up to,' she would sigh, indulging her blue-eyed boy (who got up to nothing).

Shoes were the only personal touch allowed him, even if these would stay fixed to the foot of his prosthetics, with Kevin having removed the standard issue that came with the frame (solid black, patent leather).

A pop fanboy, who knew how to draw looks (with his distinctive style), Kevin would, naturally, make amendments, though he surprisingly decided against the unwieldy platforms he had first considered and plumped for 'James Bond' shoes instead – dreaming of bright gadgets and derring-do. These were dress shoes, with a fully functioning compass fitted into the heels.

His first task was to navigate the playground, Kevin traversing the uneven weather-beaten concrete with a stuttering tread. Ahead of him, though he barely looked – taking each careful step at a time – were two of the other thalidomide children, Kenny Pollock and David Parry, who both had regular legs, but reduced arms (and an assortment of fingers).

They were skipping rope, oblivious, when, like leaves caught in a sudden squall, they chased into Kevin's teetering path and caught him flush (with their flailing arms and cantering legs), tipping him hard to the ground.

Kenny Pollock can still remember the surreal silence that followed, as the adults towered around him and he tried to make sense of the accident. Knocked unconscious at his feet, Kevin was a dark, oddly-shaped mass that refused to yield, despite his howls of entreaty. Kenny never forgot – he hadn't meant to hurt him. They were both a mere eight years old.

Kevin fell heavily and lacking the arms to shield, or to break, that headlong descent he was knocked out cold by the blow to the back of his head. The ambulance took him to Alder Hey, where he regained consciousness and was given the first seven stitches of his young life (there would be more, in time). Three days later, when his local GP removed the stitched sutures that had been so hastily applied, Kevin would scream the place down while being given a lollipop he didn't want.

Kevin was knocked unconscious three times, during his enforced high-wire career, the falls more severe with each incremental hike. Over the years, he would suffer eighteen stitches to the back of his head (having early acquired the technique of flipping his face aside, before impact), two broken noses (spitting out blood he could do nothing to quell) and he still wears a deep, guttering gash over his lip, below his misshapen nose. All of Kevin's front teeth have been cracked and smashed – and are false.

Returning from school in a hackney cab, with Old Bill at the wheel, Kevin's first action, upon arrival (later than most of his friends), would be to kick off those accursed legs.

'When did you stop using them?' I ask, wondering whether there had been a particular point – the last pair he wore still stand, on the cistern, in one of the bathrooms.

'When I was about fourteen,' he says, 'though that wasn't quite the end of them.'

For, as he went on to explain, he would make a final try of those legs when, aged twenty and studying at college, he found love – or so he thought – in the robust form of Aileen Howard.

'She was probably a bit out of my league, if I'm honest,' he admits, and thus running diligently through all the possible obstacles to their being together, he had hit on the obvious: that she was big and he was small.

He needed to measure up and new legs seemed the best method.

Despite burgeoning desires and careful attentions their relationship had so far been strictly platonic. If Aileen was kind and solicitous – which she was – Kevin's greedy eyes could not help but notice that she was like that with everyone, while he wanted something more exclusive.

Beyond the physical attraction, Kevin was also drawn to Aileen on account of her socio-economic class: she was 'posh totty', as he joked to friends, giving access to a stratum of society he had no knowledge of.

'Mummy, Daddy, this is Kevin,' the prodigal daughter proclaimed confidently, when she first whisked him into her house.

Minding his Ps and Qs – and not knowing where to put himself – Kevin was immediately sold: this was exotic; a world apart.

Aileen had attended Streatham House – a private girls' school on Victoria Road (in Crosby) – just like her inseparable friend, Alison, and, just like her friend, had disappointed in her recent A-levels. Trooping back together, with their certificated results – a short skip, in a bright blanket of light – the two girls had felt a sense of embarrassment at their shared failure.

Reacting with muted fury over the wasted investment, Aileen's parents had insisted that she take her resits at Hugh Baird and, thus, Aileen had found herself mixing, for the first time in her sheltered life, on an equal footing with 'ordinary' folk.

Taking surreptitious pleasure from her naturally blinkered and practically narrow perspective, Kevin had gloried in the heady certainties of privilege and power, while Aileen had welcomed the unlikely range and mix of the students she now encountered.

Sporting a wheelchair, the formative beginnings of a moustache and an avowedly proto-socialist agenda, Kevin was just someone else to drag home and scandalise her parents with.

The distinctions were not quite so sharp, however, with Aileen's home – a dilapidated bungalow on St Andrews Road – the accommodation of a wealthy family fallen on hard times. The old iron gutters were crumbling (and leaked); the original sash windows were still fitted with just a single pane of glass; while the path, where their Volvo Estate lounged (at its lugubrious leisure), was a patchwork of cracked, uneven paving stones, with grass spouting intermittently across its sorry expanse.

'And, this is the old homestead,' Aileen announced facetiously.

A sizeable property, in a well-to-do area, Kevin was slightly surprised that a girl with such a clear, blue-blooded accent – who had been educated privately and went skiing once a year – didn't live somewhere grander, realising, with a start, that his own home compared favourably.

On being formally introduced, Mr and Mrs Howard smiled down with unremitting decorum, even if Kevin knew within bald seconds that they didn't really like him, this being more to do with his social standing – and his inadequately submerged Scouse accent – than the wheelchair he was sat in.

'Pleased to meet you, Mr and Mrs Howard...' he announced, with formal propriety, 'I'm Kevin Donnellon, a college friend of your daughter.'

The Howards, of course, didn't consider Hugh Baird a real college... and there was the accent again, that – try as he might – Kevin couldn't mask or subdue. Aileen was scowling at her parents the whole time, Kevin recognising that parental disapproval, in this case, would only improve his appeal in the rebellious eyes of their only daughter.

Once safely out of range and carefully ensconced in Aileen's sweetly-scented bedroom, Kevin had dragged himself, independently, up over the small pouf to the bed itself.

'Nice place,' he said, tipping casually back onto the Laura Ashley duvet.

Aileen gave an emphatic turn to the key in the door and Kevin could hardly believe that he had her to himself, without the prying eyes and attentions of Bernard, Boris, Dick and Alison. He was hoping that, left to their own devices – the evening their own – something more would develop.

'Music,' Aileen muttered, with sudden inspiration, flipping the dial of the small transistor radio that, sat on the bedside table, she had set fast to Radio 1: Mike Read on the breakfast show; teatime with Peter Powell.

'I don't think your parents like me,' Kevin tried, as Aileen squatted down on the bed beside him, her curvaceous legs folded away in a sort of curtsey, her chest heaving, as she caught her breath.

He was hoping to draw her protection and gain her trust, though it was hard to have a clear plan when Aileen gazed affectionately back at him from her long, thin face, her smile showing perfectly aligned teeth.

'They're idiots,' she snorted, and Kevin liked that high-flown, yet whimsical, tone.

Her lips looked soft; the nose just a delicate smudge. When she reached across to the radio, to turn up what was a favourite song – the bedsprings creaking – Kevin noted the fine golden threads of hair running down the instep of her freckled forearm; the pale folds of puppy fat that softened every angle and flavoured every nook.

Removing her purple suede pixie boots, when she climbed onto the bed, Aileen's short rah-rah skirt would ride up her thighs to reveal the thick woollen tights she wore below (shaping those same curves). It was 1982.

Perhaps, Kevin would muse, whenever they found themselves alone and at leisure once more – hiding one piece of the obvious, behind another more fragmented truth – *if we were the same height...*

Following this stray thought through to its practical conclusion – and without telling a soul – Kevin arranged an appointment at the specialist Prosthetics wing of the Mill Road Hospital and the following week, while making out that he was off to college, he took a taxi there instead.

On the short drive, Kevin imagined the result of this labour of love – that, one day, he and Aileen would be walking out hand in hand on a proper date, as the birds chirped and the breeze tore through her russet locks (though her hair was actually more of a mousey-brown and the weather was already on the turn). He imagined their plans; their declarations of love; the everyday domesticity of 'playing house' in a home of their own... then, the driver hissing his irritation, the taxi clipped a kerb, and Kevin looked up to see that they were now entering the hospital's main drag.

If, in his dreams, Kevin is always, by nature, disembodied, in his waking moments he is often too quick – his haste, optimistic – to dismiss the physical rigours of reality. Thus, he had already quite forgotten what he now went through, again – the secret agony of the plaster cast.

Picking his legs up a month later, that pain had been forgotten, in turn.

Hoisted between a set of parallel wooden bars, to test the new legs, Kevin was strapped in tight. He believed, for no good reason, that these new prosthetics would be better than those of his youth: that he would be better able to take the rigours and strains. The doctors went blithely along with the fiction.

'You're very brave, after all these years...'

Kevin took the compliment, giving a smirk to the nurses.

'How long's it been since you last used prosthetics?' one of them asked.

'About five years,' he told them.

'Well, the technology has certainly moved on,' the doctor said. 'I think you'll be pleasantly surprised...'

They didn't have a fucking clue, of course. For, whatever his conceits, Kevin could – in fact – barely stand, his back no longer able to support that forgotten bulk (that had only increased with time).

He had been deluding himself... though, in his dreams, Kevin is pointedly disembodied.

Returning home with those heavy, hollow legs laid helplessly over his lap, it was no surprise when his mother started in on him, calling him 'a fool' and 'incapable' – admonishing his inability to 'think things through'.

It was a relief to his increasingly maudlin sense of perspective – that sudden, sombre self-awareness – when his mother promptly declared:

'And, if you think I'll be getting you into those crazy legs every morning, you've got another thing coming. Don't you remember all the problems you had before?'

Kevin didn't need to be told – he knew, already – though he welcomed the reprise that saved him the torment of lingering hope.

I can barely stand, he had thought, holding on to the bars with all the strength his pride could muster. At a push, and with the assistance of three junior nurses, he could totter upright, for a few bitter seconds, before being forced to grapple and grab at the bars for balance again (keeling, like a capsized swimmer).

If Kevin's 'legs' had proved impossible in a secondary modern, with fifteen-hundred teenagers chasing about – impossible, on those unevenly pebbled yards and bowed corridors (scuffed to the sheen of a thousand different shoes) – they were no less impossible now.

I remember Kevin telling me all this, as he leaned back against the squat table that his computer was sat on, his spine still suffering the effects of those daily, doctored – and *pointless* – exertions of forty years before.

Whether it was the beer that had softened me – I had been out drinking – or something else altogether, I was drawn deeper, for the moment, into everything he had said, appreciating for the first time, with a heavy heart, the connections between his life and my own. I said nothing, listening – my eyes an unresponsive blank.

For, I remembered, too: the taxi driving away, as I stood dumbfounded in the quickening rain (and nothing more) – in shock, already withdrawn. I thought you owed me something, but I couldn't speak – even now – and I didn't lay a glove on you. I am a coward. I let you go without a fight.

With his earthy humour and his uneven keel, Kevin has the fortunate capacity to bring a person back to the present. Thus, having allowed the sadness of those legs – and those stifled possibilities – to settle, he almost immediately punctured the gravity of everything he had just said.

'When I'm online, in chat rooms,' he expostulated, 'I always brag about the length of my cock – the fact that I have to flip it out of the way when I walk, so that I don't trip over it!'

We were both laughing, while I thought: *these stories are gold dust.*

Kevin did eventually go on a date with Aileen, he told me – resuming – after she had solicitously agreed, taking her to see Dexys Midnight Runners, at Southport Floral Hall (the stage bestrewn with straw) on Friday 1 October 1982.

It had long been a running joke to adapt the close-fitting refrain of that band's biggest hit to their beloved friend.

'Come on Eileen!' they would cry, when they were late and Aileen was lagging, hitting the chorus as one (to great amusement).

That night, Aileen drove, and when she dropped him home, Kevin – his wild eyes filled with desperate longing – asked for a kiss. Aileen refused and that was the end of it (legs or no legs).

The rejection brought as much anger as sorrow, with Kevin knowing, now, that he would never pretend again, or seek false acceptance – and never again balance himself atop those ridiculous stilts.

In the brief moment of unbroken silence that followed his forlorn request, he had also learned to never again *ask* for a kiss, but to take it, if that was what he wanted. *It's pathetic to beg*, he considered, or to make apologies for needs and desires.

There are no counterfactuals and there is no way to know how Aileen would have responded if Kevin had boasted of legs (or been taller), but it was particularly galling to discover that Aileen had been seeing Boris behind his back the whole time.

'We didn't know how to tell you,' Boris admitted sheepishly.

Kevin appeared to take it well, but was biting down on his resentment when he considered the shared conversations and confidences.

I even asked Boris for advice, he thought, fighting the urge to go on the attack.

'Well, I suppose that's okay, if that's what you both want,' he conceded, 'but you really should have told me.'

Later, pissed at the foot of the home bar that he had sneaked down to, unseen, Kevin had somehow managed to make his inebriated way back up those two flights of stairs, to the phone in his room, to call Aileen and unload a torrent of abuse.

When Mrs Howard took charge of the phone and suggested that he calm down – and tell her what the problem was – he kept on asking after Aileen; when she declared that he was never to call again, he told her to fuck off.

He was still bawling into the headset after she had hung up.

Then, he was in tears, all the pain and grief of that rejection – and the fact that his friends had misled him in such a way – coursing through.

It was a pattern that would repeat over time, with Kevin reacting to such rejections by taking down everything in his path...

It took him less than a week to understand that Aileen was simply a girl he had fancied and little more: that he had let his emotions run away with him (another pattern).

Following that failed date and the excitement of the attempt, Kevin had little more to do with Aileen, finding – in the process – that he hardly missed her. Such a drift was only natural, given how he was now nearly a year out of college and already in full-time employment.

He continued to see Boris, who had soon enough been dumped by Aileen, however, displaying in this his own twisted sense of loyalty – the fact that he didn't hold grudges; that a woman wouldn't ever come between him and his friends.

He was changing though, and those college friendships were already on borrowed time, with Kevin no longer prepared to accept the way they would take his mother's side, seeing his cries for freedom as some kind of joke.

Sometimes, he felt like they didn't even know him.

Kevin was humming a tune, which it took him several minutes to place: 'Spasticus Autisticus' by Ian Dury. He smiled, considering – with a sneer – how a song that had set out to ridicule the hubristic notion of the UN designating 1981 as the International Year of Disabled Persons had, inconceivably, been deemed offensive and banned by the BBC. The UN project's motto had been 'a wheelchair in every room': they hadn't a fucking clue.

Spitting along with the discordant sibilants of its abrasive lyrics – fired by a sudden invective – Kevin had recognised the emotion of the song (the anger and irony both) before the end of the first verse.

Fuck them, he thought, of his friends – dropped without a moment's regret – *they'll never walk in my shoes (or know what I know).*

Kevin had just turned twenty-two.

Chapter 26

The 'paid holiday' at Ellesmere House would hobble on, in a variety of forms, until the intemperate summer of 1985. Having discovered practical applications for Kevin's undoubted abilities, Sefton Council – it seemed – could no longer do without their thalidomide employee.

Thus, though the Manpower Services funding had long since run its course, Kevin's position was extended on a yearly basis. First, rather hangdog, it was Mark Cameron.

'We've got finance for the next twelve months, if you want to stay?'

With waves of smoke suffusing his small office, by the following year it was Martin Waterhouse.

'We'd like to keep you on, if you're interested?'

Without a single piece of accredited training to his name, Kevin stepped, thoughtlessly, up to the role of information officer twelve months later. The fact that he would no longer be based at Ellesmere House came as a relief by this point, given the fraught nature of the last few months under Mr Black (and the fact that so many of his friends had already moved on). The increase in salary was a welcome inducement, too.

Kevin would now spend Mondays and Wednesdays at St George's House in Bootle – in a building without a ramp – and Tuesdays and Thursdays at Litherland Town Hall. There was work to be found in the former, at least, with the social workers who shared Kevin's open-plan office regularly sending across those they considered to be suffering from some form of disability. The doors to the rooms were open to the wind at all times and Kevin can still recall the day when a particularly disgruntled member of the public had run down the full length of the corridor, slamming them all shut again.

'I've been promoted!' he preened, proudly, to his mother – they were on talking terms again – with no idea where such steps were leading.

'Very good,' Agnes replied, in her peremptory manner.

'See you Sunday, then,' Kevin signed off.

It had been a slow introduction, but once posters had been circulated to promote the services of the new welfare advice officer, Kevin was soon being rushed off his feet.

Leading the petitions for clients refused mobility or attendance allowance, Kevin was eloquent, but forceful, while boasting an eye for detail. Having long since exhausted the bluff and bluster of Tom Black's much vaunted 'experience', Kevin had come to rely on his own resources.

In establishing a point of law, he would turn to the Welfare Advice handbook first; failing this, he would ring through to Citizens Advice, glossing over blind spots with the veil of authority and a literacy far exceeding the browbeaten characters he usually represented.

'Mr Irving and his family have been left with no means of support, while your assessments labour on,' he chided. 'It's already been three months – how are they supposed to live?'

The phrasings came easy and Kevin enjoyed the theatricality, while his wheelchair added natural legitimacy. Sometimes, fate itself seemed to take his side.

'You've won,' the verdict delivered before he had even entered the room.

'But, I haven't...' Kevin began, turning about in confusion (thinking of his carefully prepared notes).

'You don't bloody need to, son,' his adversary explained, with recent government legislation having changed the terms of debate overnight.

Kevin's victories were soon stacking up. He would have another one the following week after his stout defence of a middle-aged man who had been refused attendance allowance on account of his alleged ability to walk the requisite one hundred metres.

'Look at me,' the client protested, from his chair, struggling to raise his heavy sticks. 'I could barely make it across the foyer – how do they expect me to walk?'

Feeling a personal affront, Kevin sued the case with the flourish of a man who can be said to know, securing both the desired compensation and an additional two years of back pay.

'I can't believe what you've done for me,' the man cried, in tears, outside. 'You've given me my life back!'

The work kept coming, and Kevin – who hadn't seen the posters – had no idea why, until he chanced into a conversation with a union representative.

'They're certainly getting their money's worth,' his interlocutor chuckled.

'I do what I can,' Kevin returned dryly.

'I hope they know that – and that you're properly remunerated...'

'I hadn't really considered...' Kevin replied, his brow pulling tight.

'Well, you should, because a welfare rights officer's got a lot of clout.'

'Oh, I see,' Kevin broke in, with a smile. 'You've misunderstood – I'm only an information officer.'

'But the work you're doing is of a much higher grade,' the rep assured him, 'and at any other council you'd be ten pay scales higher by now... you need to speak to your manager.'

'Oh, it's okay – I wouldn't want to rock the boat,' Kevin stuttered back.

He wasn't in a union either (but was signed up that same day).

Seeing the posters in which he so prominently featured, Kevin was flattered and understood, now, why there was always a queue waiting outside when he rolled up to the office. The caseload continued to grow. Feeling increasingly out of his depth, Kevin eventually rang through to Pauline Farrell, the Head of Social Services.

'It's too much,' he pleaded. 'I can't keep up.'

'With anyone else, I'd tend to agree, but you're doing absolute wonders, Kevin, so – please – hang on in there!'

It was meant to be a pep talk, but – with the union representative's words still running through his head – Kevin bristled at having been kept in the dark in such a way. When he learned that he had been employed on an illegal basis and had been working well beyond his pay grade for months, his anger grew, but there was loyalty, too (at the way he had been initially taken on) and he hesitated before taking the next step.

He had only gone over to Ellesmere House to catch up with his friends, but walked in on a general meeting of staff. Parking his chair at the back of the room, he was soon stifling laughter as Nicky offered increasingly callous opinions on the bigwigs standing out front (with Andrew giving droll asides of his own).

Pauline Farrell was running through their monthly targets and strategies – with Nicky tittering in bewilderment – when Kevin had the sudden sense that he should be up there, with those managers. He wondered why he hadn't been invited, or known about such a meeting, given that most of the decisions they made would directly affect him.

When the speaker referred to Kevin by name, in lauding Sefton Council as 'an equal opportunities employer', who believed in employing staff 'on merit rather than prejudice', Kevin felt the words stick in his chest. *Then, why am I sat at the back,* he thought, *and why aren't you paying me what I deserve?*

He blushed, with what seemed like modesty, as the heads turned his way – and Nicky gave an exuberant cheer – but it was more closely embarrassment. *They'll be on twenty grand, at least,* he considered bitterly: the die was cast, with Kevin finally agreeing to take his employees to a tribunal.

After accepting the responsibility of 'taking to the stand', it was a disappointment to be told that his presence wasn't required at their first sitting, which decided in his favour, as expected (with Kevin moved up to Grade 2).

'It's just the start,' the rep explained. 'As far as we're concerned, you've been working nearer the level of a senior officer, so that's what we're pushing for.'

Taking the lift up to the fourteenth floor of the Triad building in Bootle, Kevin would attend the second session in person. He was well prepared – had been through a series of questions (and answers).

'But, don't worry, I've got something up my sleeve,' his representative added, with a smile.

Kevin had forgotten that promise – or threat – by the time a young orderly, who represented the council, stood up to read out the list of Kevin's duties from his official job description. It was the first Kevin had heard of such a document.

'So, as you can see,' the orderly concluded, 'Mr Donnellon's contract clearly states that he is employed as an information officer, and – whatever he may claim – Mr Donnellon has never, at any point, been employed, by Sefton Council, as a welfare advice officer.'

A murmur of assent passed along the apparently independent panel; Kevin looked to the floor.

His counsel meanwhile, was already up on his feet.

'With permission,' he said, pulling out one of the posters showing Kevin, in all his glory, and holding it up for them to see. 'These posters, as I'm sure you're aware, have been plastered over the Sefton borough for the past two months – without Mr Donnellon's permission, I might add… and, it says right here, in black and white – Kevin Donnellon, welfare advice officer, with the council stamp in the bloody corner! It can't be any clearer than that now, can it?'

The award Kevin won, which included a further two years of

back pay, was the biggest salary jump in the history of NALGO, with Kevin moving from Scale 1 to Scale 9 in a single, legless leap.

Called into head office the following day, Kevin was informed that the council would no longer be able to provide the staff to help him up the steps into St George's House and that he was therefore being transferred.

It was only when he arrived at his new quarters – the Health Centre, on Marian Square – that he saw this manoeuvre for the act of retribution it was. With the queues here even bigger and more vociferous than before, Kevin was informed that the patients in this centre were not even required to make an appointment. His second placement – Bootle Health Centre, on Park Street – was no improvement, Kevin learning, in due course, the notoriety of both locations in council circles.

Kevin didn't phone home to announce his promotion on this occasion but, with typical resilience, he simply got down to work, resisting the urge to walk back out again.

It took him less than a day to find his bearings and to recognise that the demographic he now served knew the system inside out (and knew how to play it).

'It's me giro…' was the most frequent opener.

Kevin would give an amiable smile, knowing by now that in most of the cases that came before him, the client would have already cashed their legitimate allowance and be there to see him 'on the bounce' (under the misapprehension that he had a cupboard full of giros).

'Give it a couple of days,' Kevin would insist, 'and, if you've still not heard anything, come back in.'

'But, I need it now, lad,' the response hissed, with no little aggression, as Kevin wheeled out from behind his desk, in order to usher them to the door.

'They seemed to think I could pull a rabbit from a hat,' he tells me, seeing the humour now, though at the time, with his reputation going before him – and the days and the weeks running on – his blood pressure had been off the scale.

It was a gruelling period and, with Kevin recognising that the council was out to get him (and unlikely to stop), the pressure eventually told.

'I'm stressed, depressed... *losing it*,' he wailed disconsolately.

Sitting him down, the doctor ran through a series of questions, before cordially agreeing to sign him off for six months: 'nervous debility', the sick note read.

'What the fuck's that?' Nicky asked, grudgingly calling in to see the patient (there were no grapes).

Kevin didn't deign to enlighten her.

While the plaintiff was still in recovery, the union continued to sue on his behalf, with Kevin's salary now raised to the much more commensurate rate of an MO1 (considering the job he had been doing for the past two years).

The money had never been the problem, but – rather – the job itself, which had grown increasingly onerous, with Kevin resigning just as soon as his convalescence was through.

His notice was refused, by first post, Pauline Farrell writing – in a fairly emotive plea – of his importance to the project. Kevin, who had been fooled before and wouldn't be again, immediately wrote back to make his reasons clear.

'Surely there's something we can do?' Pauline tried again, on the phone. 'You have such good prospects...'

'I've made my decision,' Kevin told her, civil (through clenched teeth).

'Well, you'll be a genuine loss and we'd be pleased to have you back any time...' She paused, emboldened by her own flattering tone. 'And what is it you're actually thinking of doing next?'

'Not a clue,' Kevin chuckled, feeling like a child again.

He had – in fact – already put in a claim for sick benefit through the DSS; he would welcome the assessor into his home a day or two later.

'So, how are you?' she asked, stepping into the lounge.

'I'm alright, I suppose,' Kevin replied, gratified to find her sympathetic.

'And you get on okay here, by yourself?' the assessor continued. 'The benefits cover everything you need?'

'Yes,' Kevin said, quickly clarifying, 'though I'm hardly living on caviar and champagne.'

That comment drew laughter, as Tony Pirkis – who was up from Brighton for a flying visit – stepped across with the drinks.

'He's got the Thalidomide Trust money, too, remember?' he interjected.

Kevin coloured, feeling exposed, but his luck was changing.

'Yes, well, we know about that,' the assessor returned, 'but that's a *discretionary* fund and not considered as income… so, it doesn't come into our figures.'

Kevin was blushing, but smiling, too – in the belief that he deserved a break. The extra money was a security and a luxury that he came to enjoy… and, it wasn't until the laws all started to change again, that he felt the pinch once more.

He didn't mention the funds that were sitting secure in his bank, or take his guest outside to show her the flashy amendments he had recently made to his car.

By 1990 that period seemed a lifetime away, though when Kevin ran into that same union rep – who placed an arm about his shoulder (his stolid Lancashire accent as familiar as his face) – the events came flooding back.

'That was some case, wasn't it?' the rep recalled. 'One of the biggest successes in NALGO's history… I mean – really – well done! And, do you know,' he continued, 'we still teach that case on training sessions, as an example of what can be achieved.'

Kevin left with the congratulations still ringing in his ears.

His memory of that tribunal would be stirred up once more, twenty-seven years later – in April 2016 – when, invited to chair an Ability Network talk for the Sefton Council Voluntary Service, there was another unexpected sighting.

'It's Kevin Donnellon, isn't it?' the man asked, and he often got that – who could forget *Kevin* – though he wasn't recognised in turn; it was only when he started to explain that Kevin saw the clean-shaven young man in the middle-aged figure now presenting: hair thinning on top; clear blue eyes showing behind rimless glasses.

'Oh, hi,' he returned sheepishly, wondering at yet another ghost.

'I'm director of human resources now, for my sins,' the man explained; owning to a sudden sense of responsibility, Kevin was pleased to see that the man's career hadn't suffered. 'That was one of the first cases I ever sued, and you really put me in my place.'

'Sorry.'

'Don't be – you were right, in the end, weren't you? Besides, I was young and just doing what I was told – didn't know any better... and, I learnt a lot from those proceedings, too.'

Kevin, who would spend the rest of the meeting thinking about the different lives they had both gone on to lead, nodded back before wheeling away.

When, a month later – looking over the notes for the conference he was next set to chair – Kevin happened upon the name Martin Waterhouse, he was stopped in his tracks, once more.

It must be, he thought, remembering his former colleague at Ellesmere House, who had since risen to be the director of social services. Looking forward to renewing their friendly hostilities, he snickered to himself at the thought of a room full of smoke.

He was disappointed when, in the event, Mr Waterhouse pulled out, wondering whether seeing his familiar name – as chair – had prompted the withdrawal.

It was the end of a legacy – five years of rapid change (within set parameters), with Kevin's continued presence within Sefton Social Services giving legs to the fact that Sefton Council was an equal opportunities employer.

Perhaps it was, but in May 1986, at the age of twenty-four, Kevin was finally free and ready for a new challenge.

Chapter 27

The next challenge would be active politics, which was a social and emotional journey for Kevin as much as an ethical one.

Gary was overwrought.

'I'm so proud of you,' he declared; bemused by the absurdity of the situation, Kevin beamed ambivalently back.

Another officer had now been enlisted, his peaked cap joining the others in a comic pile on the turf. Trying out various grips and holds, they each took a shuffling turn around the chair, before finally heaving it up together, staggering as they went, while Kevin sat on, serene, aboard his makeshift throne – immobile, but shaking with laughter.

'Move back, out of the way!' one of the officers screeched, straining under the burden, as they forced their way through the small crowd (now letting off sarcastic hoots).

'Fucking pigs!' someone shouted, with more aggression, but the sight of Kevin – smiling his easy-going smile – was enough to quell them.

Standing proudly upright, tears moistening his eyes – a thin, comradely smile held concertedly on his reddening face – Gary was at Kevin's side the whole time and, after his friend had been rather absurdly charged with 'disturbing the peace', he was there when Kevin emerged from the police station three hours later.

Winding down the window to expel the fumes from his cigarette, while Kevin skipped the Ford Escort across the packed mud and out, onto the paved road, Gary repeated the same words: 'I'm so proud of you'.

While Kevin was long accustomed to the heady mix of emotions that would surface during these fervid encounters, this was Gary's first *up-close* campaign – putting into physical practice what he had only previously affiliated with from a distance – and the experience left its mark.

Requisitioned as a stopover point for cruise missiles, the military base at Burtonwood – with the resplendent Stars and Stripes flapping over the main building – was just a short half-hour drive down the motorway, but they started early, to beat the expected tumult of weekend traffic.

Slotting the mixtape into the deck after climbing aboard, Gary had immediately sprung the coils into life (and the day, too). They shared a look: The Style Council's 'My Ever Changing Moods' felt like the perfect choice as they set off on yet another adventure.

The protest they arrived at – ready for battle – was not what they had in mind, or what Gary had been led to expect: Burtonwood was no Greenham Common. Instead, a lone, midsized tent was pitched beside a rundown camper van, with a group of thirty or so activists – sitting or standing, under thick layers – holding tight to tin mugs (of bitter coffee), which they would draw, periodically, from tartan flasks (the bright morning reluctant to thaw).

Misted breaths held in the air as they conversed, in what seemed like whispers – with no great excitement and no great hurry. Kevin cut the music, which was suddenly out of place, and watched with curiosity as Gary jumped out and lit up a cigarette, puffing with nervous energy as he acclimatised.

An old hat, who had seen it all before, Kevin looked on with an indulgent smile.

This particular gathering, as Kevin had told his friend, was a small part of the burgeoning Snowball Campaign, which he had first encountered earlier in the month.

He had been attending a Green Party meeting on the Wirral, when a crazed-looking priest, with a thick head of erratic white hair, had come bounding across the room. *Looks like Tom Baker,* Kevin had thought, noting the scarf (of psychedelic swirls) falling from the narrow shoulders to the stick-like thighs, the deep lines on his face set against crisp, snowy-white supercilia; the starched dog collar, sitting rigid at his wrinkled throat, brought the rest to order.

'I like your scarf,' Kevin offered in passing, which proved enough to stall the man, inviting conversation.

'Ah, my fine young friend,' the priest returned, as he drew to a halt, his genial brown eyes gazing down on his interlocutor as he laid on hands. 'We're part of the Snowball Campaign,' he said, explaining how three pensioners had initiated the action by cutting through a piece of the fence at a military base, in protest against the nuclear weapons contained within. 'They promised to return to that same base every day, with ever greater numbers, until the weapons were removed.'

They would tie white ribbons – bearing messages of peace – to the fence too, he said.

'And how many people have actually signed up?' Kevin asked, wide-eyed.

'Well, at the last count,' pausing for effect, 'there have been similar – Snowball – campaigns at forty-two different army bases... which makes it pretty clear what ordinary people think about nuclear weapons being stored and deposited on our soil, don't you think?'

Kevin was nodding enthusiastically and already considering where and when to add his own 'flakes' to that growing ball of snow, with Burtonwood bringing a political dimension to their already regular drives.

There would be music playing on those trips, more often than not – a *Juke Box Jury* of recent releases. By the start of June that year, they were keen to get their hands on the latest Smiths LP – whose tracklist had been released in the previous week's NME – with Kevin driving them across to Crown Records, first thing.

'What do you think?' he asked, as Gary jumped back in – turning the LP about, after tearing through the plastic wrap.

'Looks good,' he replied, opening up the gatefold to a picture of the group – which he showed to Kevin – before pulling out the sleeve notes and squinting through the lyric sheet.

'Read some,' Kevin said, as he turned out of the car park, cutting into the stuttering traffic with his usual panache.

Gary read on – with great mirth – though nothing could prepare them for the record itself. Back home, playing it through for a second time, Gary inserted a tape and ran them off a copy for the car, writing out the songs on the insert.

It was *this* album that would be blaring from the open windows, on their trip to Burtonwood; this album, too, that would accompany their lonely sojourn to Sellafield, on a trip that – meandering guilelessly through the imposingly glacial Lakes – seemed a distillation of everything they believed in.

Passing through numerous quaint villages along the way, Gary – who was following the map – would call out their names, relishing the sound of them (an abstract form of poetry). When they sailed through what Gary identified, with a wry smile, as 'Bootle' – momentarily disconsolate at the beauty on display – Kevin heaved a sigh.

'If only *our* Bootle was like this!'

In such a manner, they bounded at pace through the countryside, noting the contrast between these beautiful, bucolic surroundings and those they had left behind. It was a state of mind, as much as anything, and they recognised that fact – the sense that they, for once, were positive agents of change.

Those trips were transformational: Mr Black and Ellesmere House – and Nunsford Close – couldn't have seemed further away, as Kevin bounced about in the driver's seat and Gary cast his head from the open window, his hair lapping back in the breeze.

'Stop the car! Stop the car!' Gary cried suddenly, and – turning his head left to right, in a panic – Kevin pushed down on the brake lever and was thrown into the steering column, while Gary juddered to a halt against the line of his belt.

Silence, the rush of adrenalin still running through their veins; then, no harm done, they were smiling again.

'Just look at it,' Gary gasped in wonder, gesturing towards the trees and fields surrounding them. 'It's absolutely beautiful!'

Turning his head guilelessly to the window, to the rambling green hills and the hedges that ran through ears of corn – the grazing cattle; the rustle of birds in flight – Kevin could only agree.

Turning skyward, he could now discern the beginnings of a sunset, the yellows and reds darkening into a fine wash of shaded bands, and – all the while – the thin, vibrating speakers in his car pumped out the sort of music that was pure release.

Gauging, now, whether such combinational beauty was *really* the reason he had been admonished to make an emergency stop, Kevin looked incredulously to his friend.

Releasing his seat belt, Gary pulled the switch on the door and stepped out, his face lifted to the sky. Kevin was wondering whether to disembark, too, when Gary hitched himself up and over a stile before chasing off into an adjacent field.

He returned with an armful of plucked flowers, and – before Kevin could stop to ask – he was off again, rushing back and forth for a full ten minutes until he had the dash and the front seat deep in vegetation, with an array of stiff stems twisted around the wiper blades.

He's mad, Kevin thought, rocking with laughter, as the music played on and the sun edged away on the horizon. At that moment, drawing in their scent like nectar, Kevin was utterly at peace.

With his hands on his knees, catching his breath, Gary suddenly straightened, before flinging out his arms, in an all-encompassing gesture, to address his friend.

'Look at it, Kevin! Just look at it!' he cried. 'It's so beautiful! How can there not be a God, somewhere, with a world like this?'

Kevin was holding back tears when he started up the engine and they turned for home.

That period was one of great charm, with those escapes – that had taken such a small proportion of time – having an inordinate effect. Thus, even as Kevin grew disillusioned with politics, he never let up with the protests and the demonstrations.

There were moments when it would all seem worthwhile, like on a particularly jubilant anti-apartheid march, in May 1987, when the hundred-strong crowd had parted to make room for a woman – in a flowery dress – who had crouched down to offer protection to a straggling ladybird.

The battle lines momentarily forgotten, Kevin pulled up in his chair beside her, with a renewed sense of belonging, drawn once more to the songs and the chants, the voices and the whistles lifted in optimistic accord. There were placards and coloured streamers, and he watched as a group of children glided innocently by, seemingly pulled along by the weight of their balloons.

Then, his companions were calling him and he set off in pursuit.

That moment would seem just a distant memory by the afternoon, when – at the arrival of the South African ambassador – the morning's light-hearted atmosphere descended into violence.

The ambassador was expected – was one of the reasons for the march – but, when he actually appeared, Kevin was surprised by the speed at which the pantomime boos turned into howls of derision and the joyous carnival into an angry riot: its marchers, a mob.

Kevin looked on, powerless, as the Socialist Worker Party members – who had previously been a small part of the larger whole – now forced their way, with strong-arms, to the front.

'What the hell are you doing?' he shouted, to people he had once considered friends, realising – suddenly – that the push had been planned, with the target the embassy itself.

'Get the fucker!' somebody yelled, and Kevin was shoved aside, doing well to keep his seat.

As the tumult grew around him, Kevin sat on in a state of sustained grief. Still an official member of the SWP, he wanted no part of this, but he would be trapped there for more than an hour, before he was able to fight his way back to where he had parked the van (a little over a mile away).

Fuckers, he spat, noting the pleasure they took in pushing and pulling, the sneers of hurled abuse.

Some of the protesters were now involved in a brawl, trampling their colleagues underfoot, and – his eyes burning with frustration – Kevin knew he didn't belong. *Bastards,* he thought, though – even as the chaos fomented with increasing force – he felt no fear, with the whole event just a dream he had no control over.

Thus, when the banner he had been clutching uncomfortably in his hand slipped to the floor, Kevin shut his eyes and let it go (making no attempt to retrieve it).

'There you are,' a voice sounded, to his left, Kevin turning to find that a police officer was handing the banner back.

Kevin gave an apologetic roll of his eyes, and – in a brief moment of lucidity – peace was struck. Almost immediately, the banner was being slapped out of his hands once more.

'Get the fuck away from him, you fucking pig!' Jill Benson – an old friend – roared, as Kevin took up a protective crouch. 'He doesn't want it, now you've had your filthy hands on it!'

Kevin turned away – from everything he thought he believed – and set off, at a despairing push, against the crowd (knowing only that he had to get out).

He would wonder at Jill, always such a shy and sensitive presence, as he made his way home. They had once sold the SWP newspapers together – outside the Black Bull, on County Road – and she had always been generous company.

'She took everything to heart, I suppose,' Kevin recalled, remembering the last time they had been out, when she had been subjected to racist abuse, on account of the anti-apartheid message on the cover.

An old man had come right up to her and was already bawling into her face before anyone noticed. They had soon scared him off – with abuse of their own – but Jill was shaking and could hardly speak.

Kevin had taken her home, considering even then that Jill wasn't really suited to such work – you needed thick skin to front up to the public like that.

On election night, in 1992, she would call Kevin up in tears.

'I can't believe that the Tories have got in again,' she cried inconsolably. 'It's never going to change,' she whined, 'because people are just too selfish…'

Kevin tried to placate her – told her that the fight wasn't over.

'Next time…'

'There won't be a next time,' she hissed.

Andrew Kavanagh phoned the following day to tell him that Jill had taken her own life.

'No, that's not right,' Kevin suddenly interjects, remembering that her premature death had come later, in 2001 – recalling the spirit (and the pain), if not the detail (or the date). 'There's a plaque dedicated to her in the Casa,' (on Hope Street) he tells me, and that feels apt.

Kevin's heart had long since taken on a more spiritual form by then, steering sharp from the political to the religious.

The latter had seemed to be almost seeking him out during those weeks, with Kevin receiving visits from the Jehovah's Witnesses, the Evangelical Church and the Mormon Sacrament, within the space of a single twenty-four hours.

He had reason to reject them all.

'I even got into paganism for a while,' he admits. 'Had the words 'Peace, Love and Harmony' painted onto a huge canvas, in the mystical runes of the witchcraft alphabet.'

Joan had mounted it, and the banner was still hanging there when a group of gaunt Evangelicals came to call.

'This is the devil's work, young man – do you not know it?' their leader pronounced, with rather more sympathy than approbation, as they set about Kevin's home for further evidence of moral failing.

Kevin stood, dumbfounded, as they scurried about him,

speaking in tongues to cast off the spells they believed were besieging the very walls.

Kevin's books on witchcraft were rooted out and pulled from the shelves, along with Bertrand Russell's *Why I Am Not a Christian*, which seemed to cause particular offence. After the leader had pronounced Kevin 'truly possessed', the group had suddenly made a run for it.

Kevin followed them out in his chair. He was something of a lost sheep at the time and they all seemed to know it – looking from his wheels to his eager face, and back again.

The Mormons came next, in the form of a pair of 'stunning blondes', rapping at his door with fixed smiles held to smooth, high cheeks, their salutations echoing eerily down the hall as they stepped inside – cautious to enter a house whose door had opened by itself.

'Hello – is anybody there?' the girls called, peeping through to the lounge, to find Kevin sprawled out on the floor. That stopped them. 'Hello, sir?' they tried uncertainly, as Kevin gazed back in wonder at their long legs (in denim shorts) and their sparkling blue eyes.

'Oh, hi,' Kevin replied, gathering himself.

Suddenly there were smiles and pearl-white teeth, Kevin hardly able to think.

'Good morning, sir. We're here today to tell you about *The Book of Mormon*!'

'Oh,' Kevin said, 'then I suppose you'd better come in.'

He was star-struck – they were hard to refuse – even if the doctrine they carefully outlined sounded increasingly absurd.

'But they were bloody gorgeous,' he concedes, owning up to the loss he felt when – their message delivered – they duly trooped right out of his life again (registering, with a catch of regret, that the Mormon faith practised polygamy).

He was still savouring the sweet memory of that delightful pair – 'I think they might have been twins' – when he was approached on the street by an elderly man in a bright blue shell suit, the challenge laid down with a ghostly smile.

'I bet you a tenner that if you come to my place of worship, you'll leave as a believer.'

Kevin gave a shake of the head, before shooting away, full throttle, wondering why everyone was suddenly so interested in his soul.

There were signs there if we care to look – the religious vocation only ever a matter of time for Kevin… Love, too – and infatuation – that reaching out we all do, in one way or another, for a friend, or for something more…

Chapter 28

Stepping across to the window, Karen drew the curtain carefully into place; then, without a word, she hurried up the stairs, and Kevin could hear her up in the bedroom, too.

'All done,' she declared, dropping down to the sofa.

She didn't settle, though, and – peering about, with her head inclined – seemed to be listening for something.

'What's wrong?' Kevin asked, his eyes narrow.

'It's the neighbour – the guy at the back,' Karen replied. 'I caught him looking across here the other day… He was stood in the window, staring right in!'

'Did you say anything?' Kevin asked, shuffling closer.

'No… course not,' Karen answered quickly, 'but I always make sure I close the curtains over, just in case I get up in the night, to use the loo, or something, and he's there, watching me!' She paused, stubbing out her cigarette. 'I never used to bother… didn't even think about it. But,' she continued – with just the hint of a smile – 'well, I usually sleep naked… and I've no intention of giving some dodgy bloke an eyeful!'

She was laughing now, and Kevin couldn't resist.

'You sleep *naked*?'

'Yeah, except in the winter, when I might wear a t-shirt.'

Standing up, to clear away the tea things, Karen took everything back through to the kitchen. Kevin's eyes followed her out, enjoying every aspect of that slow, familiar drawl, the stray ends of her jeans catching on her grubby heels, the worn-down socks.

Kevin had already hit the tipping point, and he knew now, for sure, what he had known – on one level or another – for the past twelve months: that he was in love, and there was no going back…

◊

There are several people sitting on the cupped plastic seats set off to the side of the corridor, in a small alcove, when I step in, as directed. Nurses pass, in pairs; soft-shoed orderlies push trolleys, while disorientated patients shuffle by in ill-fitting robes.

The corridors are indistinguishable, one to the next, with signs pointing the way to particular wards… to the toilets and the lifts. The smooth, scuffed floors absorb the sounds of the passing traffic. I feel light-headed.

I know two of the people by sight and another two bring a glimmer of recognition, but it's too late. I should have been here hours ago, instead of wandering in now, in unwashed jeans, with no idea how to proceed.

I sit and wait – in dreamlike silence – and I might have sat there forever, but for the arrival of her mother, who emerges from a room further down the corridor and reaches out to me. I force myself up to greet her, surprised that she remembers me, or should be seeking me out above all the others.

'Would you like to see her?' she asks, her exhausted eyes unyielding as she leads me away.

I nod – it's all I can do – and she beckons me into another room, the door closing silently behind us.

There are six identical stretcher beds laid out in two symmetrical lines (of three) and no movement coming from any of them, though each has a series of tubes, leads, twisted drips and electrical devices, leading off from the back of the frame.

Caroline lies prone on top of the covers of the second bed on the right.

She is unrecognisable.

Stepping round to the side in a daze, I lean over you, taking in the pale bloated face – blotched with bruises – and your neck, resting like a dead weight on the starched vinyl pillow.

I am meant to look, so I move closer, peering down on your heavy-lidded eyes – shut tight – that have a fine criss-cross of blue veins running over them. The lips are dry, as they often were – a drained, cracked cerise shading into amaranth.

I look, and I look (in vain)… testing for signs of life, for familiarity, as your chest – wrapped to the neck, in a drab hospital smock – lifts, and then falls, in a steady, unbroken rhythm… forcefully inflated with air, the chest pumped taut, before falling, again, motionless.

I continue to stand, and I continue to look down on you, for some time – your hollow body held by the light blue gown; the dark roots already encroaching in the dulling platinum of your disordered hair.

I leave by the back stairs.